GAUGE 0 COMPENDIUM

Chris and Julie Graebe

A listing of Hornby
Gauge 0 production
and principal variants
made at Binns Road
for the UK market from
1920 to 1970.

FRANK HORNBY
1863–1936

New Cavendish Books

LONDON

INTRODUCTION

Quite some time has passed since we sat down to put the finishing touches to Volume 5 in this series. Interest in Hornby Gauge O Trains has grown steadily in the meantime, while collecting has become more difficult . . . . and more expensive! But it stays just as interesting, with important new discoveries still being made even now, some twenty years after the Hornby Railway Collectors' Association was founded. For example, the newly discovered Great Eastern Railway wagon . . . .

**First edition published in Great Britain
by New Cavendish Books – 1989**

The Hornby Companion Series

Copyright © New Cavendish Books – 1989
All rights reserved, this book or parts thereof
may not be reproduced in any form without
permission in writing from the publisher.

Design – John B. Cooper
Editorial direction – Allen Levy & Narisa Chakra
Printed and bound in England

New Cavendish Books
3 Denbigh Road, London W11 2SJ

ISBN 0 904568 90 3

Now, what is the book that you hold in your hands? We have tried to present a preliminary list of the most important Hornby O Gauge variants made in Binns Road for the UK market in the 1920 to 1970 period. We can only envy our Hornby Dublo colleagues, who have a more or less complete list of Dublo Train production; the detail variations in O gauge make it very difficult to compile an equivalent.

We have presented here only the most important changes. That means we have had to make arbitrary choices on what to put in, and what to leave out. We have included major changes of shape (such as wagon underframes), colour (except for minor changes in shade) and lettering. But we have left out, for example, changes of coupling, loco mechanism, and trademark, together with minor details that moderately myopic authors might be expected to miss at a distance of a foot or so. Taken in conjunction with Appendix V, most details of coupling, transfer, wheel type etc can be inferred from the production dates we quote in the second column, for each variant. (The opportunity has also been taken to make minor changes to certain dates suggested in Volume 5.) We have not tackled packaging changes.

Control System and Electric Sets and Locos have been listed together with their clockwork equivalents. While 1936 has been given as the final date for black locos (and sets containing them), since that was when they were dropped from the catalogues, they could be obtained to special order or for export up to the end of production in 1941. Since locos and tenders were sold separately it is impossible to define correct pairings; this list gives the most likely combinations, but others may be just as valid in the overlap periods.

Changes between subsequent versions of the same item have been given in bold type, in an attempt to make the changes easier to pick out. We have not been pedantic about the product names given in the list, but have given the most readily understood catalogue names; please refer to Volume 5 pp. 301-11 if you want further details of catalogue name changes. Concise colour descriptions are difficult, but reference to the photographs in Volume 5 should resolve any misunderstandings; the page references in the first column of the list form an index to the illustrations in Volume 5. "PLAIN" is used to denote items not carrying company lettering. Abbreviations used include SO for special order, while PU (production unconfirmed) has been used for a wide variety of items which, by logical inference, seem likely to have been made, but which we have not yet recorded seeing. It does not necessarily indicate rarity; but we do ask, if you have any of these items, or others that have not been listed, that you let us know. This list was first compiled around 1980, before we started work on Volume 5. As you can imagine, it has needed much revision since then, and some errors probably remain. We would be pleased to be told about these, too!

Many people have been more than kind in their comments on Volume 5 and its illustrations; we would like to thank them most sincerely for their encouragement. We would like to take the opportunity to thank the publishers for the generous scope they gave us for the inclusion of colour photographs in Volume 5.

Once again, we gratefully acknowledge the help we have received from friends near and far, in the compilation of this appendix. Although they are not all listed here (many are in any case mentioned in Volume 5), some names are given in the "additional information" section. Many thanks to you all.

We are particularly grateful to Roy Paton for helping to check these lists, and to Nicholas Oddy who has again given us much useful extra information, while involving us in a long game of Finial Pursuit by extending the section on Signals. We had hoped that Bruce Baxter would assist us, as he did so ably with Volume 5, to save us from our worst mistakes; but sadly we learnt just before publication of Bruce's death. We would like to acknowledge his expertise and his enthusiasm for Hornby Trains by dedicating this book to his memory.

(Vol. 5A page numbers have been given an A prefix, to avoid confusion with Vol. 5 references.)

VOLUME 5: ADDITIONAL INFORMATION

p12: A single (perfectly genuine) constructional Hornby Wagon with "GE" clip-on lettering has been found, probably dating from the 1921-22 season; previously only wagon sides had been known, in LMS and LNER livery but slotted for GE letters. *(Jeff Knight)*

p70: The December 8th 1945 issue of Picture Post carried a Meccano Ltd advertisement promising that a limited supply of Meccano and Hornby Trains would be ready before Christmas. *David Salisbury* remembers buying items when his local shop received a parcel of Hornby Trains just before Christmas in 1945; these were, however, of prewar manufacture (for example a No. 4E Station and a No. 2E Double Arm Signal), released from the Binns Road store. Regular manufacture does not appear to have started until 1946, and the first known catalogue listing was in March 1947. Only Meccano Sets and Dinky Toys were included in the November 1945 and November 1946 price lists.

p89: The Automatic Reversing Rail was to have been a very close copy of a rail made by Bing.

p91: Electric Points on Solid Base with Ground Disc were actually made, to special order. The examples known are in blue, and are similar to those shown on p209 except for the addition of centre rails. Certain of their ground discs lack the red and green hand finishing on the surrounds to the celluloid aspects. *(Jim Gamble)*

p102: J. H. Butcher & Co. of Birmingham are now known to have made transfers for Hornby Trains. *Don Palmer* has shown us LNER 326 No. 1 Tank Loco and GW 2710 transfers marked with the maker's name.

p110: It should be mentioned that locomotives sent back for repair would often be returned with new wheels and therefore confuse dating. For example a pre 1927 uncoupled No. 1 Loco sent for repair would, from 1927, be returned fitted with coupling rods, and, from circa 1929, with red wheels. This becomes confusing when, say, a 1928-29 uncoloured wheel No. 1 has been sent back for repair a year or two later and has consequently been fitted with red wheels of the same pattern; thus trying to plot the introduction of red wheels is difficult. Other common replacements were No. 1 Special wheels fitted to No. 2 Mechanisms after 1929, and 8 spoke coupled wheels fitted to 1931-36 M3 Tank Locos after 1936. *(Nicholas Oddy)*

p115: The post-1937 clockwork No. O Locos were fitted with a dummy firebox, to conceal the mechanism in its revised position when it was moved back to clear the cylinders. Whereas certain EO20 Locos with cylinders had this dummy firebox, it was more usually omitted from the electric locos. *(David Uttley)*

p116: An early 1920 version of the GN green Hornby Loco, with green chimney and cylinders, nickel baseplate (without red valances but with red front buffer beam), and having an all-green tender, has appeared; we are now looking out for the LNWR equivalent.

p117: A few green No. 1 Tenders circa 1923-24 were lettered "LNER", using the same transfers as for the "L&NER" tender (p18) but with the ampersand cut out.

p117: A number of interesting No. 1 Locomotives have been seen which were probably marketed in 1925-26 as a means of using up obsolete parts and stock. These locomotives seem to have been supplied separately, or in sets with 1920-21 series tenders and open wagons, and are assembled from an assortment of 1924-25 season and 1920-21 season components. Both green and black varieties have been seen. Usually cab, boiler and baseplate are 1924 issue (and are painted in that style with LNER coats of arms, transfer lining, and boiler bands on green, and LMS equivalents on black). Cab roofs, splashers and handrails are 1920 style (therefore the LH splasher bears the "MLdL" decal and the RH one is plain, while the paint is a different shade to that of the more modern components). Mechanisms are 1924-25 style. A most interesting feature of these locos is that they are fitted with 1920-style 3 link couplings; it seems that, after the frames had been painted, and fitted with drop link couplings, the drop links were crudely removed and the buffer beams drilled to take the earlier type. As with much reissued stock the whole body is usually revarnished after final assembly with details such as couplings in position. *(Nicholas Oddy)*

p119: *Nicholas Oddy* has found a No. 1 Loco 8324 in LNER green with LMS gold lining, circa 1930-31, similar to the No. O version mentioned on p115. Its tender is lined in LNER style using old 2710 transfers, but with the numbers removed and replaced by LNER lettering from the 463/623 No. 1 Tank Loco transfer.

p119: A Southern No. 0/1 Tender in black with "Southern 1504" transfers has been reported to us by *Bruce Perrot*, although we have not seen it; this revised number for the A504 tender would be expected on transfers made after 1932. The No. 1 Special Tender number 2343 has also appeared on some early loco number lists; again this number would be expected if the B343 transfers had been revised, but it has so far been impossible to trace an original example.

p120: The last batch of No. 50 Locomotives sport much broader transfer lining than the earlier ones.

p122: GW locos with domes have often been rumoured; now *Nicholas Oddy* has traced a GW No. 1 Tank Loco, with the earliest 1926-style transfers, which has a polished brass dome rather than a cast or polished brass safety valve cover. A similar GW No. 2 Tank with a brass dome has been seen.

p122: The No. 1 Tank in LNER green numbered 463 was made in a transitional version with a green dome, but with a green smokebox and green smokebox door. Both LNER (green) 463 and (black) 326 appeared on earlier 1927-28 season locos with brass domes and short wheelbase mechanisms. *(Nicholas Oddy)*

p122: A late version of the black LMS 623 No. 1 Tank Loco (circa 1930) had a low profile black-finished dome.

p122: Towards the end of the old body style, the GW No. 1 Tank Loco appeared as noted with "Great Western" lettering, without crest, and with LMS-style lining. A similar version without crest but with normal GW lining was also made.

p122: We have seen an Electric No. 1 Tank (Permanent Magnet) in LNER black livery, number 326, with the 1932 "Liverpool" transfer trademark on the bunker back, and fitted with an automatic coupling. It has fixed lamps, and does not have a bulbholder; nonetheless production of these locos continued longer then we had thought!

p122: Coincident with the adoption of the universal base in 1937, a rounded-end bracket (apparently shaped to fit inside the cab underframe of the E120 Tank) was designed for the E120 motor.

p123: A red LMS No. 1 Special Loco (circa 1930) has been discovered with the number 4525, more usually used for the black version.

p124: The SR No. 1 Special Loco number was changed from A179 to 1179, not from A759 to 1179.

p124: A950 transfers for the black SR No. 1 Special Tank Loco were first used in 1930.

p127: We have seen a 2711 Loco with 3 boiler bands, mid 1924, with "L&NER" on both splashers, and tender lettered "L&NER".

p127: Existence of LNER green 2711 Locos with green running plates and with red-finished valances has been confirmed.

p129: Brush caps for the electric No. 2 Loco were of solid insulator material, rather than a brass cap covered with insulator as on later mechanisms.

p140: The L1 rear splashers were separate parts, not embossed on the firebox sides.

p140: An interesting early lined-cab L1 Loco has appeared; it has a nickel-plated bogie, and holes for fitting Compound cylinders (although these holes are unused); the smokebox door lacks the "Hornby" trademark. *(David Uttley)*

p146: The late 3.1290 Riviera Blue Train Loco cabside transfers had plain gold lining, instead of the gold/red/black lining used for the 31801 Locos; this was a better match for the tender lining.

p147: A recently discovered red coal rail tender, with sans serif plain gold "LMS" lettering, circa 1929, was possibly intended for the No. 3 Royal Scot with "6100" cabside number.

p158: The coats of arms illustrated on No. 1 Coaches in early advertising literature can be more clearly seen in the photograph that accompanied the registered design depositions. They are Great Central, not Great Eastern.

p158: A substantial number of LNWR No. 1 Coaches were produced in a very dark olive green and white, rather than the more usual brown and white. These coaches probably date from 1922.

p158: It seems that it took a long time for all the constructional No. 1 Coaches to be sold out. Both GN and MR versions appeared with Hornby Series labels on their solebar ends, and with late pattern embossed trademarks. Were these sold as Zulu Passenger Train Coaches in the 1924-25 season, in order to use up obsolete parts? *(Nicholas Oddy)*

p159: A substantial batch of LMS and LNER Guard's Vans with unembossed sides were produced in 1927-28. *(Nicholas Oddy)*

p159: Crimped bases with reduced buffer height may have been introduced late in 1930 rather than 1931. There are examples of the GW M3 Open, LMS and SR No. 1 Coaches and LMS Guard's Van, all on crimped bases with drop link rather than automatic couplings.

p159: From 1932 the GW No. 1 Coach doors were lettered "3" and "1" instead of "Third" and "First"; the revised doors were used first on the black-base then on green-base versions.

p161: One printing of the SR Corridor Brake/Composite Coach had the "load 3 tons" lettering at the passenger end on one side of the coach.

p163: The tinplate "ventilators" on the ends of the No. 2 Special Pullman roofs are actually roof footwalks. *(John Metcalfe)*

p167: Nickel-plated rather than black-enamelled wheels were used for the late electrically lit Metropolitan Coaches, for the purely practical reason that they gave good electrical contact. *(John Metcalfe)*

p167: One batch of Box Cars circa 1930 had plain yellow-cream enamelled doors.

p167: The Tank Car also appeared in a 1930 version lettered "Hornby Lines", and with "Made in USA" painted out. The body was secured to the base by eyelets rather than the later method of fixing by Meccano nuts and bolts. *(Stan Peachey)*

p170: "No. 1 Brake Van" solebar lettering appeared on at least one batch of LNW Brake Vans, which are also unusual in that they are varnished in the same manner as the LMS and LNER versions of the same season.

p170: An early (constructional) GW Brake Van appeared with close spaced No. 2 Van lettering, similar to the LMS equivalent. *(Len Champion)*

p170: A 1931-32 LMS Brake Van (dark grey, smaller gold lettering, "Manf'd by" transfer, autos with DRGM on side) has been found with the reversed GW body pattern of 1930-31 with the verandah cutout in the van end.

p170: One early batch of the Breakdown Van and Crane was fitted with cast doorhandles (see p331), presumably to use up old stock. *(Stan Peachey)*

p171: One batch of LMS Breakdown Vans circa 1934 had red-lined cranes with the later jib head (instead of green-lined); NE, GW and SR versions may also exist.

p171: We have now seen a postwar version of the Breakdown Van and Crane. The base was matt black, with a postwar grey trademark transfer; the body was standard LMS postwar brown, with small gold "LMS" letters. Lamp brackets (shown on the archive drawings) were not fitted. The crane was in the usual postwar red, but of course lacked the counterbalance weight used on the Crane Truck. Another version, found complete with 1949 box, had lamp brackets but was unlettered on body or crane; colours and trademark were the same. *(Stewart and Bernard Simpson, David Taylor)*

p172: Circa 1926, the LNER No. 1 Cattle Truck was lettered "LN(door)ER" on the body, while the solebars of the olive green base were plain. Thus between 1924 and 1926 LNER lettering moved from the body to the solebar, then to the body again. Equivalent LMS and GW versions may have appeared before the colour change to blue bases.

p173: The 1927-33 colour for No. 2 Cattle Truck bogies was black, not blue.

p177: Although not specifically mentioned, the Nord Brake Van did appear in the early blue/pale blue livery with the revised standard wagon underframe, circa 1930.

p178: It is possible that a French-type Wagon we have seen recently, with the unlikely combination of "Manf'd by" transfer, open axleguard base, and cranked automatic couplings with the Swiss patent number, in a matt red box, may have been old stock updated for sale by Meccano Ltd. The same

may apply to certain Double and Single Wine Wagons which also have features of mixed age.

p178: Circa 1930, the UK Double Wine Wagon appeared on the French crimped-axleguard long thin base (as used for French Barrel Wagons and French Coaches etc; see p331 for description) but with the English "Wine Wagon" transfers. This was a temporary change, with 1931-36 versions appearing on variants of the UK long thin base.

p179: *Nicholas Oddy* reports a Gas Cylinder Wagon circa 1933-34 with black base but with pressed straps painted blue, evidently a short lived transitional version. Furthermore, when the colours changed back at the end of the '30s to red and black, blue straps on the existing stock of cylinders were overpainted black to match the revised base colour.

p180: A very early version of the LNWR Gunpowder Van had the normal red body eyeletted to an early wagon base with oval transfer trademark; the "Gunpowder Van" lettering on the doors was in black instead of the usual white. Brass buffers were fitted.

p180: GW Gunpowder Van sliding doors had stencil-sprayed red crosses, not transfers.

p181: Surprisingly, there was a dark green Hopper Wagon circa 1927 lettered LNER, not NE; an early grey Hopper lettered NE would have seemed a more likely transitional version. *(Tony Maxey)*

p182: 1940 versions of the Hopper Wagon in SR red with black base and white letters, and in green with black base and white serif LMS letters, have been sighted. *(Michael Daws, Nicholas Oddy)*

p182: A plain green postwar Hopper Wagon of 1949, without LMS lettering, has been discovered; like other unlettered wagons of that year, it may have been intended for export.

p183: The 1927-33 colour for No. 2 Luggage Van bogies was black, not blue.

p185: A postwar No. 2 Lumber Wagon in 1949 box has been reported from Australia; details are awaited.

p186: The Nestles transfer with all blue trademark was also used on some blue-based wagons.

p186: Both LMS and GW Milk Traffic Vans in the 1927 version with blue roof and sides and olive green base have now been discovered.

p187: An early postwar (1948?) Milk Traffic Van has the normal postwar green body, and black underframe without overpainted solebars, but with a fully planked and slatted body lacking lettering panel and "Southern" transfer. It looks like the 1930 green version except that it lacks axlebox slots, and has lamp brackets, and an embossed postwar trademark on the base. *(Bruce Perrot)*

p188: Constructional wagons with slotted sides also appeared with GW transfers; one example is known, on an open axleguard base and with slots for "LNWR" letters.

p188: Open Wagons in LMS and NE livery, presumably circa 1930, are known in an unusual form with grey-enamelled sides (having medium size white lettering transfers, and gold "Manf'd by" trademarks), on a black open axleguard base. If these were sold as No. 1 Wagons then the sequence would be untidy (gold lettered with open axleguard base, then white lettered with open axleguard base, then gold lettered with standard wagon base, then white lettered with standard wagon base). The alternative possibility is that they were sold as No. 0 Wagons, produced in that form due to a temporary shortage of tinprinted sides. One LMS version has, however, been found in a No. 2 Mixed Goods Set with 1930 guarantee slip; thus sale as No. 1 Wagons seems the more likely.

p196: The 1929 SR Refrigerator Van had black letters on a white body, not pink. *(David Ramsey)*

There was also a sliding door SR version in white. *(Peter Dunk)*

p196: Large-lettered SR Refrigerator Vans were still being produced in 1938; 1939 is therefore a more likely date than 1937 for the change to smaller SR letters. *(Jon Larson)*

p198: A couple of grey on black Rotary Tipping Wagons of the 1925-26 season have been seen (with McAlpine transfers both sides, heavily varnished, and with "Hornby Series" transfer centred on the tipper saddle); this may have been a separate batch produced between the grey on green and the orange varieties, rather than updating of old stock for the current season. *(Nicholas Oddy)*

p198: The earliest version of the Side Tipping Wagon was finished in grey with black stencil-sprayed lining, and had a black open axleguard base lettered "Tilting Wagon"; the version described (and shown) with red stencil sprayed lining would have appeared very shortly afterwards.

p199: A few of the very last No. 1 Side Tipping Wagons of 1956-57 were fitted with green tippers sporting No. 50 ("Civil Engineering Contractors") transfers. *(Nicholas Oddy)*

p199: There was a Snowplough with black constructional base, grey body and red lining, lettered "NE" on the body instead of the solebar. LMS and GW equivalents may, therefore, exist.

p200: Another Snowplough variation appeared circa 1933, with light green base and roof, yellow body, blue lining and lamp, and green sliding doors. The fan was in a darker green.

p200: Some of the earliest non opening door Snowploughs (circa 1934) did not have their doors picked out in blue, although their windows were picked out.

p200: The Snowplough wheels from 1923-28 were of the same pattern as 1920-21 No. 1 Loco driving wheels; during 1928 it seems that uncoloured Mansell wheels were used for a short time; and then from 1928 to 1941 the wheels were of the same pattern as the M1 Loco (2526) driving wheels. *(Nicholas Oddy)*

p201: No. 1 Timber Wagons in red with yellow stanchions were produced late in 1931, or perhaps early in 1932, rather than 1933. There are earlier versions in red with green stanchions.

p202: *Geoff Taylor* has told us about his postwar Trolley Wagon; it is grey with red bolsters, gloss varnished, with grey postwar trademark transfer underneath; the wheels are diecast, and the bogies have axleboxes. The printer's code on the box is 6.5M 7-49.

p212: The Engine Room Attendant (based on the Ticket Collector casting) appeared in an early version with dark blue overalls.

p216: The No. 1 and No. 2 Engine Sheds appeared circa 1934 with blue ridge tiles, equivalent to those of the concurrently available Nos. 1A and 2A. There were almost certainly equivalent E1E and E2E versions. Incidentally, the shed shown third from left on p215 lacks dark detail printing on the skylight sides; *Nicholas Oddy* has seen a late No. 2 version fitted with stencil sprayed skylight sides, presumably when litho sheet was running out.

p223: A different version of the large Wakefield Castrol Poster was lettered "272 MPH. Campbell smashes world's land speed record using....". *(Tony Maxey)*

p225: An early postwar set of posters has been discovered; it contains twelve posters, in a clear cellophane packet with blue lettering (not marked as Set A or Set B). The posters are identical to prewar versions, with matt surfaces. It seems likely these are prewar leftovers, repackaged. *(Richard Packham)*

p227: The brazier with small black dots on a red fire background appears to have been a late wartime issue.

p228: *Bob Parry* tells us that the first 2E Signal Cabins of 1932 used the black mortar printings.

p228: After the war, No. 2 Signal Cabins with hinged roofs and backs, with tinprintings identical to the pre-1941 style, were made. They were sold in the buff boxes with yellow labels characteristic of the 1946-48 period. *(John Pentney)*

p231: A transitional version of the No. 1 Signal Gantry (Home) of early 1939, had a white bridge and black levers, but had red-topped posts. Other signals of the same period had red tops and black levers; for example the 2E Junction Signal on p277.

p231: Some very interesting early lattice-post postwar Signals, in buff boxes with yellow labels, have recently come to light. These differ from the later versions (eg that on p76 lower right) in having the bottom of the post finished black, although the base is the normal green. The post cap and the lever are black. This version is shown on p76 (upper picture), although we had not noticed it before publication. Home, Distant and Double Arm versions are all known. *(Nicholas Oddy)*

p234 There were yet more transitional versions of the No. 2E Reading Station and the No. 2 Margate Station (and therefore possibly the others). These used the normal No. 2 building printings and chimneys, but had the later green tinprinted roof and speckled platform. *(Harry Walker)*

p234: The earliest postwar No. 3 Stations appeared in buff boxes with yellow labels; the tinprintings were identical to the final prewar style, with the same tinprinted trademark. *(Nicholas Oddy)* By the way, the revised tinprintings for the orange roof No. 3 Station had the Hornby advertisement on one end altered to remove the words "Accurate models"!

p236: No. 2E Turntable rails were plain tinplate, not aluminium-finished like those of the No. 2.

p239: The earliest version of the "K" Type Oil Can was much smaller than the later type; it had the "Meccano" trademark engraved on the filler, not stamped underneath. The spout was folded from sheet, not drawn from tube; the "K" on the side was a separate piece in brass sheet, not embossed as later. The HBT usually showed a version with copper body and brass spout; although this is not the most frequently encountered version, it was made. Another version of the can has steel body and copper spout; the only example we know has no Meccano Ltd trademark, but is of course marked "K" like the others. The most common version, with copper body and copper tube, usually has the "Meccano" trademark embossed on the filler or underneath, but sometimes the "Meccano" stamping is missing. It is not impossible that Messrs Kaye sold this can through other outlets. (Nicholas Oddy, Peter Dunk)

p240: The earliest Diecast Spoked Wheels were identical in pattern to those used for the No. 1 Special and No. 2 Special Tenders. From around 1936, Spoked Wheels were of a somewhat smaller size; these were used for the new High Capacity Wagon etc. The tender wheels were unchanged.

p240: At first, the Mansell Wheels boxed for separate sale were plain castings, not finished in the usual black with white rims, although this colouring was soon universally applied to Mansell Wheels. Plain Diecast Spoked Wheels may also have been sold for a while.

p243: The early Rheostat illustrated in the French No. 2 Electric Loco instructions (see p130), and for some time afterwards, was shown with sides perforated like the Meccano Lattice Girder. It is not clear if the Rheostat actually appeared in this form.

p243: A Redline-blue Speed and Reverse Switch

has been discovered; blue-bodied 6 volt Resistance Controllers were also manufactured.

p244: 20 volt Meccano Motors were first planned, and announced in trade leaflets but not catalogued, in 1930; this pre-dated the first known Hornby 20 volt trains, which appeared in the UK in 1932. The instructions for these early No. 20 Meccano Motors are combined with instructions for a 20 volt version of the Ferranti transformer, which gave an output of 24 volts at 1 amp, and was available for supplies of 100 to 250 volts. (Roger Beardsley)

p244: Alan Cliff has told us about an exotic transformer with controller, similar to the T20A but labelled T20S. It is for 250V 25 cycle supply, and gives 15V 16VA output. Presumably it was made to special order; it appears to have been made around 1936.

p248: An early dark red version of the MO Wagon had wagon numbers tinprinted on the ends as well as the sides. (Stan Peachey)

p249: One unusual postwar MO Crane Truck had the normal green base, but its jib was in a lighter than usual blue, matching the base of the Dinky Goods Yard Crane. It had the embossed "Hornby Series" trademark which was usual circa 1952; the winder handle was Brunofix finished.

p249: An interesting 4-page colour leaflet published circa 1934 listed no less than four British Express Train Sets, and included brief instructions for running. Set No. 1 (4/-) contained Loco, Tender and Wagon; the No. 2 Set had Loco, Tender, and two Passenger Coaches, for 5/-. Set No. 3, also 5/-, had Loco, Tender and one Passenger Coach, with a Wayside Halt and Signal; the 6/- No. 4 Set was the largest, having Loco, Tender, two Passenger Coaches, Country Station, Signal Box and Signal. Each set had a circle of MO-type Rails, one fitted with brake. Thus to acquire each item in the British Express range, you

would have had to buy at least three of the sets. It seems from this list that M Telegraph Poles were not included in the British Express range. (Peter Matthews)

p250: The mechanism for the very earliest 2526 M1 Loco had nickel-plated sideplates. The M2930 Loco and Tender was unusual in being sold in a single box, of the normal light blue-grey M series style, with end flaps rather than a lifting lid, for economy. Although sold as the M2930 Loco and Tender from 1930 to 1933, the actual Loco and Tender numbers were in some cases 2728.

p252: Around 1947, the LMS M1 Wagon appeared in light grey, with grey inside walls.

p254: There are two major versions of the early small-size Tinprinted Train mechanism. The first, with blued sideplates, is a close copy of the Bing version (but not an exact copy) with very thin stamped gears which have a tendency to eat each other. The second, with nickel-plated sideplates, is the same in pattern, but the gearing is more substantial, being properly cut - Meccano fashion. (Nicholas Oddy)

p255: Certain Tinprinted Train Locos for the French market carried the French garter transfer on top of the boiler. (Peter Dunk)

p255: An interesting M3 Loco of 1927-28 period had boiler and baseplate tinprinted in GN green. These were, however, the only tinprinted parts, the rest being enamelled plain green, including dome, splasher sides, cab sides and roof, and cylinder sides. No cabside transfers were applied, nor were there any embossed, transfer or tinprinted trademarks, the box being the only indication of the manufacturer's identity. (John Harwood)

p256: A transitional version of the GW M3 Wagon was enamelled in grey, with white letters, but had no buffers. There may have been an LMS equivalent.

p258: Early 8 spoke M3 Tank Loco wheels were cast using old uncoupled No. 0/1 wheel patterns and were probably quite cheap. The later 12 spoke wheels were a much more expensive development, without any obvious explanation; it is not clear whether the French market 12 spoke wheels first used for the PO-type loco were based on the M3 wheel, or vice versa. Certain M3 Tanks have a mixture of 12 spoke and 8 spoke uncoupled wheels, possibly as a result of repairs to the earliest locos after 1932!

p263: When introduced, the French Fibre Wagon was on a red long thin wagon base, and had eight stanchions against only six on the shorter UK version, which was on the standard wagon base.

p267: The Late 1930s section was scrambled by the printers; the fourth line of the section continues at the head of the centre column.

p278: The Bognor Regis Station and yellow crossing sign shown are not Hornby. We are much obliged to *Pat Flynn* for providing this picture.

p280: The yellow and green hinged door export version of the Fyffes Van had a door transfer reading "Fyffes" only, not "Fyffes Blue Label", and there were no diagonal "Bananas" transfers on the van side. Export Single and Double Wine Wagons did not have "Wine Wagon" transfers on the barrels. *(Bendt Zinck)*

p282: An intriguing 1930-31 Meccano Products catalogue for the Canadian market lists the M-style US Hornby Loco in 15 volt as well as clockwork versions. The sets were CM1 and EM1 Passenger, with red/black loco and green/gold coaches; CM2 and EM2 Passenger, with green/black loco and yellow/black coaches; also CM and EM Freight Train Sets, with red/black loco, yellow Box Car, red Tank Car, and green Caboose.

p285: Two interesting early Hornby Train folders have been discovered, one for 1922 and one for 1923. They are in the same format as the 1924 folder; a single sheet folded into six vertical-format pages. They show the complete Hornby ranges for the appropriate seasons; unexpectedly, they also list the Hornby Train Component Parts, which otherwise were listed only on train set instructions.

p293: MO Straight and Curved Rails appeared in pale blue boxes in 1948.

p293: Several items of firmly postwar manufacture were packed during the early postwar years in old stock of prewar or wartime boxes, and these boxes were often clearly stamped with postwar stock codes (p295). We have recently found an MO Wagon and an MO Coach of 1952 manufacture in 1940 boxes, with rubber-stamping suggesting 1952 packing. *Nicholas Oddy* has found a Gas Cylinder wagon and a No. 1 Level Crossing, both in 1940 boxes with circular rubber-stamped packers' codes, circa 1948-49.

p293: In the 1930s certain boxes were rubber stamped "OS" to denote old stock; for example a 1928 LMS No. 1 Passenger Coach in a box of 1931 or later. This may have been for the 1935 stock clearance mentioned on p54.

p295: The first Hornby train set box label, used earlier for the Raylo set, showed a Great Central loco, not Great Northern. For a short while in 1921, these early Hornby Train Set boxes were covered in brown leatherpaper, the lids being embossed with the gilt Hornby Train picture in place of the printed labels; they were soon replaced by the improved and enlarged crimson-lined style. Old stock of these transitional boxes was used for No. O Goods Sets around 1925.

p296: The Tinprinted Train Sets were the first to use the picture of the LNWR 4-6-0 departing from a terminus. This label was last used for some M Train Sets in 1926.

p296: From 1930 fixed partitions were fitted in the corrugated cardboard train set boxes; this change therefore pre-dated the change to rigid boxes.

p298: The 1922 series of 9" radius rails had the normal sleepers of the period, but were not fitted with locking wires. It should perhaps have been mentioned that the 1930 series MO rail sleepers were similar in shape to those of the 1922 series. Post-1938 MO rails were embossed with 6 "bumps" instead of the previous 4, because of the M Connecting Clips.

p327: The 1932-36 and 1938-39 trademark transfer with line under "Meccano" were as shown; nevertheless it is (just!) possible to distinguish the 1939-41 version. On this the line continues to the end of the "O" of Meccano; on the earlier type the line stops just short of the end of the "O". The postwar gold transfers were similar to the pre-1939 version. *(Gordon Selby)*

p327: *Nicholas Oddy* tells us that the "gold" of the later transfers is an opaque gold ink, while that of the earlier is a translucent yellow ink through which the "silver" leaf backing of the transfer reflects. The opaque gold of the later transfers looks muddy in comparison to that of the earlier.

p330: Some early postwar wagon bases were spot welded in 4 places to secure the underframe; others were not. We have not yet discovered any rhyme or reason to it. *(Bruce Macdonald)*

p331: Axles for the 1920s nickel-plated wheels varied slightly in diameter, subsequent to the major change from Meccano rod diameter. Furthermore, late black tinplate wheels had plunged holes for the axles, presumably to improve the bearing surface. *(Gordon Selby)*

	PREWAR TRAIN SETS	

This section lists details of locos and rolling stock included over the years in the Hornby Train Sets. Rails, lamps, keys, literature and other sundry items are not listed. Electric sets had contents similar to those of the clockwork equivalent, except where noted.

MO GOODS SET; clockwork only
- 1930-41 Red MO Loco and Tender, two MO Wagons
- 1930-41 Green MO Loco and Tender, two MO Wagons

MO MIXED GOODS SET; clockwork only
- 1936-41 Red MO Loco and Tender; MO Petrol Tank, MO Side Tipping and MO Rotary Tipping Wagons
- 1936-41 Green MO Loco and Tender; MO Petrol Tank, MO Side Tipping and MO Rotary Tipping Wagons

M8 COMPLETE MODEL RAILWAY; clockwork only
- 1934-41 Red MO Loco and Tender, two MO Wagons, M Signal, M Signal Cabin, two Trees with Stands, M8 Set Tunnel, M Wayside Station, M Footbridge
- p248 1934-41 Green MO Loco and Tender, otherwise same contents

M9 COMPLETE MODEL RAILWAY; clockwork only
- 1934-41 Red MO Loco and Tender, two MO Pullman Coaches, M Signal, M Station, M Footbridge, M Signal Cabin, M Level Crossing, Guard, Porter, two Trees with Stands, two Hikers
- 1934-41 Green MO Loco and Tender, otherwise same contents

M10 COMPLETE MODEL RAILWAY; clockwork only
- 1933-41 Red MO Loco and Tender, two MO Pullman Coaches, M Footbridge, M Station, M Wayside Station, M Signal Cabin, two M Telegraph Poles, two M Signals, M Loading Gauge, No. O Tunnel, No. O Cutting, M Level Crossing, three Trees, six Figures
- 1933-41 Green MO Loco and Tender, otherwise same contents

MO PASSENGER SET; clockwork only
- 1930-41 Red MO Loco and Tender, two MO Pullman Coaches
- 1930-41 Green MO Loco and Tender, two MO Pullman Coaches

BRITISH EXPRESS TRAIN SET No. 1; clockwork only
- 1932-36 British Express Loco and Tender, Wagon

BRITISH EXPRESS TRAIN SET No. 2; clockwork only
- 1932-36 British Express Loco and Tender, and two Coaches

BRITISH EXPRESS TRAIN SET No. 3; clockwork only
- 1932-36 British Express Loco and Tender, Coach, Signal and Wayside Halt

BRITISH EXPRESS TRAIN SET No. 4; clockwork only
- 1932-36 British Express Loco and Tender, two Coaches, Signal, Signal Box and Country Station

A10

M1 GOODS SET; also EM16 1934-38, EM120 1934-38
-     1929-30   Green non-reversing M Loco and Tender, two LMS M Wagons
-     1929-30   Green non-reversing M Loco and Tender, two NE M Wagons
-     1929-30   Green non-reversing M Loco and Tender, two GW M Wagons
-     1929-30   Green non-reversing M Loco and Tender, two SR M Wagons

-     1930-41   Red Loco and Tender, two LMS M1 Wagons
-     1930-41   Green Loco and Tender, two NE M1 Wagons
-     1930-41   Green Loco and Tender, two GW M1 Wagons
-     1930-41   Green Loco and Tender, two SR M1 Wagons
-     1931-34   Dark Red Loco and Tender, two LMS M1 Wagons

MO PASSENGER SET; clockwork only (M1-style Loco)
-     1929-30   Green non-reversing M Loco and Tender, one M Pullman Coach

M1 PASSENGER SET; also EM16 1934-35, EM120 1934-38
-     1926-30   Green non-reversing M Loco and Tender, two M Pullman Coaches

-     1930-41   Green Loco and Tender, two M1 Pullman Coaches
-     1930-41   Red Loco and Tender, two M1 Pullman Coaches
-     1931-34   Dark Red M1 Loco and Tender, two M1 Pullman Coaches

M2 PASSENGER SET; also EM26 1934-35, EM220 1934-35
-     1926-30   Green non-reversing M Loco and Tender, three M Pullman Coaches

-     1930-41   Green Loco and Tender, three M1 Pullman Coaches
-     1930-41   Red Loco and Tender, three M1 Pullman Coaches
-     1931-34   Dark Red M1 Loco and Tender, three M1 Pullman Coaches

TINPRINTED/GEORGE V/No. OO TRAIN; clockwork only
-     1920-26   Green GN tinprinted Loco and Tender, two GN Tinprinted Train Coaches
-     1920-26   Red MR tinprinted Loco and Tender, two MR Tinprinted Train Coaches
-     1920-26   Black LNWR tinprinted Loco and Tender, two LNW Tinprinted Train Coaches

M3 GOODS SET; clockwork only
-     1926-28   Tinprinted GN Green Loco and Tender, two GW M Wagons
-     1926-28   Tinprinted MR Red Loco and Tender, two LMS M wagons
-     1926-28   Tinprinted LNW Black Loco and Tender, two LMS M Wagons

-     1928-29   Enamelled No. O Type PLAIN Green Loco and Tender, two GW M Wagons
-     1928-29   Enamelled No. O Type PLAIN Red Loco and Tender, two LMS M Wagons
-     1928-29   Enamelled No. O Type PLAIN Black Loco and Tender, two LMS M Wagons

No. O "SILVER JUBILEE" SET; clockwork only

p260   1936-41   LNER "Silver Link" Loco and Tender, No. O "Silver Jubilee" Articulated Saloon Coach

No. O STREAMLINED SET; clockwork only

-    1937-40   Maroon and Cream Loco and Tender, Articulated Saloon Coach
-    1937-40   Light Green and Dark Green Loco and Tender, Articulated Saloon Coach

M11 COMPLETE MODEL RAILWAY; clockwork only

-    1934-41   LMS M3 Tank Loco, LMS M3 Wagon, Fibre Wagon, Timber Wagon, No. O Tunnel, M Station, M Signal, M Level Crossing, M Signal Cabin, M
                Footbridge, two Trees with Stands, Guard, Cow, Horse and Set of Rails with Points
-    1934-41   LNER M3 Tank Loco, NE M3 Wagon, otherwise same contents
-    1934-41   GW M3 Tank Loco, GW M3 Wagon, otherwise same contents
-    1934-41   SR M3 Tank Loco, SR M3 Wagon, otherwise same contents

M3 TANK GOODS SET; also EM36 1934-41, EM320 1934-41

-    1931-41   LMS Red Tank Loco, LMS M3 Wagon, M3 Tank Wagon, M3 Timber Wagon
-    1931-41   LNER Green Tank Loco, NE M3 Wagon, M3 Tank Wagon, M3 Timber Wagon
-    1931-41   GW Green Tank Loco, GW M3 Wagon, M3 Tank Wagon, M3 Timber Wagon
-    1931-41   SR Green Tank Loco, SR M3 Wagon, M3 Tank Wagon, M3 Timber Wagon

M3 TANK PASSENGER SET; clockwork only

-    1935-41   LMS Red M3 Tank Loco, three No. O Pullman Coaches
-    1935-41   LNER Green M3 Tank Loco, three No. O Pullman Coaches
-    1935-41   GW Green M3 Tank Loco, three No. O Pullman Coaches
-    1935-41   SR Green M3 Tank Loco, three No. O Pullman Coaches

No. O GOODS SET; also EO6 1934-35, EO20 1934-35

-    1922-23   PLAIN Black Zulu Loco and Tender, LNW Zulu Wagon
-    1923-25   LMS Black Zulu Loco and Tender, LMS Zulu Wagon

-    1924-28   LMS Black Loco and Tender, LMS Wagon
-    1924-28   LMS Red Loco and Tender, LMS Wagon
-    1924-28   LNER Black Loco and Tender, LNER/NE Wagon (NE from 1926)
-    1924-28   LNER Green Loco and Tender, LNER/NE Wagon (NE from 1926)
-    1926-28   GW Loco and Tender, GW Wagon

-    1928-29   LMS Black Loco and Tender, two LMS Wagons
-    1928-29   LMS Red Loco and Tender, two LMS Wagons
-    1928-29   LNER Black Loco and Tender, two NE Wagons
-    1928-29   LNER Green Loco and Tender, two NE Wagons
-    1928-29   GW Loco and Tender, two GW Wagons
-    1928-29   SR Black Loco and Tender, two SR Wagons
-    1928-29   SR Green Loco and Tender, two SR Wagons

	1929-36	LMS Black Loco and Tender, LMS No. O Wagon, No. 1 Timber Wagon
-	1929-36	LMS Black Loco and Tender, LMS No. O Wagon, No. 1 Timber Wagon
-	1929-39	LMS Red Loco and Tender, LMS No. O Wagon, No. 1 Timber Wagon
-	1929-36	LNER Black Loco and Tender, NE No. O Wagon, No. 1 Timber Wagon
-	1929-39	LNER Green Loco and Tender, NE No. O Wagon, No. 1 Timber Wagon
-	1929-39	GW Loco and Tender, GW No. O Wagon, No. 1 Timber Wagon
-	1929-36	SR Black Loco and Tender, SR No. O Wagon, No. 1 Timber Wagon
-	1929-39	SR Green Loco and Tender, SR No. O Wagon, No. 1 Timber Wagon

(The Timber wagons had Railway Company lettering from 1929 to 1930.)

No. O PASSENGER SET; also EO6 1934-35, EO20 1934-39

-	1922-23	PLAIN Black Zulu Loco and Tender, two LNWR Zulu Coaches
-	1923-24	LMS Black Zulu Loco and Tender, two Zulu Coaches
-	1924-28	LMS Red Loco and Tender, two LMS Passenger Coaches
-	1924-28	LNER Green Loco and Tender, two LNER Passenger Coaches
-	1926-28	GW Loco and Tender, two GW Passenger Coaches
-	1928-29	LMS Red Loco and Tender, LMS Passenger Coach and Guard's Van
-	1928-29	LNER Green Loco and Tender, LNER Passenger Coach and Guard's Van
-	1928-29	GW Loco and Tender, GW Passenger Coach and Guard's Van
-	1928-29	SR Green Loco and Tender, SR Passenger Coach and Guard's Van
-	1929-39	LMS Red Loco and Tender, two No. O Pullman Coaches
-	1929-39	LNER Green Loco and Tender, two No. O Pullman Coaches
-	1929-39	GW Loco and Tender, two No. O Pullman Coaches
-	1929-39	SR Green Loco and Tender, two No. O Pullman Coaches

No. 1 TANK GOODS SET; also Control 1927-29, E16 1934-36, LST1/20 and E120 1933-41

-	1925-36	LMS Black Tank Loco, LMS Wagon, Tank Wagon, LMS Brake Van
-	1925-41	LMS Red Tank Loco, LMS Wagon, Tank Wagon, LMS Brake Van
-	1925-36	LNER Black Tank Loco, LNER/NE Wagon, Tank Wagon, LNER/NE Brake Van (NE wagons from 1926)
-	1925-41	LNER Green Tank Loco, LNER/NE Wagon, Tank Wagon, LNER/NE Brake Van (NE wagons from 1926)
-	1926-41	GW Tank Loco, GW Wagon, Tank Wagon, GW Brake Van
-	1928-36	SR Black Tank Loco, SR Wagon, Tank Wagon, SR Brake Van
-	1928-41	SR Green Tank Loco, SR Wagon, Tank Wagon, SR Brake Van

No. 1 GOODS SET; also Control 1927-29, E16 1934-35, E120 1934-41

-	1920-23	PLAIN Black Loco and Tender, LNWR Truck
-	1920-23	PLAIN Red Loco and Tender, MR Truck
-	1920-23	PLAIN Green Loco and tender, GN Truck
-	1921-23	PLAIN Blue Loco and Tender, CR Truck
-	1923-28	LMS Black Loco and Tender, LMS Wagon
-	1923-28	LMS Red Loco and Tender, LMS Wagon

-	1924-28	LNER Black Loco and Tender, LNER/NE Wagon (NE Wagon from 1926)
-	1923-28	LNER Green Loco and Tender, LNER/NE Wagon (NE Wagon from 1926)
-	1926-28	GW Loco and Tender, GW Wagon
-	1928-36	LMS Black Loco and Tender, LMS Wagon, LMS Brake Van
-	1928-41	LMS Red Loco and Tender, LMS Wagon, LMS Brake Van
-	1928-36	LNER Black Loco and Tender, NE Wagon, NE Brake Van
-	1928-41	LNER Green Loco and Tender, NE Wagon, NE Brake Van
-	1928-41	GW Loco and Tender, GW Wagon, GW Brake Van
-	1928-36	SR Black Loco and Tender, SR Wagon, SR Brake Van
-	1928-41	SR Green Loco and Tender, SR Wagon, SR Brake Van

No. 1 PASSENGER SET; also Control 1928-29, E16 1934-35, E120 1934-35

-	1921-24	PLAIN Black Loco and Tender, two LNWR Coaches
-	1921-24	PLAIN Red Loco and Tender, two MR Coaches
-	1921-24	PLAIN Green Loco and Tender, two GN Coaches
-	1921-24	PLAIN Blue Loco and Tender, two CR Coaches
-	1924-28	LMS Red Loco and Tender, two LMS Passenger Coaches
-	1924-28	LNER Green Loco and Tender, two NE Passenger Coaches
-	1926-28	GW Loco and Tender, two GW Passenger Coaches
-	1928-41	LMS Red Loco and Tender, two LMS Passenger Coaches and Guard's Van
-	1928-41	LNER Green Loco and Tender, two LNER Passenger Coaches and Guard's Van
-	1928-41	GW Loco and Tender, two GW Passenger Coaches and Guard's Van
-	1928-41	SR Green Loco and Tender, two SR Passenger Coaches and Guard's Van

No. 1 SPECIAL TANK GOODS SET; also E120 Special Tank 1935-41

-	1935-36	LMS Black Tank Loco, LMS No. 1 Wagon, Tank Wagon, LMS Brake Van
-	1935-41	LMS Red Tank Loco, LMS No. 1 Wagon, Tank Wagon, LMS Brake Van
-	1935-36	LNER Black Tank Loco, NE No. 1 Wagon, Tank Wagon, NE Brake Van
-	1935-41	LNER Green Tank Loco, NE No. 1 Wagon, Tank Wagon, NE Brake Van
-	1935-41	GW Green Tank Loco, GW No. 1 Wagon, Tank Wagon, GW Brake Van
-	1935-36	SR Black Tank Loco, SR No. 1 Wagon, Tank Wagon, SR Brake Van
-	1935-41	SR Green Tank Loco, SR No. 1 Wagon, Tank Wagon, SR Brake Van

No. 1 SPECIAL GOODS SET; also E120 Special 1934-35

-	1929-35	LMS Black Loco and Tender, LMS No. 1 Wagon, LMS Brake Van
-	1929-35	LMS Red Loco and Tender, LMS No. 1 Wagon, LMS Brake Van
-	1929-35	LNER Black Loco and Tender, NE No. 1 Wagon, NE Brake Van
-	1929-35	LNER Green Loco and Tender, NE No. 1 Wagon , NE Brake Van
-	1929-35	GW Loco and Tender, GW No. 1 Wagon, GW Brake Van
-	1929-35	SR Black Loco and Tender, SR No. 1 Wagon, SR Brake Van
-	1929-35	SR Green Loco and Tender, SR No. 1 Wagon, SR Brake Van

No. 1 SPECIAL PASSENGER SET; also E120 Special 1934-41
- 1929-37 LMS Red Loco and Tender, two No. 1 Pullman Coaches and Composite
- 1937-41 LMS Red Loco and Tender, two LMS No. 1 Passenger Coaches and Guard's Van
- 1929-41 LNER Green Loco and Tender, two No. 1 Pullman Coaches and Composite
- 1929-37 GW Loco and Tender, two No. 1 Pullman Coaches and Composite
- 1937-41 GW Loco and Tender, two GW No. 1 Passenger Coaches and Guard's Van
- 1929-41 SR Green Loco and Tender, two No. 1 Pullman Coaches and Composite

No. 2 TANK GOODS SET; also Control 1927-29
- 1925-29 LMS Black Tank Loco, LMS Wagon, Tank Wagon, LMS Cattle Truck, LMS Brake Van
- 1925-29 LMS Red Tank Loco, LMS Wagon, Tank Wagon, LMS Cattle Truck, LMS Brake Van
- 1925-29 LNER Black Tank Loco, LNER/NE Wagon, Tank Wagon, LNER/NE Cattle Truck, LNER/NE Brake Van (NE wagons from 1926)
- 1925-29 LNER Green Tank Loco, LNER/NE Wagon, Tank Wagon, LNER/NE Cattle Truck, LNER/NE Brake Van (NE wagons from 1926)
- 1926-29 GW Tank Loco, GW Wagon, Tank Wagon, GW Cattle Truck, GW Brake Van
- 1928-29 SR Black Tank Loco, SR Wagon, Tank Wagon, SR Cattle Truck, SR Brake Van
- 1928-29 SR Green Tank Loco, SR Wagon, Tank Wagon, SR Cattle Truck, SR Brake Van

No. 2 TANK PASSENGER SET; also Control 1926-29
- 1925-28 LMS Red Tank Loco, three LMS Passenger Coaches and Guard's Van
- 1925-28 LNER Green Tank Loco, three LNER Passenger Coaches and Guard's Van
- 1926-28 GW Tank Loco, three GW Passenger Coaches and Guard's Van

- 1928-29 LMS Red Tank Loco, three No. 1 Pullman Coaches and Composite
- 1928-29 LNER Green Tank Loco, three No. 1 Pullman Coaches and Composite
- 1928-29 GW Tank Loco, three No. 1 Pullman Coaches and Composite
- 1928-29 SR Green Tank Loco, three No. 1 Pullman Coaches and Composite

No. 2 HORNBY GOODS SET; also Control 1927-29
- 1921-23 PLAIN Black Loco and Tender, two LNWR Wagons
- 1921-23 PLAIN Red Loco and Tender, two MR Wagons
- 1921-23 PLAIN Green Loco and Tender, two GN Wagons
- 1921-23 PLAIN Blue Loco and Tender, two CR Wagons

- 1923-29 LMS Black Loco and Tender, two LMS Wagons (LMS Brake Van added from 1928)
- 1923-29 LMS Red Loco and Tender, two LMS Wagons (LMS Brake Van added from 1928)
- 1924-29 LNER Black Loco and Tender, two LNER/NE Wagons (NE Wagons from 1926; NE Brake Van added from 1928)
- 1923-29 LNER Green Loco and Tender, two LNER/NE Wagons (NE Wagons from 1926; NE Brake Van added from 1928)
- 1926-29 GW Loco and Tender, two GW Wagons (GW Brake Van added from 1928)
- 1928-29 SR Black Loco and Tender, two SR Wagons, SR Brake Van
- 1928-29 SR Green Loco and Tender, two SR Wagons, SR Brake Van

No. 2 PULLMAN SET; also Control 1926-29
- 1921-23   PLAIN Black Loco and Tender, Pullman Car and LNWR Dining Saloon
- 1921-23   PLAIN Red Loco and Tender, Pullman Car and MR Dining Saloon
- 1921-23   PLAIN Green Loco and Tender, Pullman Car and GN Dining Saloon
- 1921-23   PLAIN Blue Loco and Tender, Pullman Car and CR Dining Saloon

- 1923-25   LMS Black Loco and Tender, Pullman Car and Pullman Dining Saloon
- 1923-25   LMS Red Loco and Tender, Pullman Car and Pullman Dining Saloon
- 1923-25   LNER Green Loco and Tender, Pullman Car and Pullman Dining Saloon

- 1925-29   LMS Red loco and Tender, two Pullman Cars
- 1925-29   LNER Green Loco and Tender, two Pullman Cars
- 1926-29   GW Loco and Tender, two Pullman Cars
- 1928-29   SR Green Loco and Tender, two Pullman Cars

No. 2 SPECIAL GOODS SET; clockwork only
- 1929-30   LMS Black No. 2 Special Tank Loco, two LMS Wagons, LMS Brake Van
- 1929-30   LMS Red No. 2 Special Tank Loco, two LMS Wagons, LMS Brake Van
- 1929-30   LNER Black No. 2 Special Tank Loco, two NE Wagons, NE Brake Van
- 1929-30   LNER Green No. 2 Special Tank Loco, two NE Wagons, NE Brake Van
- 1929-30   GW No. 2 Special Tank Loco, two GW Wagons, GW Brake Van
- 1929-30   SR Black No. 2 Special Tank Loco, two SR Wagons, SR Brake Van
- 1929-30   SR Green No. 2 Special Tank Loco, two SR Wagons, SR Brake Van

No. 2 MIXED GOODS SET; also E26 1934-35, LST2/20 and E220 1933-41
- 1929-36   LMS Black Tank Loco, LMS Wagon, Tank Wagon, LMS Cattle Truck, LMS Brake Van
- 1929-41   LMS Red Tank Loco, LMS Wagon, Tank Wagon, LMS Cattle Truck, LMS Brake Van
- 1929-36   LNER Black Tank Loco, NE Wagon, Tank Wagon, NE Cattle Truck, NE Brake Van
- 1929-41   LNER Green Tank Loco, NE Wagon, Tank Wagon, NE Cattle truck, NE Brake Van
- 1929-41   GW Tank Loco, GW Wagon, Tank Wagon, GW Cattle Truck, GW Brake Van
- 1929-36   SR Black Tank Loco, SR Wagon, Tank Wagon, SR Cattle Truck, SR Brake Van
- 1929-41   SR Green Tank Loco, SR Wagon, Tank Wagon, SR Cattle Truck, SR Brake Van

No. 2 SPECIAL TANK PASSENGER SET; also E220 Special Tank 1935-41
- 1935-41   LMS Red Tank Loco, No. 2 LMS Passenger Coach and Brake
- 1935-41   LNER Green Tank Loco, No. 2 NE Passenger Coach and Brake
- 1935-41   GW Tank Loco, No. 2 GW Passenger Coach and Brake
- 1935-41   SR Green Tank Loco, No. 2 SR Passenger Coach and Brake

No. 2 SPECIAL PULLMAN SET; also E220 1934-37
- 1929-37   LMS Compound Loco and Tender, No. 2 Special Pullman Coach and Composite
- 1929-37   LNER Loco and Tender, No. 2 Special Pullman Coach and Composite ("Yorkshire" 1929-35, "Bramham Moor" 1935-37)
- 1929-37   GW "County of Bedford" Loco and Tender, No. 2 Special Pullman Coach and Composite
- 1929-37   SR L1 Loco and Tender, No. 2 Special Pullman Coach and Composite

No. 2 SPECIAL PASSENGER SET; (also E220 1937-41; E220 sets contained two Coaches and one Brake)
-     1937-41   LMS Compound Loco and Tender, LMS No. 2 Corridor Coach and Brake
-     1937-41   LNER "Bramham Moor" Loco and Tender, NE No. 2 Corridor Coach and Brake
-     1937-41   GW "County of Bedford" Loco and Tender, GW No. 2 Corridor Coach and Brake
-     1937-41   SR L1 Loco and Tender, SR No. 2 Corridor Coach and Brake

No. 3C PULLMAN SET; clockwork Control only 1927-29; clockwork 1929-41; 3E (4V) 1927-29; 3E (6V) 1929-36; E320 1934-41
-     1927-28   LMS "Royal Scot" and Tender, two No. 2 Pullman Coaches
-     1927-28   LNER "Flying Scotsman" and Tender, two No. 2 Pullman Coaches
-     1927-28   GW "Caerphilly Castle" and Tender, two No. 2 Pullman Coaches
-     1928   SR "Lord Nelson" and Tender, two No. 2 Pullman Coaches

-     1928-37   LMS "Royal Scot" and Tender, No. 2 Special Pullman Coach and Composite
-     1928-37   LNER "Flying Scotsman" and Tender, No. 2 Special Pullman Coach and Composite
-     1928-37   GW "Caerphilly Castle" and Tender, No. 2 Special Pullman Coach and Composite
-     1928-41   SR "Lord Nelson" and Tender, No. 2 Special Pullman Coach and Composite
          Resistance Controller included in electric sets, to July 1934

No. 3C PASSENGER SET; (also E320, same dates; E320 Sets contained two Coaches and one Brake)
-     1937-41   LMS "Royal Scot" and Tender, LMS No. 2 Corridor Coach and Brake
-     1937-41   LNER "Flying Scotsman" and Tender, NE No. 2 Corridor Coach and Brake
-     1937-41   GW "Caerphilly Castle" and Tender, GW No. 2 Corridor Coach and Brake
          (No SR version)

No. 3C RIVIERA "BLUE" TRAIN; clockwork Control only 1926-29; clockwork 1929-41; 3E (4V) 1926-29; 3E (6V) 1929-36; E320 1934-40
-     1926-41   Nord Loco and Tender, Riviera Blue Train Sleeping Car and Dining Car

METROPOLITAN SET; HV 1925-26 and 1927-29; LV (4V) 1926-29; LV (6V) 1929-39; E320 1938-39; Control c/w 1926-29; c/w 1929-39
-     1925-41   Metropolitan Loco, 1st Class and Brake/3rd Coaches. (Rheostat included with HV Sets; Resistance Controller with LV Sets until July 1934)

PRESENTATION SET A
-     1923-24   Hornby Passenger Set, two Wagons, Brake Van, Luggage Van, Milk Traffic Van, Side Tipping Wagon, Rotary Tipping Wagon, Colman's Mustard Van, Crane Truck, Petrol Tank Wagon, Gas Cylinder Wagon, Timber Wagon, Windsor Station, Turntable, two Signals, Lamp Standard, two Telegraph Poles, Loading Gauge, Spring Buffer Stop, Lattice Girder Bridge, extra rails to make Figure 23S. Loco colours given as "Black, Chocolate and Green".

PRESENTATION SET B
p20   1923-24   No. 2 Pullman Set, two Wagons, Luggage Van, Brake Van, Milk Traffic Van, No. 2 Cattle Truck, Refrigerator Van, Colman's Mustard Van, Breakdown Van and Crane, Trolley Wagon, Petrol Tank Wagon, Gas Cylinder Wagon, No. 2 Lumber Wagon, No. 2 Timber Wagon, Side Tipping Wagon, Rotary Tipping Wagon, Hopper Wagon, Cement Wagon, Windsor Station, Turntable, three Telegraph Poles, Loading Gauge, Double Lamp Standard, three Signals, two Spring Buffer Stops, Lattice Girder Bridge, Extra track to make Figure 23L. Loco colours given as "Black, Chocolate and Green".

Please note caveat about tender pairings on page 324 of Volume 5. Safety valve cover abbreviated to "svc".

MO LOCOMOTIVE (Clockwork only)

p246   1930-32   **Green boiler, black base**; no cylinders; cutout cab windows; fixed key; single flat splasher. **4472** tender.
p247   1932-33   Green boiler, black base; no cylinders; **printed** cab windows; fixed key; single flat splasher. **2595** tender.
p247   1933-36   Green boiler, **red base**; no cylinders; fixed key; single flat splasher; 2595 tender.
p247   1933-36   Green boiler, **green base**; no cylinders; fixed key; single flat splasher; 2595 tender.
p247   1936-38   Green boiler, **black base with cylinders**; **removeable** key; single flat splasher. 2595 tender
p248   1938-41   Green boiler, black base with cylinders; removeable key; **two round splashers**. 2595 tender

p246   1930-32   **Red boiler, black base**; no cylinders; cutout cab windows; fixed key; single flat splasher. **6100** tender.
-   1932-33   Red boiler, black base; no cylinders; **printed** cab windows; fixed key; single flat splasher (PU). **6161** tender.
p247   1933-36   Red boiler, **red base**; no cylinders; fixed key; single flat splasher; 6161 tender.
p247   1933-36   Red boiler, **green base**; no cylinders; fixed key; single flat splasher; 6161 tender.
p247   1936-38   Red boiler, **black base with cylinders**; **removeable** key; single flat splasher. 6161 tender
-   1938-41   Red boiler, black base with cylinders; removeable key; **two round splashers**. 6161 tender

p249   1932-36   **BRITISH EXPRESS LOCO**; 3233 tender

M1 LOCOMOTIVE (EM120 and EM16 1934-38)
Some 1932-33 transitional versions used old tinprintings with plain black cab windows, not cut out.

p250   1926-27   Green Loco, **2526**; diecast chimney, nickel winder; green tender, **2526**. c/w only
p251   1927-28   Green Loco, **2728**; diecast chimney, nickel winder; green tender, **2728**. c/w only
-   1928-29   Green Loco, 2728; diecast chimney, **black winder**; green tender, 2728. c/w only
p251   1929-32   Green Loco, **2930**; **tin chimney**, black winder; green tender, **2930**. c/w only

p251   1930-31   **Green boiler, black base**; **cutout cab windows**; **green 3031 tender**, black base; c/w only (p251 shows loco only)
p251   1931-33   Green boiler, black base; **printed cab windows**; green **3132 tender**, black base; c/w only (p251 shows tender only)
p251   1933-34   Green boiler, **green base**; green **3133 tender**, green base; c/w
-   1934-36   Green boiler, green base; green **3435 tender**, green base; c/w, EM16, EM120
-   1934-36   Green boiler, **red base** (PU); green **3435 tender**, **red base** (PU)
p252   1936-41   Green boiler, **black base**; green 3435 tender, **black base**; c/w, EM16, EM120

p251   1930-31   **Red boiler, black base**; **cutout cab windows**; **red 3031 tender**, black base; c/w only (p251 shows tender only)
-   1931-33   Red boiler, black base; **printed cab windows** (PU); red **3132 tender**, black base (PU); c/w only
-   1933-34   Red boiler, **green base**; red 3132 tender, **green base**; c/w
p252   1934-36   Red boiler, green base; red **3435 tender**, green base; c/w, EM120, EM16
p252   1934-36   Red boiler, **red base**; red 3435 tender, **red base**; c/w, EM120, EM16
-   1936-41   Red boiler, **black base**; red 3435 tender, **black base**; c/w, EM120, EM16

| p251 | 1931-33 | **Maroon boiler, black base**; **printed cab windows**; **maroon 3132 tender**, black base; c/w only |
| - | 1933-34 | Maroon boiler, **green base**; maroon 3132 tender, **green base**; c/w only |

GEORGE V, OO and M3 LOCOMOTIVE (Clockwork only)

p254	1920-26	GN green tinprinted loco **1452**; GNR tinprinted train tender
-	1926-28	GN green mainly tinprinted loco 1452; **green 2526 tender** with coal rail cutout
-	1928	GN green part-tinprinted loco 1452; **green 2728 tender** with coal rail cutout
p256	1928-29	**Green enamelled No. O-style body**; green 2728 tender with coal rail cutout

p254	1920-26	MR red tinprinted loco, no number; MR tinprinted train tender **483**
p255	1926-27	MR red tinprinted loco, no number; **red tinprinted M1-style 2527 coal rail tender**
p255	1927-28	MR red part-tinprinted loco, no number; **red enamelled 2710 narrow base tender**
p256	1928-29	Red enamelled No. O-style body; red enamelled 2710 wide base tender without buffers

p9	1920-26	LNWR black tinprinted loco 2663 "George V"; "LNWR" tinprinted train tender
p255	1926-27	LNWR black tinprinted loco 2663 "George V"; **black tinprinted Ml-style 2527 coal rail tender**
p255	1927-28	LNWR black part-tinprinted loco 2663 "George V"; **black enamelled 2710 narrow base tender**
p256	1928-29	**Black enamelled No. O-style body**; black enamelled 2710 wide base tender without buffers

M3 TANK LOCOMOTIVE (LSTM3/20 1932-34; EM320 and EM36 from 1934)
Coupling rods and 8-spoke wheels were frequently fitted to pre-1936 locos when they were returned for repair after 1936

-	1931-32	LMS red, tinprinted loco 2270; no cylinders, 8-spoke wheels, no coupling rods; c/w only
p259	1932-36	LMS red, tinprinted loco 2270; no cylinders, **12-spoke wheels**, no coupling rods; c/w, EM36, EM3/20, EM320
p238	1936-41	LMS red, tinprinted loco 2270; **with cylinders**, **8-spoke wheels**, **with rods**; c/w, EM36, EM320

-	1931-32	LNER green, tinprinted loco **460**; no cylinders, 8-spoke wheels, no coupling rods; c/w only
-	1932-36	LNER green, tinprinted loco 460; no cylinders, **12-spoke wheels**, no coupling rods; c/w, EM36, EM3/20, EM320
p237	1936-41	LNER green, tinprinted loco 460; **with cylinders**, **8-spoke wheels**, **with rods**; c/w, EM36, EM320

p258	1931-32	GW green, tinprinted loco **6600**; no cylinders, 8-spoke wheels, no coupling rods; c/w only
p259	1932-36	GW green, tinprinted loco 6600; no cylinders, **12-spoke wheels**, no coupling rods; c/w, EM36, EM3/20, EM320
-	1936-41	GW green, tinprinted loco 6600; **with cylinders**, **8-spoke wheels**, **with rods**; c/w, EM36, EM320

-	1931-32	SR green, tinprinted loco **E126**; no cylinders, 8-spoke wheels, no coupling rods; c/w only
p258	1932-36	SR green, tinprinted loco E126; no cylinders, **12-spoke wheels**, no coupling rods; c/w, EM36, EM3/20, EM320
p215	1936-41	SR green, tinprinted loco E126; **with cylinders**, **8-spoke wheels**, **with rods**; c/w, EM36, EM320

SILVER LINK and STREAMLINED LOCOS (Clockwork only)

p260	1936-41	"Silver Link", **2509** on cabside
p260	1937-40	Streamlined Loco, light and dark green, **7391** on loco and tender
p260	1937-40	Streamlined Loco, maroon and cream, **3917** on loco and tender

No. 0 LOCOMOTIVE (EO6 1934-35; EO20 1934-41)

p17	1922-23	PLAIN black, "ZULU" on splashers, no number. Plain tender. c/w only
p115	1923-24	**LMS** black, "ZULU" on smokebox, no number on cab. **2710** tender, no lining transfer. c/w only
p22	1924-25	LMS black, **unlined crest** on cabside, black dome. 2710 tender, no lining transfer. c/w only
-	1925-26	LMS black, **lined crest** on cabside, unlined boiler, **brass** dome. **Narrow base** 2710 tender, **lining transfer**. c/w only
p113	1926-27	LMS black, lined crest on cabside, unlined boiler, brass dome. **Normal base** 2710 tender, lining transfer. c/w only
-	1927-28	LMS black, lined crest on cabside, **3 single boiler bands**, brass dome. Normal 2710 tender. c/w only
-	1928-29	LMS black, lined crest on cabside, short splasher, 3 single boiler bands, **black dome** (PU). 2710 tender. c/w only
-	1929-31	LMS black, **8327** on cabside, **long splasher**, black dome. **"L.M.S."** coalrail tender. c/w only
p41	1931	LMS black, 8327 on cabside, long splasher, black dome. **"L M S"** (no full stop) coalrail tender. c/w only
p214	1931-36	LMS black, **600** on cabside, **revised body style**. "LMS" tender. c/w, EO6, EO20
-	1924-26	**LMS red,** lined crest on cabside, unlined boiler. Narrow base 2710 tender, lining transfer. c/w only
p27	1926-27	LMS red, lined crest on cabside, unlined boiler. **Normal width,** black base 2710 tender, lining transfer. c/w only
p113	1927-28	LMS red, lined crest on cabside, **3 single boiler bands**, brass dome, red smokebox. **Red base** 2710 tender. c/w only
-	1928-29	LMS red, lined crest on cabside, short splasher, 3 single boiler bands, **red dome, black smokebox** (PU). 2710 tender. c/w only
p34	1929-31	LMS red, **8324** on cabside, **long splasher**, red dome. **"L.M.S."** coalrail tender. c/w only
-	1931	LMS red, 8324 on cabside, long splasher, red dome. **"L M S"** (no full stop) coalrail tender. c/w only
p51	1931-37	LMS red, **500** on cabside, **revised body style, no cylinders**. "LMS" tender. c/w, EO6, EO20
-	1937-38	LMS red, 500 on cabside, revised body style, **cylinders**. "LMS" tender. c/w, EO20
p209	1938-39	LMS red, **5551** on cabside, revised body style, cylinders. "LMS" tender. c/w, EO20
p66	1939-41	LMS red, **5600** on cabside, revised body style, cylinders. "LMS" tender. c/w, EO20
p115	1924-26	**LNER black,** lined crest on cabside, unlined boiler. Narrow base 2710 tender, lining transfer. c/w only
-	1926-27	LNER black, lined crest on cabside, unlined boiler. **Normal width** 2710 tender, lining transfer. c/w only
-	1927-28	LNER black, lined crest on cabside, **3 single boiler bands**, brass dome. Normal width 2710 tender. c/w only
-	1928-29	LNER black, lined crest on cabside, short splasher, 3 single boiler bands, **black dome** (PU). 2710 tender. c/w only
-	1929-31	LNER black, **small 232** on cabside, **long splasher**, black dome. **"L.N.E.R. 5097"** tender. c/w only
p113	1931-36	LNER black, **6380** on cabside, **revised body style, no cylinders**. "LNER" tender. c/w, EO6, EO20
-	1924-26	**LNER green,** lined crest on cabside, unlined boiler. Narrow base 2710 tender, lining transfer. c/w only
p115	1926-27	LNER green, lined crest on cabside, unlined boiler. **Normal width,** black base 2710 tender, lining transfer. c/w only
-	1927-28	LNER green, lined crest on cabside, **3 single boiler bands**, brass dome, green smokebox. **Green base** 2710 tender. c/w only
-	1928-29	LNER green, lined crest on cabside, short splasher, 3 single boiler bands, **green dome, black smokebox** (PU). 2710 tender. c/w only
p113	1929-31	LNER green, **small 232** on cabside, **long splasher**, green dome. **"L.N.E.R. 5096"** coalrail tender. c/w only
-	1930-31	LNER green, 8324, long splasher, **LMS-style lining transfers**. "LNER" coalrail tender, LNER-style lining. c/w only
p43	1931-36	LNER green, **5508** on cabside, **revised body style, no cylinders**. "LNER" tender. c/w, EO6, EO20
-	1935	LNER green, **2810** on cabside, revised body style, no cylinders. "LNER" tender. EO20 only (probably a production error)
-	1936-37	LNER **darker green**, 5508 on cabside, revised body style, no cylinders. "LNER" tender. c/w, EO20
p62	1937-38	LNER darker green, 5508 on cabside, revised body style, **cylinders**. "LNER" tender. c/w, EO20
p238	1938-41	LNER darker green, **4797** on cabside, revised body style, cylinders. "LNER" tender. c/w, EO20

-	1926-27	**GW**, lined crest on cabside, unlined boiler, cast svc. (PU) Black base 2710 tender. c/w only
-	1927-28	GW, lined crest on cabside, **3 single boiler bands**, cast svc. **Green base** 2710 tender. c/w only
-	1928	GW, lined crest on cabside, 3 single boiler bands, **brass svc**, green smokebox. (PU) Green base 2710 tender. c/w only
-	1928-29	GW, lined crest on cabside, short splasher, 3 single boiler bands, brass svc, **black smokebox**. (PU) Green base 2710 tender. c/w only
p36	1929	GW, **2449 numberplate**, **long splasher**, 3 single boiler bands, "**Great (crest) Western**" tender. c/w only
p36	1929-31	GW, 2449 numberplate, long splasher, **5 boiler bands**, "Great (crest) Western" tender. c/w only
p113	1931-35	GW, **2251 numberplate**, **revised body style, no cylinders.** "Great (crest) Western" tender. c/w, EO6, EO20
-	1935-37	GW, 2251 numberplate, revised body style, no cylinders. **"GWR" monogram tender.** c/w, EO6, EO20
-	1937-38	GW, 2251 numberplate, revised body style, **cylinders.** "GWR" monogram tender. c/w, EO20
p67	1938-41	GW, **5399 numberplate**, revised body style, cylinders. "GWR" monogram tender. c/w, EO20
-	1928-29	**SR black**, no number on cabside, short splasher; 4 boiler bands (PU). "Southern E509" tender. c/w only
-	1929-31	SR black, **small 232** on cabside, **long splasher**; 5 boiler bands; "Southern E509" tender. c/w only
p113	1931-36	SR black, **no number** on cabside, **revised body style, no cylinders.** "Southern A504" tender. c/w, EO6, EO20 .
-	1928-29	**SR green**, no number on cabside, short splasher; 4 boiler bands; "Southern A759" tender. c/w only
p35	1929-31	SR green, **small 232** on cabside, **long splasher: 5 boiler bands**; "Southern A759" tender. c/w only
p220	1931-33	SR green, **no number** on cabside, **revised body style, no cylinders.** "Southern E793" tender. c/w only
-	1933-37	SR green, no number on cabside, revised body style, no cylinders. **"Southern 793"** tender. c/w, EO6, EO20
p113	1937-41	SR green, no number on cabside, revised body style, **cylinders.** "Southern 793" tender. c/w, EO20

No. 1 TANK LOCOMOTIVE (Control 1927-29; Electric No. 1 Tank 6V DC 1929-34; E16 Tank 1934-36; LST1/20 1932-34; E120 Tank from 1934)

p17	1922-23	**PLAIN** black, no number, "**ZULU**" on tanks. c/w only
-	1923-24	**LMS black**, no number, "ZULU" on **smokebox door, "LMS"** on unlined tanks. c/w only
p22	1924-25	LMS black, number "0-4-0", black dome, plain smokebox door, red-lined cab windows. c/w only ("ZULU" on earliest versions only)
p121	1925-26	LMS black, number "0-4-0", **brass dome, detailed** smokebox door, red-lined cab windows. c/w only
-	1926	LMS black, number "0-4-0", brass dome, detailed smokebox door, **unlined cab windows.** c/w only
-	1926-27	LMS black, **623**, brass dome, unlined boiler. c/w only
p30	1927-28	LMS black, 623, brass dome, **2 prs boiler bands.** c/w only
-	1928-31	LMS black, 623, **black dome**, 2 prs boiler bands. c/w only
p41	1929-31	LMS black, **326**, black dome. c/w; 6V DC to 1934
p41	1930-31	LMS black, **no number**, "LMS" on lined tanks, black dome. c/w only
p47	1931-36	LMS black, **7140; revised body style.** c/w, E16, E120
-	1925	**LMS red**, number "0-4-0", brass dome, plain smokebox door. c/w only
p120	1925-26	LMS red, number "0-4-0", brass dome, **detailed smokebox door.** c/w only
p27	1926-27	LMS red, **623**, brass dome, unlined boiler. c/w only
p121	1927-28	LMS red, 623, brass dome, **2 prs boiler bands**, red smokebox. c/w only
p34	1928-29	LMS red, 623, **red dome**, 2 prs boiler bands, **black smokebox.** c/w; 6V DC to 1934
p34	1929-31	LMS red, **326**, red dome, black smokebox. c/w
p40	1930-31	LMS red, **no number**, "LMS" on lined tanks, red dome. c/w only

p45	1931-37	LMS red, **2115** (serif numbers and letters); **revised body style**. c/w, E16, E120
p61	1937-39	LMS red, 2115 (**sans-serif** numbers and letters); revised body style. c/w, E120
p70	1939-41	LMS red, 2115 (**serif** numbers and letters); revised body style (as before, but usually matt). c/w, E120
p199	1925-26	**LNER black**, number "0-4-0", brass dome, detailed smokebox door, red-lined cab windows. c/w only
-	1926	LNER black, number "0-4-0", brass dome, detailed smokebox door, **unlined cab windows**. c/w only
p220	1926-27	LNER black, **623**, brass dome, unlined boiler. c/w only
-	1927-28	LNER black, 623, brass dome, **2 prs boiler bands**. c/w only
-	1928-29	LNER black, **326**, brass dome, 2 prs boiler bands
p37	1929-31	LNER black, 326, **black dome**. c/w; 6V DC to 1934
-	1930-31	LNER black, **no number**, "LNER" on lined tanks, black dome (PU)
p121	1931-36	LNER black, **826**; **revised body style**; c/w, E16, E120
p236	1924-25	**LNER green**, number "0-4-0", brass dome, plain smokebox door, green buffer beams and chimney. c/w only
-	1925-26	LNER green, number "0-4-0", brass dome, **detailed smokebox door, red buffer beams, black chimney**. c/w only
p29	1926-27	LNER green, **623**, brass dome, unlined boiler. c/w only
p121	1927-28	LNER green, 623, brass dome, **2 prs boiler bands**, green smokebox. c/w only
-	1928	LNER green, **463**, brass dome, green smokebox. c/w only
-	1928-29	LNER green, 463, **green dome**, green smokebox. c/w only
p120	1929-31	LNER green, 463, green dome, **black smokebox**. c/w; 6V DC to 1934
p39	1930-31	LNER green, **no number**, "LNER" on lined tanks, green dome. c/w only
p50	1931-36	LNER green, **2900**; **revised body style**. c/w, E16, E120
-	1936-41	LNER **darker** green, 2900; revised body style. c/w, E120
p26	1926	**GW green**, no number, cast svc, unlined boiler; no crest. c/w only
-	1926-27	GW green, no number, cast svc, unlined boiler; **with crest**. c/w only
-	1927	GW green, no number, cast svc, **2 prs boiler bands**; with crest. c/w only
p30	1927-28	GW green, no number, **brass svc**, 2 prs boiler bands; with crest; green smokebox. c/w only
p121	1928-31	GW green, no number, brass svc, 2 prs boiler bands; with crest; **black smokebox**. c/w; 6V DC to 1934
-	1930-31	GW green, no number, brass svc, 2 prs boiler bands; **no crest**; black smokebox; GW-style tank lining. c/w only
p42	1930-31	GW green, no number, brass svc, 2 prs boiler bands; no crest; black smokebox; **LMS-style** tank lining. c/w only
p44	1931-35	GW green, **4560** on black/red/gold plate, **revised body style**, "Great Western". c/w, E16, E120
p67	1935-41	GW green, 4560 on **black/gold** plate, revised body style, "GWR" monogram. c/w, E120
p37	1928-31	**SR black, A600**. c/w; 6V DC to 1934
p45	1931-33	SR black, **E111, revised body style**. c/w, E120
p121	1933-36	SR black, **111**, revised body style. c/w, E16, E120
p37	1928-31	**SR green, B667**. c/w; 6V DC to 1934
-	1931-33	SR green, **E29, revised body style**. c/w, E120
p121	1933-41	SR black, **29**, revised body style. c/w, E16, E120

No. 1 LOCOMOTIVE (Control 1927-29; E16 1934-35; E120 from 1934)

-	1920	**PLAIN (LNWR) black** loco, nickel running plate, 2710 numberplate (PU); plain black tender
p11	1920-23	PLAIN (LNWR) black loco, **black running plate**, 2710 numberplate; plain black tender. c/w only
-	1920	**PLAIN (GN) green** loco, nickel running plate, 2710 numberplate; plain green tender, green base. c/w only
p15	1920-23	PLAIN (GN) green loco; **black running plate**, red valance; 2710 numberplate; plain green tender, **black base**. c/w only
p117	1920	**PLAIN (MR) red** loco, nickel running plate, 2710 numberplate; plain red tender, red base. c/w only
p15	1920-23	PLAIN (MR) red loco; **black running plate**, red valance; 2710 numberplate; plain red tender, **black base**. c/w only
p117	1921-23	**PLAIN (CR) blue** loco, black running plate, 2710 numberplate; plain blue tender, black base. c/w only

p18	1923	**LMS black**, 2710 numberplate, white lined "LMS" rh splasher, unlined boiler; plain tender. c/w only
-	1923-24	LMS black, 2710 numberplate, **gold lined "LMS" rh splasher**, unlined boiler; plain tender. c/w only
-	1924-25	LMS black, **lined crest on cab, gold lined "LMS" both splashers, 3 single boiler bands; 2710 tender**, no lining transfer. c/w only
p119	1925-26	LMS black, lined crest on cab, "LMS" splashers, **5 boiler bands; narrow base** 2710 tender, **lining transfer**. c/w only
p27	1926-28	LMS black, lined crest on cab, "LMS" splashers, 5 boiler bands; **normal width** 2710 tender, lining transfer. c/w only
-	1928-29	LMS black, lined crest on cab, short "LMS" splashers, 5 boiler bands, **black dome** (PU); normal width 2710 tender, lining transfer. c/w only
-	1929-31	LMS black, **8327** on cabside, **long splasher**, black dome; **"L.M.S."** coal rail tender. c/w only
-	1931	LMS black, 8327 on cabside, long splasher, black dome; **"L M S"** (no full stop) coal rail tender. c/w only
p211	1931-36	LMS black, **2290** on cabside, **revised body style**; "LMS" tender. c/w, E16, E120

p18	1923	**LMS red**, 2710 numberplate, white lined "LMS" rh splasher, unlined boiler; plain tender. c/w only
-	1923-24	LMS red, 2710 numberplate, **gold lined "LMS" rh splasher**, unlined boiler; plain tender. c/w only
p23	1924-25	LMS red, **lined crest on cab, gold lined "LMS" both splashers, 3 single boiler bands; 2710 tender**, no lining transfer. c/w only
-	1925-26	LMS red, lined crest on cab, "LMS" splashers, **5 boiler bands**, black running plate; **narrow base** 2710 tender, **lining transfer**. c/w only
-	1926-27	LMS red, lined crest on cab, "LMS" splashers, 5 boiler bands, **red running plate; normal width** black base 2710 tender, lining transfer. c/w only
p30	1927-28	LMS red, lined crest on cab, "LMS" splashers, 5 boiler bands, red running plate; normal width **red base** 2710 tender, lining transfer. c/w only
p128	1928-29	LMS red, lined crest on cab, short "LMS" splashers, 5 boiler bands, **red dome, black smokebox**; normal width 2710 tender, lining transfer. c/w only
p34	1929-31	LMS red, **8324** on cabside, **long splasher**, red dome; **"L.M.S."** coal rail tender. c/w only
-	1931	LMS red, 8324 on cabside, long splasher, red dome; **"L M S"** (no full stop) coal rail tender. c/w only
p119	1931-36	LMS red, **1000** on cabside, **revised body style**; "LMS" tender. c/w, E16, E120
-	1936-38	LMS red, **serif 5600** on cabside, revised body style; "LMS" tender. c/w, E120
p70	1938-41	LMS red, **sans-serif** 5600 on cabside, revised body style; "LMS" tender. c/w, E120

p24	1924-25	**LNER black**, lined crest on cab, "LNER" both splashers; 3 single boiler bands; 2710 tender, no lining transfer. c/w only
p25	1925-26	LNER black, lined crest on cab, **5 boiler bands; narrow base** 2710 tender, **lining transfer**. c/w only
-	1926-28	LNER black, lined crest on cab, 5 boiler bands; **normal width** 2710 tender, lining transfer. c/w only
-	1928-29	LNER black, lined crest on cab, short splasher, 5 boiler bands, **black dome** (PU); normal width 2710 tender, lining transfer. c/w only
p118	1929-31	LNER black, **small 232** on cabside, **long splasher**, black dome; **"L.N.E.R. 5097"** tender. c/w only
p119	1931-36	LNER black, **6097** on cabside, **revised body style**; "LNER" tender. c/w, E16, E120

p18	1923-24	L&NER green, 2710 numberplate, "L&NER" rh splasher, unlined boiler; plain tender, or "L&NER" tender with no lining transfer. c/w only
-		(also with "LNER" tender, no lining transfer)
-	1924-25	L&NER green, **lined crest on cab**, "**L&NER" both splashers, 3 single boiler bands**; **2710 tender**, no lining transfer. c/w only
p25	1925-26	LNER green, lined crest on cab, "**LNER" splashers**, **5 boiler bands**, black running plate, red valance; **narrow base** 2710 tender, **lining transfer**. c/w only
p29	1926-27	LNER green, lined crest on cab, "LNER" splashers, 5 boiler bands, **green running plate**, red valance; **normal width** black base 2710 tender, lining transfer. c/w only
-	1927-28	LNER green, lined crest on cab, "LNER" splashers, 5 boiler bands, green running plate, **green valance**; normal width **green base** 2710 tender, lining transfer. c/w only
-	1928-29	LNER green, lined crest on cab, short "LNER" splashers, **4 boiler bands**, **green dome**, **black smokebox** (PU); normal width 2710 tender, lining transfer. c/w only
p116	1929-31	LNER green, **small 232** on cabside, **long splasher**, green dome; "**L.N.E.R. 5096**" tender. c/w only
-	1930-31	LNER green, 8324, long splasher, **LMS-style lining transfers**. "LNER" coalrail tender, LNER-style lining. c/w only
p43	1931-36	LNER green, 2810 on cabside, **revised body style**; "LNER" tender. c/w, E16, E120
p119	1936-41	LNER **darker** green, 2810 on cabside, revised body style; "LNER" tender. c/w, E120
-	1939-41	LNER darker green, **1842** on cabside, revised body style (PU); "LNER" tender
-	1926	**GW green**, lined crest on cab, 2 prs boiler bands, cast svc; broad lining; black base 2710 tender, broad lining transfer. c/w only
p26	1926-27	GW green, lined crest on cab, 2 prs boiler bands, cast svc; **narrower lining**; black base 2710 tender, **narrower lining** transfer. c/w only
p30	1927-28	GW green, lined crest on cab, 2 prs boiler bands, **brass svc**, green smokebox; **green base** 2710 tender, lining transfer. c/w only
p32	1928-29	GW green, lined crest on cab, short splasher, 2 prs boiler bands, brass svc, **black smokebox**; green base 2710 tender, lining transfer. c/w only
p119	1929-31	GW green, 2449 numberplate, **long splasher**, brass svc; "**Great (crest) Western**" coal rail tender. c/w only
-	1931-35	GW green, 4300 on cabside, **revised body style**; "Great (crest) Western" tender. c/w, E16, E120
p59	1935-38	GW green, 4300 on cabside, revised body style; "**GWR**" monogram tender. c/w, E120
p175	1938-41	GW green, **9319** on cabside, revised body style; "GWR" monogram tender. c/w, E120
p119	1928-29	**SR black**, no cabside number, short splasher; 4 boiler bands; "Southern E509" tender. c/w only
-	1929-31	SR black, **small 232** on cabside, **long splasher**; **5 boiler bands**; "Southern E509" tender. c/w only
-	1931-36	SR black, no cabside number, **revised body style**; "Southern **A504**" tender. c/w, E16, E120
p31	1928-29	**SR green**, no cabside number, short splasher; 4 boiler bands; "Southern A759" tender. c/w only
p35	1929-31	SR green, **small 232** on cabside, **long splasher**; **5 boiler bands**; "Southern A759" tender. c/w only
-	1931-33	SR green, no cabside number, **revised body style**; "Southern **E793**" tender. c/w only
p119	1933-41	SR green, no cabside number, revised body style; "Southern **793**" tender. c/w, E16, E120 (p119 shows E793 tender)

No. 1 SPECIAL TANK LOCOMOTIVE (EPM16 1934-39; E120 Special Tank from 1934)

-	1929-31	**LMS black, 16045**, shadowed sans-serif letters and numbers. c/w only
p124	1931-36	LMS black, 16045, shadowed **serif letters** and numbers. c/w, E120 Special, EPM16
-	1929	**LMS red, 6418**, shadowed sans-serif letters and numbers. 7 boiler bands. c/w only
p34	1929-30	LMS red, 6418, shadowed sans-serif letters and numbers. **8 boiler bands**. c/w only
p45	1930-33	LMS red, **2120**, shadowed **serif letters** and numbers; black/gold/red tank lining. c/w only
-	1933-34	LMS red, 2120, shadowed serif letters and numbers; **black/gold** tank lining. c/w only

p217	1934-36	LMS red, **15500**, shadowed serif letters and numbers. c/w, E120 Special, EPM16
p174	1936-37	LMS red, **70**, shadowed serif letters and numbers. c/w, E120 Special, EPM16
-	1937-39	LMS red, 70, shadowed **sans-serif letters** and numbers. c/w, E120 Special, EPM16
-	1939-41	LMS red, 70, shadowed **serif letters** and numbers (as before, but usually matt). c/w, E120 Special

| p124 | 1929-30 | **LNER black, 8108**. c/w only |
| p39 | 1930-36 | LNER black, **2586**. c/w, E120 Special, EPM16 |

-	1929	**LNER green, 8123**, 7 boiler bands (PU) c/w only
p37	1929-35	LNER green, 8123. **8 boiler bands.** c/w, E120 Special, EPM16
p125	1935-36	LNER green, **2162**. c/w, E120 Special, EPM16
-	1936-41	LNER **darker green**, 2162. c/w, E120 Special, EPM16

-	1929	**GW green, 3580**, 7 boiler bands. c/w only
p36	1929-30	GW green, 3580, **8 boiler bands.** c/w only
p42	1930-32	GW green, **5500** not on plate, "Great Western" on tanks. c/w only
p210	1932-36	GW green, 5500 **on plate**, "Great Western" on tanks. c/w, E120 Special, EPM16
p124	1936-41	GW green, 5500 on plate, **"GWR" monogram** on tanks. c/w, E120 Special, EPM16

| p124 | 1929-30 | **SR black, A129**. c/w only |
| - | 1930-36 | SR black, **A950** (serif letters). c/w, E120 Special, EPM16 |

p35	1929-30	**SR green, A950** (outlined sans-serif letters). c/w only
p124	1930-35	SR green, **B28.** (**serif letters**) c/w, E120 Special, EPM16
p125	1935-41	SR green, **516**. c/w, E120 Special, EPM16

No. 1 SPECIAL LOCOMOTIVE (E120 Special from 1934)

| p37 | 1929-30 | **LMS black, 4525** on cabside; lined tender with unshadowed gold "LMS" letters. c/w only |
| p123 | 1930-36 | LMS black, 4525 on cabside; lined tender with **shadowed serif** "LMS" letters. c/w, E120 Special |

p34	1929-30	**LMS red, 4312** on cabside; unlined tender with unshadowed gold "LMS" letters. c/w only
-	1930	LMS red, **4525** on cabside; unlined tender with unshadowed gold "LMS" letters. c/w only (but similar 20V loco circa 1935; production errors?)
p50	1930-31	LMS red, **4312** on cabside; **lined tender** with **shadowed serif** "LMS" letters. c/w only
p123	1931-35	LMS red, **8712** on cabside; lined tender with shadowed serif "LMS" letters. c/w, E120 Special
p211	1935-41	LMS red, **2700** on cabside; lined tender with shadowed serif "LMS" letters. c/w, E120 Special

| p123 | 1929-36 | **LNER black, 2691** on small numberplate; "LNER 2691" tender. c/w, E120 Special |

-	1929	**LNER green, 2694** on small numberplate, black boiler bands; "LNER 2694" tender. c/w only
p124	1929-31	LNER green, 2694 on small numberplate, **white boiler bands**; "LNER 2694" tender. c/w only
p53	1931-36	LNER green, **1368** on cabside; **"LNER" tender.** c/w, E120 Special
-	1936-41	LNER **darker green**, 1368 on cabside; "LNER" tender. c/w, E120 Special

p36	1929-34	**GW green, 2301**; "Great (crest) Western" tender. c/w only
-	1934-36	GW green, **4700**; "Great (crest) Western" tender. c/w, E120 Special
p59	1936-41	GW green, 4700; **"Great (GWR monogram) Western"** tender. c/w, E120 Special
p123	1929-36	**SR black, B343** on small numberplate; "Southern B343" tender. c/w, E120 Special
p35	1929-35	**SR green, A179** on small numberplate; **"Southern A179"** tender. c/w, E120 Special
p215	1935-41	SR green, **1179** on small numberplate; **"Southern 1179"** tender. c/w, E120 Special

No. 2 TANK LOCOMOTIVE (Clockwork only; Control 1926-29)

-	1923	**LMS black**, "LM&SR 1019"; 3 boiler bands, lined tanks, unlined bunker (PU)
p132	1923-24	LMS black, **no number**, lettered **"LM&S"**; 3 boiler bands, **unlined tanks, lined bunker**
-	1924	LMS black, **"LMS 4-4-4"**; no crest; 3 boiler bands, **lined tanks**, lined bunker
p23	1924-25	LMS black, "LMS 4-4-4"; no crest; **5 boiler bands**
p133	1925-26	LMS black, "LMS 4-4-4"; **crest on cab front**; 5 boiler bands
-	1926	LMS black, "LMS 4-4-4"; **crest on bunker**; 5 boiler bands (PU)
p133	1926-28	LMS black, **"LMS 2052"**; crest on bunker; brass dome; 5 boiler bands
-	1928-29	LMS black, "LMS 2052"; crest on bunker; **black dome**; 5 boiler bands
-	1928	LMS black, "LMS 2052"; crest on bunker; **brass dome**; 3 boiler bands (one single, one pair)
-	1928-29	LMS black, **"2107"**, **no company lettering**; crest on bunker; **black dome**; 5 boiler bands
-	1928-29	LMS black, "2107"; **"LMS" plate on bunker**; black dome; 5 boiler bands
p33	1928-29	LMS black, **"2051"**; "LMS" plate on bunker; black dome; 5 boiler bands
-	1923	**LMS red**, "LM&SR 1019"; 3 boiler bands; lined tanks, unlined bunker (PU)
-	1923-24	LMS red, **no number**, lettered **"LM&S"**; 3 boiler bands, **unlined tanks, lined bunker** (PU)
p133	1924	LMS red, **"LMS 4-4-4"**; no crest; 3 boiler bands; **lined tanks**, lined bunker
-	1924-25	LMS red, "LMS 4-4-4"; no crest; **5 boiler bands**; black running plate
-	1925	LMS red, "LMS 4-4-4"; **crest on cab front**; 5 boiler bands; black running plate (PU)
-	1925-26	LMS red, "LMS 4-4-4"; **crest on bunker**; 5 boiler bands; **maroon running plate**
p27	1926-28	LMS red, **"LMS 2052"**; crest on bunker; brass dome, red smokebox; 5 boiler bands
p133	1928-29	LMS red, **"2107"**; **no company lettering**; crest on bunker; **red dome, black smokebox**; 3 boiler bands
-	1928-29	LMS red, "2107"; **"LMS" plate on bunker**; red dome, black smokebox; 3 boiler bands
p32	1928-29	LMS red, **"2051"**; "LMS" plate on bunker; red dome, black smokebox; 3 boiler bands
-	1928-29	LMS red, "LMS 2052"; **no crest or plate** on bunker; red dome, black smokebox; 3 boiler bands
p32	1928-29	LMS red, "LMS 2052"; **crest on bunker**; red dome, black smokebox; 3 boiler bands
-	1924-26	**LNER black**, "LNER 4-4-4"; crest on cab front; brass dome; 5 boiler bands
p133	1926-28	LNER black, "LNER 4-4-4"; **crest on bunker**; brass dome; 5 boiler bands
	1928	LNER black, "LNER 4-4-4"; crest on bunker; **black dome**; 5 boiler bands (PU)
p133	1928-29	LNER black, **"LNER 460"**; crest on bunker; black dome; 5 boiler bands
-	1928-29	LNER black, "LNER 460"; **no crest** on bunker; black dome; 5 boiler bands

p19	1923	**LNER green**, no number, lettered "L&NER"; 3 boiler bands, unlined tanks, lined bunker
p133	1923-24	LNER green, **"L&NER 1534"**; no crest; 3 boiler bands, **lined tanks**, lined bunker
p24	1924.	LNER green, **"L&NER 4-4-4"**; no crest; 3 boiler bands
-	1924-25	LNER green, "L&NER 4-4-4"; no crest; **5 boiler bands**
-	1925	LNER green, "L&NER 4-4-4"; **crest on cab front**; 5 boiler bands
p217	1925-26	LNER green, **"LNER 4-4-4"**; crest on cab front; 5 boiler bands; black running plate, red valance
p29	1926	LNER green, "LNER 4-4-4"; crest on cab front; 5 boiler bands; **green running plate**, red valance
-	1926-27	LNER green, **"LNER 460"**; crest on cab front; brass dome; 5 boiler bands; green running plate, **green valance**
p29	1927-28	LNER green, "LNER 460"; **crest on bunker**; brass dome; green smokebox; 5 boiler bands; green running plate, green valance
-	1928-29	LNER green, "LNER 460"; crest on bunker; **green dome**; black smokebox; **3 boiler bands**
-	1928-29	LNER green, **"LNER 5165"**; **no crest on bunker**; green dome; black smokebox; 3 boiler bands
p133	1928-29	LNER green, "LNER 5165"; no crest on bunker; green dome; black smokebox; **4 boiler bands**
p132	1926-27	**GW green**; no number; lettered "Great Western"; crest on cab front
p133	1927	GW green; **7202**; "Great (crest) Western"; black svc; green smokebox; 4 boiler bands
-	1927-28	GW green; 7202; "Great (crest) Western"; **brass svc**; green smokebox; 4 boiler bands (PU)
p32	1928-29	GW green; 7202; "Great (crest) Western"; brass svc; **black smokebox; 3 boiler bands**
p32	1928-29	GW green; **2243**; "Great (crest) Western"; brass svc; black smokebox; 3 boiler bands
p132	1928-29	**SR black; E492;** black dome
p132	1928-29	**SR green; B604;** green dome

No. 2 LOCOMOTIVE (Clockwork only, except special order and export; see pp130-1. Control 1926-29.)

p15	1921-23	**PLAIN (LNWR) black**; 2711 on numberplate; plain tender
p13	1921-23	**PLAIN (GN) green**; 2711 on numberplate; plain tender
p15	1921-23	**PLAIN (MR) red**; 2711 on numberplate; plain tender
p126	1921-23	**PLAIN (CR) blue**; 2711 on numberplate; plain tender
p126	1923-24	**LMS black**; 2711 on numberplate, unlined **"LM&S" both splashers**; unlined boiler; plain tender
-	1923-24	LMS black; 2711 on numberplate, lined **"LMS" splasher lhs only**; unlined boiler (PU). Plain tender
-	1923-24	LMS black; 2711 on numberplate, lined **"LMS" both splashers**; unlined boiler (PU). Plain tender or **"LMS" tender**
p127	1924	LMS black; 2711 on numberplate, lined "LMS" both splashers; **3 boiler bands**; "LMS" tender (p127 shows unlined 2711 tender)
-	1924-25	LMS black; **lined crest on cab**; lined "LMS" both splashers; **5 boiler bands**; **unlined 2711 tender**
p27	1925-28	LMS black; lined crest on cab; lined "LMS" both splashers; 5 boiler bands; brass dome; **lined 2711 tender**
-	1928-29	LMS black; lined crest on cab; lined but **unlettered splashers**; 5 boiler bands; **black dome**; lined 2711 tender
p126	1923-24	**LMS red**; 2711 on numberplate, unlined **"LM&S" both splashers**; unlined boiler; plain tender
-	1923-24	LMS red; 2711 on numberplate, lined **"LMS" splasher lhs only**; unlined boiler; plain tender
p126	1923-24	LMS red; 2711 on numberplate, lined **"LMS" both splashers**; unlined boiler; **"LMS" tender**
-	1924	LMS red; 2711 on numberplate, lined "LMS" both splashers; **3 boiler bands** (PU). "LMS" tender
-	1924-25	LMS red; **lined crest on cab**; lined "LMS" both splashers; black running plate; **5 boiler bands; unlined 2711 tender**
p131	1924	LMS red; lined crest on cab; lined "LMS" both splashers; black running plate; 5 boiler bands; red dome. **Electric mechanism, special order.**

p30	1925-28	LMS red; lined crest on cab; lined "LMS" both splashers; **maroon running plate**; red smokebox; 5 boiler bands; brass dome; **lined 2711 tender**
-	1928	LMS red; lined crest on cab; lined "LMS" both splashers; maroon running plate; **black smokebox; 3 boiler bands; red dome**; lined 2711 tender
-	1928-29	LMS red; lined crest on cab; lined but **unlettered splashers**; maroon running plate; black smokebox; 3 boiler bands; red dome; lined 2711 tender

p24	1924-25	**LNER black**; lined crest on cab; lined "LNER" both splashers; 5 boiler bands; brass dome; unlined 2711 tender
p127	1925-28	LNER black; lined crest on cab; lined "LNER" both splashers; 5 boiler bands; brass dome; **lined 2711 tender**
p29	1928-29	LNER black; lined crest on cab; lined but **unlettered splashers**; 5 boiler bands; **black dome**; lined 2711 tender

-	1923	**L&NER green**; 2711 on numberplate, **GN crests both splashers**; unlined boiler; plain tender
p19	1923	L&NER green; 2711 on numberplate, **"L&NER" splasher lhs , GN crest rhs**; unlined boiler; plain tender
p18	1923-24	L&NER green; 2711 on numberplate, **"L&NER" both splashers**; unlined boiler; **"L&NER" tender**
-	1924	L&NER green; 2711 on numberplate, "L&NER" both splashers; **3 boiler bands**; "L&NER" tender
-	1924-25	L&NER green; **lined crest on cab**; lined "L&NER" both splashers; black running plate, red valance; **5 boiler bands; unlined 2711 tender**
-	1925	**LNER green**; lined crest on cab; lined "LNER" both splashers; black running plate, red valance; 5 boiler bands; **lined 2711 tender**
-	1925-27	LNER green; lined crest on cab; lined "LNER" both splashers; **green running plate**, red valance; 5 boiler bands; lined 2711 tender
-	1927-28	LNER green; lined crest on cab; lined "LNER" both splashers; green running plate, **green valance**; 5 boiler bands; brass dome; green smokebox; lined 2711 tender
-	1928-29	LNER green; lined crest on cab; lined but **unlettered splashers**; **3 boiler bands; green dome; black smokebox**; lined 2711 tender

p128	1926-27	**GW green**; lined crest on cab; "GW" splashers; 4 boiler bands, cast svc; 2711 tender, wide lining
p26	1927	GW green; **7283 on cab**; "Great (crest) Western" splashers; 4 boiler bands, green smokebox; cast svc; 2711 tender, **narrow lining**
-	1927-28	GW green; 7283 on cab; "Great (crest) Western" splashers; 4 boiler bands, green smokebox; **brass svc**; 2711 tender, narrow lining
-	1928-29	GW green; 7283 on cab; lined but **unlettered splashers**; **3 boiler bands, black smokebox**; brass svc; **"Great (crest) Western" tender**

| p129 | 1928-29 | **SR black**; no cabside number, unlettered splashers; black dome, green lining; "Southern E510" tender |

| p129 | 1928-29 | **SR green**; no cabside number, unlettered splashers; green dome; "Southern A760" tender |

No. 2 SPECIAL TANK LOCOMOTIVE (No. 2 Electric Tank 6V 1930-34; E26 Special Tank 1934-41; LST2/20 1933-34; E220 Special Tank 1934-41)

| p142 | 1929-31 | **LMS black; 6781**, shadowed sans-serif "LMS" and number transfers. c/w only |
| p51 | 1931-36 | LMS black; 6781, shadowed **serif "LMS"** and number transfers. c/w, 20V, 6V |

p141	1929	**LMS red; 2323**, shadowed sans-serif "LMS" and number, small numberplate on smokebox door. c/w only
p34	1929-30	LMS red; 2323, shadowed sans-serif "LMS" and number, **no numberplate on smokebox door**. c/w only
p51	1930-36	LMS red; **2180**, shadowed **serif "LMS"** and number transfers. c/w, 6V, 20V
-	1936-37	LMS red; **6954**, shadowed serif "LMS" and number transfers. c/w, 6V, 20V
p61	1937-39	LMS red; 6954, shadowed **sans-serif** "LMS" and number transfers. c/w, 6V, 20V
p142	1939-41	LMS red; 6954, shadowed **serif** "LMS" and number transfers (as before, but usually matt). c/w, 6V, 20V

| p142 | 1929-36 | **LNER black; 5154.** c/w, 6V, 20V |

p37	1929-32	**LNER green**; **6**. c/w, 6V, 20V
p142	1932-36	LNER green; **1784**. c/w, 6V, 20V
-	1936-41	LNER **darker green**; 1784. c/w, 6V, 20V
p36	1929-30	**GW green**; **4703**. c/w only
p143	1930-32	GW green; **2221**, number not on numberplate; lettered "Great Western". c/w , 6V
p49	1932-36	GW green; 2221, **number on numberplate**; lettered "Great Western". c/w, 6V, 20V
p142	1936-41	GW green; 2221, number on numberplate; **"GWR" monogram**. c/w, 6V, 20V
p142	1929-30	**SR black**; **E492**, number on bunker; sans-serif letters. c/w only
p45	1930-33	SR black; E492, **number on tank**; **serif letters**. c/w, 6V
-	1933-36	SR black; **492**, number on tank. c/w, 6V, 20V
p143	1929-30	**SR green**; **B329**, number on bunker; sans-serif letters. c/w only
p143	1930-33	SR green; B329, **number on tank**; **serif letters**. c/w, 6V
p211	1933-35	SR green; **2329**. c/w, 6V, 20V
p142	1935-41	SR green; **2091**. c/w, 6V, 20V

No. 2 SPECIAL LOCOMOTIVE (and E220 from 1934)

p135	1929-30	**LMS Compound**; plain gold 1185 on cabside and smokebox; maroon running plate; cabtop with narrow-spaced emboss, narrow black strip; 3 boiler bands; unlined sans-serif "LMS" tender. c/w only
-	1930-31	LMS Compound; **shadowed serif 1185** on cabside, **white 1185 on smokebox door**; **black running plate**; cabtop with narrow-spaced emboss, **wider black strip**; **2 boiler bands**; **lined shadowed serif "LMS" tender**. c/w only
-	1931-32	LMS Compound; shadowed serif 1185, black running plate; cabtop with narrow-spaced emboss, wider black strip; **3 boiler bands**; lined shadowed serif "LMS" tender. c/w, E220
p57	1932-37	LMS Compound; shadowed serif 1185, black running plate; cabtop with **wider-spaced emboss**, wider black strip; 3 boiler bands; lined shadowed serif "LMS" tender. c/w, E220
p61	1937-38	LMS Compound; shadowed **sans-serif 1185**, black running plate; lined shadowed **sans-serif "LMS"** tender. c/w, E220
p137	1938-41	LMS Compound; shadowed **serif 1185**, black running plate; lined **serif "LMS"** tender; (usually matt finish). c/w, E220
p136	1938	**LMS black 2P**, 700. Special order
p135	1929-30	**LNER "Yorkshire"**; **234** on small cabside numberplate; green running plate; **"LNER 234"** tender. c/w only
p138	1930-31	LNER "Yorkshire"; **234 on cabside**; green running plate; **"LNER"** tender. c/w only (Loco and small letter tender p138; Loco also sold with large letter tender p147, and with normal letter tender p139)
p139	1931-35	LNER "Yorkshire"; 234 on cabside; **black running plate**; "LNER" tender, normal letters. c/w, E220
p55	1935-36	**LNER "Bramham Moor"**; **201** on cabside; green, with black running plate; "LNER" tender, normal letters. c/w, E220
p62	1936-41	LNER "Bramham Moor"; 201 on cabside; **darker green**, with black running plate; "LNER" tender, normal letters. c/w, E220
p135	1929-30	**GW "County of Bedford"**; **3821**, green running plate, gold/black/red name and numberplates; "Great (crest) Western" tender. c/w only
-	1930-36	GW "County of Bedford"; 3821, **black running plate, black/gold** name and numberplates; "Great (crest) Western" tender. c/w, E220
p140	1936-41	GW "County of Bedford"; 3821, black running plate, black/gold name and numberplates; **"GWR" monogram tender**. c/w, E220

p135	1929-30	**SR L1 Class Loco**; A759 on small cabside numberplate; black running plate; lined cabside; **unlined "SOUTHERN A759"** tender. c/w only
p138	1930-35	SR L1 Class Loco; A759 on small cabside numberplate; black running plate; **unlined cabside; lined** "SOUTHERN A759" tender. c/w, E220
p215	1935-41	SR L1 Class Loco; **1759** on small cabside numberplate; black running plate; unlined cabside; lined **"SOUTHERN 1759"** tender. c/w, E220

No. 3C RIVIERA BLUE TRAIN LOCOS (Control only 1926-29; clockwork 1929-41; 3E 4V 1926-29; 3E 6V 1929-34; E36 1934-36; E3/20 1933-34; E320 1934-40)

p144	1926-28	**Nord, 31240** on black/gold/red lined cab; no deflectors, brown smokebox, black smokebox door, black running plate, brass domes; **31801 tender.** c/w, 4V
-	1928-29	Nord, 31240 on black/gold/red lined cab; no deflectors, brown smokebox, black smokebox door, **brown running plate, brown domes**; 31801 tender. c/w, 4V, 6V
p145	1929-30	Nord, **31801** on black/gold/red lined cab; no deflectors, brown smokebox, black smokebox door, brown running plate, brown domes; 31801 tender. c/w, 6V
p144	1930-34	Nord, 31801 on black/gold/red lined cab; no deflectors, **black smokebox**, black smokebox door, brown running plate, brown domes; 31801 tender. c/w, 6V, 20V
p145	1934-36	Nord, 31801 on black/gold/red lined cab; **black deflectors**, black smokebox, black smokebox door, brown running plate, brown domes; 31801 tender. c/w, 6V, 20V
-	1936-38	Nord, 31801 on black/gold/red lined cab; **brown deflectors, brown smokebox, brown smokebox door**, brown running plate, brown domes; 31801 tender. c/w, 20V (31801 tender with revised bogies in 1937-38 season)
p146	1938-41	Nord, **3.1290 on gold lined cab**; brown deflectors, smokebox, smokebox door, running plate, domes; **3.1290 tender** with revised bogies. c/w, 20V

No. 3C LOCOMOTIVE (Control only 1927-29, clockwork 1929-41; 3E 4V 1927-29; 3E 6V 1929-34; E36 1934-36; E3/20 1933-34; E320 1934-41)

-	1927-28	**"Royal Scot"**, lined crest on cab; brass dome; red smokebox; 5 boiler bands; **6100 tender.** c/w, 4V
p34	1928-29	"Royal Scot", lined crest on cab; **red dome; black smokebox; 4 boiler bands**; 6100 tender. c/w, 4V, 6V
p34	1929-30	"Royal Scot", **plain gold 6100 on cab**; black smokebox; 4 boiler bands; 6100 or **"LMS" coal rail tenders**, or **unlined "LMS" No. 2 Special tender!** c/w, 6V
-	1930-31	"Royal Scot", plain gold 6100 on cab; black smokebox; **5 boiler bands; lined "LMS"** No. 2 Special tender. c/w, 6V
-	1931-33	"Royal Scot", plain gold 6100 on cab; black smokebox; **4 boiler bands**; no deflectors; solid rear splasher lining; lined "LMS" No. 2 Special tender. c/w, 6V
p148	1933-36	"Royal Scot", **shadowed 6100 on cab**; black smokebox; 4 boiler bands; no deflectors; **outline rear splasher lining**; lined "LMS" No. 2 Special tender. c/w, 6V, 20V
p239	1936-41	"Royal Scot", shadowed 6100 on cab; black smokebox; 4 boiler bands; **smoke deflectors**; outline rear splasher lining; lined "LMS" No. 2 Special tender. c/w, 6V, 20V

-	1927-28	**"Flying Scotsman"**; lined cab with LNER crest; brass dome; green smokebox; 5 boiler bands; **"LNER 4472"** tender. c/w, 4V
p147	1928-29	"Flying Scotsman"; lined cab with LNER crest; **green dome; black smokebox; 4 boiler bands**; "LNER" or "LNER 4472" coal rail tender. c/w, 4V, 6V
p147	1929-33	"Flying Scotsman"; **plain gold 4472 on cab**; black smokebox; 4 boiler bands; solid rear splasher lining; red/gold nameplate; "LNER" **No. 2 Special** tender. c/w, 6V (c1929 with "LNER" coal rail tender)
-	1933	(also a transitional version with black/gold nameplate and black/gold outline rear splasher lining)
p148	1933-36	"Flying Scotsman"; **shadowed 4472** on cab; black smokebox; 4 boiler bands; **black/white outline rear splasher lining; black/gold nameplate**; green; "LNER" No. 2 Special tender. c/w, 6V, 20V
p149		(version circa 1935 with deflectors)
p65	1936-41	"Flying Scotsman"; shadowed 4472 on cab; black smokebox; 4 boiler bands; outline rear splasher lining; black/gold nameplate; **darker green**; "LNER" No. 2 Special tender. c/w, 20V

p149	1937	**LNER black** E320 loco, 1368
p147	1927-28	"Caerphilly Castle"; 4073 on cab; number not on plate; green smokebox; 5 boiler bands; solid rear splasher lining; brass and cast svcs; "Great (crest) Western" coal rail tender. c/w, 4V
-	1928-29	"Caerphilly Castle"; 4073 on cab; number not on plate; **black smokebox; 4 boiler bands**; solid rear splasher lining; brass svc only, **brass whistle**; "Great (crest) Western" coal rail tender. c/w, 4V, 6V
p49	1929-33	"Caerphilly Castle"; 4073 on cab; number not on plate; black smokebox; 4 boiler bands; solid rear splasher lining; brass svc, brass whistle; "Great (crest) Western" **No. 2 Special tender.** c/w, 6V, 20V
p148	1933-36	"Caerphilly Castle"; 4073 on cab; **number on plate**; black smokebox; 4 boiler bands; solid rear splasher lining; brass svc, brass whistle; red/gold nameplate; "Great (crest) Western" No. 2 Special tender. c/w, 6V, 20V
p63	1936-39	"Caerphilly Castle"; 4073 on cab; number on plate; black smokebox; 4 boiler bands; solid rear splasher lining; brass svc, brass whistle; red/gold nameplate; **"GWR" monogram** No. 2 Special tender. c/w, 20V
p67	1939-41	"Caerphilly Castle"; 4073 on cab; number on plate; black smokebox; 4 boiler bands; solid rear splasher lining; brass svc, brass whistle; **black/gold nameplate**; "GWR" monogram No. 2 Special tender. c/w, 20V
p146	1928-29	"**Lord Nelson**"; black smokebox; 5 boiler bands; solid rear splasher lining; "SOUTHERN E850" coal rail tender. c/w, 4V, 6V
-	1929-30	"Lord Nelson"; black smokebox; **3 boiler bands**; solid rear splasher lining; "SOUTHERN E850" **No. 2 Special tender**, rectangular lining. c/w, 6V
-	1930-33	"Lord Nelson"; black smokebox; 3 boiler bands; solid rear splasher lining; "SOUTHERN E850" No. 2 Special tender, **normal lining.** c/w, 6V
-	1933-36	"Lord Nelson"; black smokebox; 3 boiler bands; **outline rear splasher lining**; no deflectors; "**SOUTHERN 850**" No. 2 Special tender, normal lining. c/w, 6V, 20V
p60	1936-41	"Lord Nelson"; black smokebox; 3 boiler bands; outline rear splasher lining; **smoke deflectors**; "SOUTHERN 850" No. 2 Special tender, normal lining. c/w, 20V

No. 4 "ETON" LOCOMOTIVE (Clockwork and E420)

p150	1937-41	"Eton", **900** on small cabside plate; "Southern 900" tender. c/w, 20V

"PRINCESS ELIZABETH" LOCOMOTIVE (20 volt only)

p151	1937	"**Princess Elizabeth**", 6201; serif number on cab, serif "LMS" on tender; sand-colour inside cab. 20V
p153	1937-38	"Princess Elizabeth", 6201; **sans-serif** number on cab, **sans-serif** "LMS" on tender; sand-colour inside cab. 20V
p153	1938-40	"Princess Elizabeth", 6201; sans-serif number on cab, sans-serif "LMS" on tender; **maroon inside cab.** 20V

LEC1, LE1/20 and LE120 LOCOMOTIVE (LE1/20 1932-34, LE120 1934-36)

p156	1932-33	**10655; dark green, grey roof.** c/w, 20V
p156	1933-36	10655; **light green, cream roof.** c/w, 20V
p156	1933-36	10655; **red, cream roof.** c/w, 20V
p156	1933-36	10655; **cream, red roof.** c/w, 20V
p156	1933-36	10655; **blue, yellow roof.** c/w, 20V

LE220 LOCOMOTIVE (electric only; LE2/20 1932-34, LE220 1934-36)

p157 1932-33 **10655; dark green, grey roof**, 20V

-     1933-36 10655; **light green, cream roof**. 20V (PU)
p157 1933-36 10655; **red, cream roof**. 20V
p157 1933-36 10655; **cream, blue roof**. 20V

METROPOLITAN LOCOMOTIVE (Control only 1926-29; clockwork 1929-39; HV 1925-26 and 1927-29; LV 4V 1926-29; LV 6V 1929-34; E36 1934-39; 20V 1938-39)

p154 1925-39 **Metropolitan** locomotive, **2**

-	1922-24	**ZULU PASSENGER COACH; LNWR**
p158	1921-23	**No. 1 PASSENGER COACH; LNWR**, constructional; brass-lettered doors
p19	1923-24	**No. 1 PASSENGER COACH; LNWR**, constructional; **tinprinted doors**
p158	1921-24	**No. 1 PASSENGER COACH; MR**, constructional; brass-lettered doors
p158	1921-24	**No. 1 PASSENGER COACH; GN**, constructional; brass-lettered doors
p158	1921-23	**No. 1 PASSENGER COACH; CR**, constructional; brass-lettered doors
p159	1924-25	**No. 1 PASSENGER COACH; LMS**, long thin base, clerestory roof; yellow lining; doors "FIRST"/"1", "THIRD"/"3"
-	1925-28	**No. 1 PASSENGER COACH; LMS**, long thin base, clerestory roof; **gold lining**; doors "FIRST"/"1", "THIRD"/"3"
-	1928-30	**No. 1 PASSENGER COACH; LMS**, long thin base, **non-clerestory roof**; gold lining; doors "FIRST"/"1", "THIRD"/"3"
p159	1930-33	**No. 1 PASSENGER COACH; LMS**, black **crimped long thin base**, dark grey non-clerestory roof; gold lining; **doors blank/"1", blank/"3"**
p50	1933-34	**No. 1 PASSENGER COACH; LMS**, **red** crimped long thin base, **cream** non-clerestory roof; gold lining; doors blank/"1", blank/"3"
p159	1934-41	**No. 1 PASSENGER COACH; LMS**, **revised style with non-opening doors**; black coach base, grey roof
-	1924-25	**No. 1 PASSENGER COACH; LNER**, long thin base, clerestory roof; yellow lining; doors "FIRST"/"1", "THIRD"/"3", numbers shadowed
p159	1925-28	**No. 1 PASSENGER COACH; LNER**, long thin base, clerestory roof; **gold lining**; doors "FIRST"/"1", "THIRD"/"3"; numbers shadowed
-	1925-28	**No. 1 PASSENGER COACH; LNER**, long thin base, clerestory roof; gold lining; doors "FIRST"/"1", "THIRD"/"3"; **numbers unshadowed**
-	1928-30	**No. 1 PASSENGER COACH; LNER**, long thin base, **non-clerestory roof**; gold lining; doors "FIRST"/"1", "THIRD"/"3"; numbers unshadowed
-	1930-33	**No. 1 PASSENGER COACH; LNER**, black **crimped long thin base**, dark grey non-clerestory roof; gold lining; doors "FIRST"/"1", "THIRD"/"3"
p159	1933-34	**No. 1 PASSENGER COACH; LNER**, **green** crimped long thin base, **cream** non-clerestory roof; gold lining; doors "FIRST"/"1", "THIRD"/"3"
p159	1934-41	**No. 1 PASSENGER COACH; LNER**, **revised style with non-opening doors**; black coach base, grey roof
p159	1926-28	**No. 1 PASSENGER COACH; GW**, long thin base, clerestory roof; gold lining; doors "FIRST"/blank, "THIRD"/blank
-	1928-30	**No. 1 PASSENGER COACH; GW**, long thin base, **non-clerestory roof**; gold lining; doors "FIRST"/blank, "THIRD"/blank
p159	1930-32	**No. 1 PASSENGER COACH; GW**, black **crimped long thin base**, dark grey non-clerestory roof; gold lining; doors "FIRST"/blank, "THIRD"/blank
-	1932-33	**No. 1 PASSENGER COACH; GW**, black crimped long thin base, dark grey non-clerestory roof; gold lining; **doors blank/"1", blank/"3"**
p49	1933-34	**No. 1 PASSENGER COACH; GW**, **green** crimped long thin base, **cream** non-clerestory roof; gold lining; doors blank/"1", blank/"3"
p159	1934-41	**No. 1 PASSENGER COACH; GW**, **revised style with non-opening doors**; black coach base, grey roof
p159	1928-30	**No. 1 PASSENGER COACH; SR**, long thin base, non-clerestory roof; yellow lining; doors "FIRST"/blank, "THIRD"/blank; number 1728
p159	1930-32	**No. 1 PASSENGER COACH; SR**, black **crimped long thin base**, dark grey non-clerestory roof; yellow lining; doors "FIRST"/blank, "THIRD"/blank; number 1728
-	1932-33	**No. 1 PASSENGER COACH; SR**, black crimped long thin base, dark grey non-clerestory roof; yellow lining; doors "FIRST"/blank, "THIRD"/blank; **number 2891**
-	1933-34	**No. 1 PASSENGER COACH; SR**, **green** crimped long thin base, **cream** non-clerestory roof; yellow lining; doors "FIRST"/blank, "THIRD"/blank; number 2891
p159	1934-41	**No. 1 PASSENGER COACH; SR**, **revised style with non-opening doors**; black coach base, grey roof

p159	1924-28	**GUARD'S VAN; LMS**, long thin base, clerestory roof; yellow lining; door lettered "GUARD"
-	1928-30	**GUARD'S VAN; LMS**, long thin base, **non-clerestory roof**; yellow lining; door lettered "GUARD"
p159	1930-33	**GUARD'S VAN; LMS**, black **crimped long thin base**, dark grey non-clerestory roof; yellow lining; door lettered "GUARD"
p50	1933-34	**GUARD'S VAN; LMS**, **red** crimped long thin base, **cream** non-clerestory roof; yellow lining; door lettered "GUARD"
p159	1934-41	**GUARD'S VAN; LMS**, **revised style with non-opening doors**; black coach base, grey roof
p159	1924-28	**GUARD'S VAN; NE**, long thin base, clerestory roof; yellow lining; door lettered "GUARD"
-	1928-30	**GUARD'S VAN; NE**, long thin base, **non-clerestory roof**; yellow lining; door lettered "GUARD"
p159	1930-33	**GUARD'S VAN; NE**, black **crimped long thin base**, dark grey non-clerestory roof; yellow lining; door lettered "GUARD"
-	1933-34	**GUARD'S VAN; NE**, **green** crimped long thin base, **cream** non-clerestory roof; yellow lining; door lettered "GUARD"
p159	1934-41	**GUARD'S VAN; NE**, **revised style with non-opening doors**; black coach base, grey roof
p26	1926-28	**GUARD'S VAN; GW**, long thin base, clerestory roof; gold lining; door lettered "GUARD"
p159	1928-30	**GUARD'S VAN; GW**, long thin base, **non-clerestory roof**; gold lining; door lettered "GUARD"
p159	1930-33	**GUARD'S VAN; GW**, black **crimped long thin base**, dark grey non-clerestory roof; gold lining; door lettered "GUARD"
p49	1933-34	**GUARD'S VAN; GW**, **green** crimped long thin base, **cream** non-clerestory roof; gold lining; door lettered "GUARD"
p159	1934-41	**GUARD'S VAN; GW**, **revised style with non-opening doors**; black coach base, grey roof
p159	1928-30	**GUARD'S VAN; SR**, long thin base, non-clerestory roof; yellow lining; door lettered "GUARD"
-	1930-32	**GUARD'S VAN; SR**, black **crimped long thin base**, dark grey non-clerestory roof; yellow lining; door lettered "GUARD"
p159	1932-33	**GUARD'S VAN; SR**, black crimped long thin base, dark grey non-clerestory roof; yellow lining; **doors unlettered**
-	1933-34	**GUARD'S VAN; SR**, **green** crimped long thin base, **cream** non-clerestory roof; yellow lining; doors unlettered
p159	1934-41	**GUARD'S VAN; SR**, **revised style with non-opening doors**; black coach base, grey roof
p160	1935-41	**No. 2 PASSENGER COACH; LMS** 1st/3rd
p160	1935-41	**No. 2 PASSENGER COACH; LMS** brake/3rd
p160	1935-41	**No. 2 PASSENGER COACH; NE** 1st/3rd
p160	1935-41	**No. 2 PASSENGER COACH; NE** brake/3rd
p160	1935-41	**No. 2 PASSENGER COACH; GW** 1st/3rd
p160	1935-41	**No. 2 PASSENGER COACH; GW** brake/3rd
p60	1935-41	**No. 2 PASSENGER COACH; SR** 1st/3rd
p60	1935-41	**No. 2 PASSENGER COACH; SR** brake/3rd
p161	1937-41	**No. 2 CORRIDOR COACH; LMS** 1st/3rd
p161	1937-41	**No. 2 CORRIDOR COACH; LMS** brake/composite
p161	1937-41	**No. 2 CORRIDOR COACH; NE** 1st/3rd
p161	1937-41	**No. 2 CORRIDOR COACH; NE** brake/composite
p161	1937-41	**No. 2 CORRIDOR COACH; GW** 1st/3rd
p161	1937-41	**No. 2 CORRIDOR COACH; GW** brake/3rd
p161	1937-41	**No. 2 CORRIDOR COACH; SR** 3rd class
p161	1937-41	**No. 2 CORRIDOR COACH; SR** brake/composite

p249	1932-36	**BRITISH EXPRESS COACH**
p246	1930-33	**MO PULLMAN COACH; JOAN**, brown roof, brown name panel
-	1933-34	**MO PULLMAN COACH; JOAN, red roof**, brown name panel
p247	1934-35	**MO PULLMAN COACH; JOAN**, red roof, **red name panel**
p247	1935-41	**MO PULLMAN COACH; JOAN, cream roof**, red name panel
p246	1930-33	**MO PULLMAN COACH; ZENA**, brown roof, brown name panel
-	1933-34	**MO PULLMAN COACH; ZENA, green roof**, brown name panel
p247	1934-35	**MO PULLMAN COACH; ZENA**, green roof, **red name panel**
p247	1935-41	**MO PULLMAN COACH; ZENA, cream roof**, red name panel

| p250 | 1926-27 | **M1/2 PULLMAN COACH**; no name, "PULLMAN" below windows; grey roof |
| p251 | 1927-28 | **M1/2 PULLMAN COACH**; no name, "PULLMAN" below windows; **brown roof** |

p251	1928-31	**M1/2 PULLMAN COACH; MARJORIE**; brown roof, black base; lilac door windows
-	1931-33	**M1/2 PULLMAN COACH; MARJORIE**; brown roof, black base; **red door windows**
p251	1933-34	**M1/2 PULLMAN COACH; MARJORIE; yellow roof, yellow base**
-	1933-34	**M1/2 PULLMAN COACH; MARJORIE; red roof, red base**
p252	1934-35	**M1/2 PULLMAN COACH; MARJORIE**; red roof, **black base**
p252	1935-41	**M1/2 PULLMAN COACH; MARJORIE; cream roof**, black base

p251	1928-31	M1/2 PULLMAN COACH; AURELIA; brown roof, black base; lilac door windows
-	1931-33	**M1/2 PULLMAN COACH; AURELIA**; brown roof, black base; **red door windows**
p251	1933-34	**M1/2 PULLMAN COACH; AURELIA; yellow roof, yellow base**
p252	1934-35	**M1/2 PULLMAN COACH; AURELIA**; yellow roof, **black base**
-	1935-41	**M1/2 PULLMAN COACH; AURELIA; cream roof**, black base

p251	1928-31	**M1/2 PULLMAN COACH; VIKING**; brown roof, black base; lilac door windows
-	1931-33	**M1/2 PULLMAN COACH; VIKING**; brown roof, black base; **red door windows**
p251	1933-34	**M1/2 PULLMAN COACH; VIKING; green roof, green base**
p252	1934-35	**M1/2 PULLMAN COACH; VIKING**; green roof, **black base**
-	1935-41	**M1/2 PULLMAN COACH; VIKING; cream roof**, black base

-	1931-33	**No. O PULLMAN COACH; MARJORIE**; brown roof, black base; red door windows
-	1933-34	**No. O PULLMAN COACH; MARJORIE; red roof, red base**
-	1934-35	**No. O PULLMAN COACH; MARJORIE**; red roof, **black base**
-	1935-41	**No. O PULLMAN COACH; MARJORIE; cream roof**, black base

-	1931-33	**No. O PULLMAN COACH; AURELIA**; brown roof, black base; red door windows
-	1933-34	**No. O PULLMAN COACH; AURELIA; yellow roof, yellow base**
-	1934-35	**No. O PULLMAN COACH; AURELIA**; yellow roof, **black base**
-	1935-41	**No. O PULLMAN COACH; AURELIA; cream roof**, black base

p116	1931-33	**No. O PULLMAN COACH**; **VIKING**; brown roof, black base; red door windows
-	1933-34	**No. O PULLMAN COACH**; VIKING; **green roof, green base**
-	1934-35	**No. O PULLMAN COACH**; VIKING; green roof, **black base** (PU)
-	1935-41	**No. O PULLMAN COACH**; VIKING; **cream roof**, black base

p132	1928-30	**No. 1 PULLMAN COACH**; **CORSAIR**; cream roof, black base; opening doors
-	1930-33	**No. 1 PULLMAN COACH**; CORSAIR; **grey roof**, black base; opening doors
p162	1933-34	**No. 1 PULLMAN COACH**; CORSAIR; **green roof, green base**; opening doors
-	1933-34	**No. 1 PULLMAN COACH**; CORSAIR; **red roof, red base**; opening doors
p162	1934-35	**No. 1 PULLMAN COACH**; CORSAIR; **green roof, black base**; opening doors
-	1934-35	**No. 1 PULLMAN COACH**; CORSAIR; **red roof, black base**; opening doors
-	1935-41	**No. 1 PULLMAN COACH**; CORSAIR; **cream roof**, black base; **non-opening doors**

p132	1928-30	**No. 1 PULLMAN COACH**; **CYNTHIA**; cream roof, black base; opening doors
-	1930-33	**No. 1 PULLMAN COACH**; CYNTHIA; **grey roof**, black base; opening doors
-	1933-34	**No. 1 PULLMAN COACH**; CYNTHIA; **green roof, green base**; opening doors
p162	1933-34	**No. 1 PULLMAN COACH**; CYNTHIA; **red roof, red base**; opening doors
-	1934-35	**No. 1 PULLMAN COACH**; CYNTHIA; **green roof, black base**; opening doors
-	1934-35	**No. 1 PULLMAN COACH**; CYNTHIA; **red roof, black base**; opening doors
p162	1935-41	**No. 1 PULLMAN COACH**; CYNTHIA; **cream roof**, black base; **non-opening doors**

p162	1928-30	**No. 1 PULLMAN COACH**; **NIOBE**; cream roof, black base; opening doors
p162	1930-33	**No. 1 PULLMAN COACH**; NIOBE; **grey roof**, black base; opening doors
-	1933-34	**No. 1 PULLMAN COACH**; NIOBE; **red roof, red base**; opening doors
-	1933-34	**No. 1 PULLMAN COACH**; NIOBE; **blue roof, blue base**; opening doors
-	1934-35	**No. 1 PULLMAN COACH**; NIOBE; **red roof, black base**; opening doors
-	1934-35	**No. 1 PULLMAN COACH**; NIOBE; **blue roof, black base**; opening doors
-	1935-41	**No. 1 PULLMAN COACH**; NIOBE; **cream roof**, black base; **non-opening doors**

p132	1928-30	**No. 1 PULLMAN COMPOSITE**; **ANSONIA**; cream roof, black base; opening doors
-	1930-33	**No. 1 PULLMAN COMPOSITE**; ANSONIA; **grey roof**, black base; opening doors
-	1933-34	**No. 1 PULLMAN COMPOSITE**; ANSONIA; **coloured roof, coloured base**; opening doors (PU)
-	1934-35	**No. 1 PULLMAN COMPOSITE**; ANSONIA; coloured roof, **black base**; opening doors (PU)
p162	1935-41	**No. 1 PULLMAN COMPOSITE**; ANSONIA; **cream roof**, black base; **non-opening doors**

p162	1930-33	**No. 1 PULLMAN COMPOSITE**; **AURORA**; grey roof, black base; opening doors
-	1933-34	**No. 1 PULLMAN COMPOSITE**; AURORA; **red roof, red base**; opening doors
-	1933-34	**No. 1 PULLMAN COMPOSITE**; AURORA; **green roof, green base**; opening doors
-	1934-35	**No. 1 PULLMAN COMPOSITE**; AURORA; **red roof, black base**; opening doors
p162	1934-35	**No. 1 PULLMAN COMPOSITE**; AURORA; **green roof, black base**; opening doors
-	1935-41	**No. 1 PULLMAN COMPOSITE**; AURORA; **cream roof**, black base; **non-opening doors**

-	1921	**DINING SALOON**; **LNWR** crest, green and cream; fixed doors; white window surrounds (PU)
-	1921-22	DINING SALOON; LNWR crest, green and cream; fixed doors; **gold window surrounds**; black gas cylinders
-	1922-23	DINING SALOON; LNWR crest, green and cream; fixed doors; gold window surrounds; **green gas cylinders**
-	1921	DINING SALOON; **GN** crest, green and cream; fixed doors; white window surrounds
-	1921-22	DINING SALOON; GN crest, green and cream; fixed doors; **gold window surrounds**; black gas cylinders
-	1922-23	DINING SALOON; GN crest, green and cream; fixed doors; gold window surrounds; **green gas cylinders**
-	1921	DINING SALOON; **MR** crest, green and cream; fixed doors; white window surrounds
-	1921-22	DINING SALOON; MR crest, green and cream; fixed doors; **gold window surrounds**; black gas cylinders
-	1922-23	DINING SALOON; MR crest, green and cream; fixed doors; gold window surrounds; **green gas cylinders**
-	1921	DINING SALOON; **CR** crest, green and cream; fixed doors; white window surrounds (PU)
p126	1921-22	DINING SALOON; CR crest, green and cream; fixed doors; **gold window surrounds**; black gas cylinders
-	1922-23	DINING SALOON; CR crest, green and cream; fixed doors; gold window surrounds; **green gas cylinders**
p19	1923-24	DINING SALOON; **PULLMAN** crest, green and cream; **opening doors with celluloid windows**; gold window surrounds
p163	1924-25	DINING SALOON; PULLMAN crest, green and cream; opening doors with **printed windows**; gold window surrounds
p13	1921	**No. 2 PULLMAN COACH**; green and cream; fixed doors; white window surrounds
-	1921-22	No. 2 PULLMAN COACH; green and cream; fixed doors; **gold window surrounds**; black gas cylinders
p163	1922-23	No. 2 PULLMAN COACH; green and cream; fixed doors; gold window surrounds; **green gas cylinders**
p163	1923-24	No. 2 PULLMAN COACH; green and cream; **opening doors with celluloid windows**; gold window surrounds
-	1924-25	No. 2 PULLMAN COACH; green and cream; opening doors with **printed windows**; unlined "PULLMAN" transfer
-	1925	No. 2 PULLMAN COACH; green and cream; opening doors with printed windows; **lined "PULLMAN" transfer**
p163	1925-28	No. 2 PULLMAN COACH; **brown and cream**; opening doors with printed windows; lined "PULLMAN" transfer
p163	1927?	No. 2 PULLMAN COACH; brown and cream; **plain opening doors**; lined "PULLMAN" transfer; constructional body style
p165	1927-28	**No. 3 PULLMAN COACH**; brown and cream, **revised body style with corridor connection**
-	1930-32	No. 2 PULLMAN COACH; brown and cream, with corridor connection; brown "PULLMAN" name panel; large crests (reintroduction)
-	1932-33	No. 2 PULLMAN COACH; brown and cream, with corridor connection; **dark "PULLMAN" name panel**; large crests
-	1933-35	No. 2 PULLMAN COACH; brown and cream, with corridor connection; dark "PULLMAN" name panel; **small crests**
p165	1935-41	No. 2 PULLMAN COACH; brown and cream, with corridor connection; **brown "PULLMAN" name panel**; small crests
p163	1928	**No. 2 SPECIAL PULLMAN COACH**; **IOLANTHE** (new transfer on old No. 3 body style)
p36	1928-30	No. 2 SPECIAL PULLMAN COACH; IOLANTHE; cream roof
-	1930-34	No. 2 SPECIAL PULLMAN COACH; IOLANTHE; **grey roof**
p164	1929-30	No. 2 SPECIAL PULLMAN COACH; **ZENOBIA**; cream roof
-	1930-41	No. 2 SPECIAL PULLMAN COACH; ZENOBIA; **grey roof**
p164	1930-41	No. 2 SPECIAL PULLMAN COACH; **GROSVENOR**; grey roof
p164	1934-41	No. 2 SPECIAL PULLMAN COACH; **LORAINE**; grey roof
p36	1928-30	**No. 2 SPECIAL PULLMAN COMPOSITE**; **ARCADIA**; cream roof
-	1930-32	No. 2 SPECIAL PULLMAN COMPOSITE; ARCADIA; **grey roof**; cream across luggage doors
-	1932-35	No. 2 SPECIAL PULLMAN COMPOSITE; ARCADIA; grey roof; **brown luggage doors**
p164	1929-30	No. 2 SPECIAL PULLMAN COMPOSITE; **ALBERTA**; cream roof
-	1930-32	No. 2 SPECIAL PULLMAN COMPOSITE; ALBERTA; **grey roof**; cream across luggage doors
-	1932-41	No. 2 SPECIAL PULLMAN COMPOSITE; ALBERTA; grey roof; **brown luggage doors**

p164	1930-32	**No. 2 SPECIAL PULLMAN COMPOSITE; MONTANA**; grey roof; cream across luggage doors
-	1932-41	**No. 2 SPECIAL PULLMAN COMPOSITE; MONTANA**; grey roof; **brown luggage doors**
p164	1935-41	**No. 2 SPECIAL PULLMAN COMPOSITE; VERONA**; grey roof; brown luggage doors
p165	1930-41	**SALOON COACH, LMS**
p165	1930-35	**SALOON COACH, LNER**; gold letters, shadowed blue
-	1935-41	**SALOON COACH, LNER**; gold letters, **shadowed red**
p165	1926-41	**RIVIERA BLUE TRAIN SLEEPING CAR**
p165	1926-41	**RIVIERA BLUE TRAIN DINING CAR**
-	1931-34	**No. 3 MITROPA COACH, DINING CAR** (speisewagen); ends black
p165	1934-41	**No. 3 MITROPA COACH, DINING CAR** (speisewagen); **ends red**
p45-	1931-34	**No. 3 MITROPA COACH, SLEEPING CAR** (schlafwagen); ends black
p165	1934-41	**No. 3 MITROPA COACH, SLEEPING CAR** (schlafwagen); **ends red**
-	1931-33	**No. 0 MITROPA COACH, DINING CAR** (speisewagen); red enamel over tinprinted body
-	1933-36	**No. 0 MITROPA COACH, DINING CAR** (speisewagen); red enamel, **gold transfers** (PU)
p166	1936-41	**No. 0 MITROPA COACH, DINING CAR** (speisewagen); red **tinprinted body**
-	1931-33	**No. 0 MITROPA COACH, SLEEPING CAR** (schlafwagen); red enamel over tinprinted body
p166	1933-36	**No. 0 MITROPA COACH, SLEEPING CAR** (schlafwagen); red enamel, **gold transfers**
p166	1936-41	**No. 0 MITROPA COACH, SLEEPING CAR** (schlafwagen); red **tinprinted body**
p156	1930-33	**PULLMAN CAR, AMERICAN TYPE; MADISON, green body**; black base, grey roof
-	1933-34	**PULLMAN CAR, AMERICAN TYPE; MADISON**, green body; **red base, red roof**
-	1934-36	**PULLMAN CAR, AMERICAN TYPE; MADISON**, green body; **black base**, red roof
-	1936-41	**PULLMAN CAR, AMERICAN TYPE; MADISON**, green body; black base, **cream roof** (PU)
p166	1930-33	**PULLMAN CAR, AMERICAN TYPE; MADISON, yellow body**; black base, grey roof
-	1933-34	**PULLMAN CAR, AMERICAN TYPE; MADISON**, yellow body; **orange base, orange roof**
p166	1934-36	**PULLMAN CAR, AMERICAN TYPE; MADISON**, yellow body; **black base**, orange roof
p166	1936-41	**PULLMAN CAR, AMERICAN TYPE; MADISON**, yellow body; black base, **cream roof**
p166	1930-33	**PULLMAN CAR, AMERICAN TYPE; WASHINGTON, green body**; black base, grey roof
-	1933-34	**PULLMAN CAR, AMERICAN TYPE; WASHINGTON**, green body; **red base, red roof**
p166	1934-36	**PULLMAN CAR, AMERICAN TYPE; WASHINGTON**, green body; **black base**, red roof
p166	1936-41	**PULLMAN CAR, AMERICAN TYPE; WASHINGTON**, green body; black base, **cream roof**
p166	1930-33	**PULLMAN CAR, AMERICAN TYPE; WASHINGTON, yellow body**; black base, grey roof
p166	1933-34	**PULLMAN CAR, AMERICAN TYPE; WASHINGTON**, yellow body; **orange base, orange roof**
-	1934-36	**PULLMAN CAR, AMERICAN TYPE; WASHINGTON**, yellow body; **black base**, orange roof (PU)
-	1936-41	**PULLMAN CAR, AMERICAN TYPE; WASHINGTON**, yellow body; black base, **cream roof** (PU)

-	1926-39	**METROPOLITAN COACH C**; 1st class
-	1926-39	**METROPOLITAN COACH C**; brake/3rd
p154	1925-39	**METROPOLITAN COACH E**; 1st class (plug and socket connection for HV; roller pickup for LV)
p154	1925-39	**METROPOLITAN COACH E**; brake/3rd (plug and socket connection for HV; roller pickup for LV)
p9	1920-26	**TINPRINTED TRAIN COACH, LNWR**
p254	1920-26	**TINPRINTED TRAIN COACH, GN**
p254	1920-26	**TINPRINTED TRAIN COACH, MR**
p260	1936-41	**No. O "SILVER JUBILEE" ARTICULATED SALOON COACH**
p260	1937-40	**No. O STREAMLINE COACH**, maroon and cream
p260	1937-40	**No. O STREAMLINE COACH**, light green and dark green

p202	1935-37	**No. O BANANA VAN;** black standard base, grey body, white roof; "Avonmouth" letters in black
p203	1937-41	**No. O BANANA VAN;** black standard base, grey body, **grey** roof; "Avonmouth" letters in **white**

No. 1 Banana Van... see FYFFES

p168	1931-32	**BARREL WAGON;** red crimped long thin base, 2 chains, no central tin clip; blue barrels, black lined, secured by nail heads and chains
p168	1932	**BARREL WAGON;** red crimped long thin base, 2 chains, **with central tin clip;** blue barrels, black lined, **secured by chains only**
p168	1932-33	**BARREL WAGON;** red crimped long thin base, 2 chains, with central tin clip; blue barrels, **yellow lined**
p168	1933-35	**BARREL WAGON;** red crimped long thin base, 2 chains, with central tin clip; **yellow barrels, black lined**
p168	1933-35	**BARREL WAGON;** red crimped long thin base, 2 chains, with central tin clip; **green barrels, black lined**
p168	1935-37	**BARREL WAGON;** red **coach-type base**, single chain; yellow barrels, black lined
p168	1935-37	**BARREL WAGON;** red **coach-type base**, single chain; green barrels, black lined
p168	1937-41	**BARREL WAGON;** red coach-type base, single chain; **yellow Castrol** barrels, black lined
p168	1937-41	**BARREL WAGON;** red coach-type base, single chain; **green Castrol** barrels, black lined

Biscuit Van... see CARR'S, CRAWFORD'S, JACOB'S

Bitumen Tank Wagon... see COLAS

-	1930	**BOX CAR;** black US base, brown roof, black footwalk, plain enamelled door
p167	1930-33	**BOX CAR;** black US base, brown roof, black footwalk, **printed door**
p167	1933-36	**BOX CAR; orange US base, orange roof, green footwalk,** printed door
p167	1936-41	**BOX CAR; black US base,** orange roof, green footwalk, printed door

p190	1927-30	**BP PETROL TANK WAGON;** cream with red line; open axleguard base; pressed filler, cast top
p190	1930-31	**BP PETROL TANK WAGON;** cream with red line; **standard base;** pressed filler, cast top; wide flanges on ends
p190	1931-32	**BP PETROL TANK WAGON;** cream with red line; standard base; pressed filler, cast top; **narrow flanges on ends**
p190	1932-34	**BP PETROL TANK WAGON;** cream, **large letters;** standard base; pressed filler, cast top; narrow flanges on ends
p190	1934-36	**BP PETROL TANK WAGON;** cream, large letters; standard base; pressed filler, **embossed top;** narrow flanges on ends

p169	1922-23	**BRAKE VAN;** LNW, grey body, early base, white "LNW"; doors one end only
p17	1923-24	**BRAKE VAN;** LNW, grey body, **open axleguard base**, white "LNW"; unlettered base
-	1924	**BRAKE VAN;** LNW, grey body, open axleguard base, white "LNW"; **"No. 1 Brake Van"** on base

-	1922-23	**BRAKE VAN;** GN, brown body, early base, white "GN"; doors both ends
p169	1923-24	**BRAKE VAN;** GN, brown body, **open axleguard base**, white "GN"; unlettered base
-	1923-24	**BRAKE VAN;** GN, brown body, open axleguard base, white "GN"; **"No. 1 Brake Van"** on base (PU)

p169	1924-25	**BRAKE VAN; LMS,** grey body, open axleguard base, white "LMS"; "No. 1 Brake Van" on base; doors one end only
-	1925-27	**BRAKE VAN; LMS,** grey body, open axleguard base, white normally-spaced "LMS"; **unlettered base**
p25	1926	**BRAKE VAN; LMS,** grey body, open axleguard base, white **closely-spaced** "LMS"; unlettered base
p169	1927-30	**BRAKE VAN; LMS,** grey body, open axleguard base, **large gold** "LMS"
-	1930-31	**BRAKE VAN; LMS,** grey body, black **standard base,** large gold "LMS"
p169	1931-33	**BRAKE VAN; LMS,** grey body, black standard base, **smaller gold** "LMS"
p169	1931-33	**BRAKE VAN; LMS,** grey body, black standard base, **white** "LMS"
-	1933	**BRAKE VAN; LMS, lighter grey** body, **green** standard base, **smaller gold** "LMS" (PU)
p50	1933-35	**BRAKE VAN; LMS,** lighter grey body, **green** standard base, sans-serif **white** "LMS"
p57	1935-39	**BRAKE VAN; LMS,** lighter grey body, **black** standard base, sans-serif white "LMS"
p169	1939-41	**BRAKE VAN; LMS,** lighter grey body, black standard base, **serif white** "LMS"
-	1924-25	**BRAKE VAN; LNER,** brown body, open axleguard base, white "LNER"; "No. 1 Brake Van" on base; doors both ends
p169	1925-27	**BRAKE VAN; LNER,** brown body, open axleguard base, white "LNER"; **unlettered base**
p118	1927-30	**BRAKE VAN; NE,** brown body, open axleguard base, **large gold** "NE"
p169	1930-32	**BRAKE VAN; NE,** brown body, black **standard base,** large gold "NE"
-	1932	**BRAKE VAN; NE,** brown body, black standard base, **smaller gold** "NE" (PU)
-	1932-33	**BRAKE VAN; NE,** brown body, black standard base, **white** "NE"
-	1933	**BRAKE VAN; NE,** brown body, **green** standard base, **smaller gold** "NE" (PU)
-	1933-35	**BRAKE VAN; NE,** brown body, **green** standard base, **white** "NE"
p169	1935-41	**BRAKE VAN; NE,** brown body, **black** standard base, white "NE" (as 1932-33)
-	1926	**BRAKE VAN; GW,** grey body, open axleguard base, white **closely-spaced** "GW"; unlettered base; doors one end only
p169	1926-27	**BRAKE VAN; GW,** grey body, open axleguard base, white **normally-spaced** "GW"; unlettered base
-	1927-30	**BRAKE VAN; GW,** grey body, open axleguard base, **large gold** "GW"
p169	1930	**BRAKE VAN; GW,** grey body, black **standard base,** large gold "GW"
p42	1930-32	**BRAKE VAN; GW,** grey body, black standard base, **smaller gold** "GW"
-	1932-33	**BRAKE VAN; GW,** grey body, black standard base, **white** "GW"
-	1933	**BRAKE VAN; GW, lighter grey** body, **green** standard base, **smaller gold** "GW" (PU)
p169	1933-35	**BRAKE VAN; GW,** lighter grey body, **green** standard base, **white** "GW"
p169	1935-41	**BRAKE VAN; GW,** lighter grey body, **black** standard base, white "GW"
p169	1928-30	**BRAKE VAN; SR,** lighter brown body, open axleguard base, **large gold** "SR"; doors both ends
-	1930-32	**BRAKE VAN; SR,** lighter brown body, black **standard base,** large gold "SR"
p45	1932-33	**BRAKE VAN; SR,** lighter brown body, black standard base, **smaller gold** "SR"
-	1932	**BRAKE VAN; SR,** lighter brown body, black standard base, **white** "SR" (PU)
p169	1933	**BRAKE VAN; SR, darker brown** body, **green** standard base, **smaller gold** "SR"
p211	1933-35	**BRAKE VAN; SR,** darker brown body, **green** standard base, **white** "SR"
p67	1935-41	**BRAKE VAN; SR,** darker brown body, **black** standard base, white "SR"

Brake Van, French Type... see French Type Brake Van

BREAKDOWN VAN and CRANE

p171	1923	PLAIN; grey body; unlettered black base, white roof; grey unstrengthened jib; red cross both sides; unlined "To lift.." one side
-	1923-24	PLAIN; grey body; **"Breakdown.." one side**; unstrengthened jib; red cross both sides; **lined** "To lift.." both sides
p171	1923-24	PLAIN; grey body; **"Breakdown.." both sides**; unstrengthened jib; **no red cross**; lined "To lift.." both sides
-	1924-25	LMS; grey body; "Breakdown.." one side; unstrengthened jib; red cross both sides; lined "To lift.." one side; "LMS" one side only; open front door
p171	1925	LMS; grey body; "Breakdown.." one side; **strengthened jib**; **red cross one side**; lined **"To lift.."** both sides; "LMS" one side only; **hinged front door**
p171	1925-27	LMS; grey body, **unlettered base**; strengthened jib; red cross one side; lined "To lift.." both sides; "LMS" one side only; hinged front door
-	1927-28	LMS; **brown body, blue base**, white roof, small gold "LMS" one side, red cross one side; white "To lift.." on jib
-	1928-30	LMS; brown body, blue base, white roof, small gold "LMS" one side, red cross one side; **gold "To lift.."** on jib; early bogies
-	1930-31	LMS; brown body, blue base, white roof, small gold "LMS" one side, red cross one side; gold "To lift.." on jib; **lowered bogies** (PU)
-	1931	LMS; brown body, blue base, white roof, small gold "LMS" one side, red cross one side; **red-lined jib**; hinged doors
-	1931-32	LMS; brown body, blue base, white roof, small gold "LMS" one side, red cross one side; red-lined jib; **sliding side doors**
-	1932-33	LMS; brown body, blue base, white roof, small gold **"LMS" both sides, no red cross**; red-lined jib; sliding side doors
-	1934?	LMS; **green body, lighter blue base and roof, green bogies**, small gold "LMS" both sides, no red cross; **blue jib**, red-lined; sliding side doors
-	1933-36	LMS; green body, lighter blue base and roof, green bogies, small gold "LMS" both sides, no red cross; blue jib, **green-lined**; sliding side doors
p171	1936-37	LMS; green body, **black base**, lighter blue roof, **black bogies**, small gold sans-serif "LMS" both sides; blue jib, green-lined; sliding side doors
-	1937-38	LMS; **grey body**, black base, lighter blue roof, black bogies, small gold **serif** "LMS" both sides; **grey jib, lined dark grey**; sliding side doors
p171	1938-41	LMS; grey body, black base, **white roof**, black bogies, small gold serif "LMS" both sides; grey jib, lined dark grey; sliding side doors
-	1939?	LMS; grey body, black base, white roof, black bogies, small **white "LMS" both sides**; grey jib, lined dark grey; sliding side doors (PU)
-	1924-25	LNER; grey body; "Breakdown.." both sides; unstrengthened jib; red cross one side; lined "To lift.." one side; "LNER" one side only; open front door
-	1925	LNER; grey body; **"Breakdown.." one side**; **strengthened jib**; red cross one side; lined **"To lift.."** both sides; "LNER" one side only; **hinged front door**
-	1925-27	LNER; grey body, **unlettered base**; strengthened jib; red cross one side; lined "To lift.." both sides; "LNER" one side only; hinged front door
p171	1927-28	**NE; brown body, blue base**, white roof, small gold "NE" one side, red cross one side; white "To lift.." on jib
p171	1928-30	NE; brown body, blue base, white roof, small gold "NE" one side, red cross one side; **gold "To lift.."** on jib; early bogies
-	1930-31	NE; brown body, blue base, white roof, small gold "NE" one side, red cross one side; gold "To lift.." on jib; **lowered bogies** (PU)
-	1931	NE; brown body, blue base, white roof, small gold "NE" one side, red cross one side; **red-lined jib**; hinged doors
-	1931-32	NE; brown body, blue base, white roof, small gold "NE" one side, red cross one side; red-lined jib; **sliding side doors**
-	1932-33	NE; brown body, blue base, white roof, small gold **"NE" both sides, no red cross**; red-lined jib; sliding side doors
-	1934?	NE; **green body, lighter blue base and roof, green bogies**, small gold "NE" both sides, no red cross; **blue jib**, red-lined; sliding side doors (PU)
p171	1933-36	NE; green body, lighter blue base and roof, green bogies, small gold "NE" both sides, no red cross; blue jib, **green-lined**; sliding side doors
-	1936-37	NE; green body, **black base**, lighter blue roof, **black bogies**, small gold "NE" both sides, no red cross; blue jib, green-lined; sliding side doors
p171	1937-38	NE; **grey body**, black base, lighter blue roof, black bogies, small gold "NE" both sides, no red cross; **grey jib, lined dark grey**; sliding side doors
-	1938-41	NE; grey body, black base, **white roof**, black bogies, small gold "NE" both sides, no red cross; grey jib, lined dark grey; sliding side doors
-	1939?	NE; grey body, black base, white roof, black bogies, small **white "NE" both sides**, no red cross; grey jib, lined dark grey; sliding side doors (PU)
p128	1926	GW; grey body, unlettered base; strengthened jib; red cross one side; lined "To lift.." both sides; "GW" one side only; hinged front door
-	1927-28	GW; **brown body, blue base**, white roof, small gold "GW" one side, red cross one side; white "To lift.." on jib
-	1928-30	GW; brown body, blue base, white roof, small gold "GW" one side, red cross one side; **gold "To lift.."** on jib; early bogies
-	1930-31	GW; brown body, blue base, white roof, small gold "GW" one side, red cross one side; gold "To lift.." on jib; **lowered bogies** (PU)
p171	1931	GW; brown body, blue base, white roof, small gold "GW" one side, red cross one side; **red-lined jib**; hinged doors
-	1931-32	GW; brown body, blue base, white roof, small gold "GW" one side, red cross one side; red-lined jib; **sliding side doors**

A42

-	1932-33	GW; brown body, blue base, white roof, small gold "GW" **both sides, no red cross**; red-lined jib; sliding side doors (PU)
-	1934?	GW; **green body, lighter blue base and roof, green bogies,** small gold "GW" both sides, no red cross; **blue jib,** red-lined; sliding side doors (PU)
-	1933-36	GW; green body, lighter blue base and roof, green bogies, small gold "GW" both sides, no red cross; blue jib, **green-lined**; sliding side doors
-	1936-37	GW; green body, **black base,** lighter blue roof, **black bogies,** small gold "GW" both sides, no red cross; blue jib, green-lined; sliding side doors
-	1937-38	GW; **grey body,** black base, lighter blue roof, black bogies, small gold "GW" both sides, no red cross; **grey jib, lined dark grey**; sliding side doors
-	1938-41	GW; grey body, black base, **white roof,** black bogies, small gold "GW" both sides, no red cross; grey jib, lined dark grey; sliding side doors
-	1939?	GW; grey body, black base, white roof, black bogies, small **white "GW" both sides,** no red cross; grey jib, lined dark grey; sliding side doors
p31	1928-30	SR; brown body, darker brown base, white roof, small gold SR one side, red cross one side; brown jib, gold "To lift.."
-	1930-31	SR; brown body, darker brown base, white roof, small gold SR one side, red cross one side; brown jib, gold "To lift.."; **lowered bogies** (PU)
-	1931	SR; brown body, darker brown base, white roof; small gold SR one side, red cross one side; brown **red-lined** jib; hinged doors
p171	1931-32	SR; brown body, darker brown base, white roof; small **gold SR both sides, no red cross**; brown red-lined jib; hinged doors
-	1932-33	SR; brown body, darker brown base, white roof; small gold SR both sides, no red cross; brown red-lined jib; **sliding side doors** (PU)
-	1934?	SR; **green body, lighter blue base and roof, green bogies,** small gold "SR" both sides, no red cross; **blue jib,** red-lined; sliding side doors (PU)
p211	1933-36	SR; green body, lighter blue base and roof, green bogies, small gold "SR" both sides, no red cross; blue jib, **green-lined**; sliding side doors
-	1936-37	SR; green body, **black base,** lighter blue roof, **black bogies,** small gold "SR" both sides, no red cross; blue jib, green-lined; sliding side doors
-	1937-38	SR; **grey body,** black base, lighter blue roof, black bogies, small gold "SR" both sides, no red cross; **grey jib, lined dark grey**; sliding side doors
-	1938-41	SR; grey body, black base, **white roof,** black bogies, small gold "SR" both sides, no red cross; grey jib, lined dark grey; sliding side doors
-	1939?	SR; grey body, black base, white roof, black bogies, small **white "SR" both sides,** no red cross; grey jib, lined dark grey; sliding side doors (PU)
p167	1930-33	CABOOSE; black US base and end rails, orange roof; monitor sides green, roof orange
p167	1933-36	CABOOSE; **red US base, green end rails, red roof, all-green monitor**
p167	1936-41	CABOOSE; **black US base,** green end rails, red roof, all-green monitor
p195	1932-33	CADBURY'S CHOCOLATE VAN; black standard base, blue body, white roof; serif letters
p195	1933-35	CADBURY'S CHOCOLATE VAN; **green standard base, lighter blue body,** white roof; serif letters
p195	1935-38	CADBURY'S CHOCOLATE VAN; **black standard base,** lighter blue body, white roof; serif letters
p195	1938-41	CADBURY'S CHOCOLATE VAN; black standard base, lighter blue body, white roof; **block letters**
p192	1924	CARR'S BISCUIT VAN; open axleguard base; blue body, white roof
p193	1924-25	CARR'S BISCUIT VAN; open axleguard base; **grey-blue** body, white roof
p193	1925-30	CARR'S BISCUIT VAN; open axleguard base; grey-blue body, **grey-blue roof**
-	1930-32	CARR'S BISCUIT VAN; **standard base**; grey-blue body and roof, hinged door (PU)
-	1932-33	CARR'S BISCUIT VAN; standard base; grey-blue blue body and roof, **sliding door** (PU)
-	1933	CARR'S BISCUIT VAN; standard base; **lighter blue** body and roof, sliding door
p193	1933-34	CARR'S BISCUIT VAN; standard base; lighter blue body and roof, **hinged door**
p193	1934-41	CARR'S BISCUIT VAN; standard base; lighter blue body and roof, **sliding door; revised transfers**
p190	1930-31	CASTROL OIL TANK WAGON; green; standard base; pressed filler, cast top; wide flanges on ends
p190	1931-34	CASTROL OIL TANK WAGON; green; standard base; pressed filler, cast top; **narrow flanges on ends**
p190	1934-41	CASTROL OIL TANK WAGON; green; standard base; pressed filler, **embossed top**; narrow flanges on ends

p172	1923	**No. 1 CATTLE TRUCK; PLAIN**, olive green open axleguard base, "No. 1 Cattle Truck" one side on solebar; grey body, white roof
-	1924-25	**No. 1 CATTLE TRUCK; LMS**, olive green open axleguard base, "No. 1 Cattle Truck" one side on solebar; small gold "LMS" both sides on grey body; white roof
p172	1924-25	No. 1 CATTLE TRUCK; LMS, olive green open axleguard base, "No. 1 Cattle Truck" one side on solebar; small gold "LMS" both sides on grey body; **dark grey-green roof**
p172	1925-26	No. 1 CATTLE TRUCK; LMS, olive green open axleguard base, **small gold "LMS" both solebars**; grey body; dark grey-green roof
-	1926-27	No. 1 CATTLE TRUCK; LMS, olive green open axleguard base; grey body, small gold "LMS" **both sides on body**, plain solebars; dark grey-green roof (PU)
p30	1927-30	No. 1 CATTLE TRUCK; LMS, **blue** open axleguard base; **pale blue/grey body**, small gold "LMS" both sides on body; **blue doors and roof**
-	1930-32	No. 1 CATTLE TRUCK; LMS, blue **standard base**; pale blue/grey body, small gold "LMS" both sides; blue doors and roof
p172	1932-33	No. 1 CATTLE TRUCK; LMS, **red** standard base; pale blue/grey body, small gold "LMS" both sides (lhs of doors); blue doors and roof
-	1933	No. 1 CATTLE TRUCK; LMS, red standard base; pale blue/grey body, small gold "LMS" both sides (**rhs of doors**); blue doors and roof
p172	1933-34	No. 1 CATTLE TRUCK; LMS, **green** standard base; grey body, small gold "LMS" both sides (lhs of doors); **green doors and roof**
-	1934-35	No. 1 CATTLE TRUCK; LMS, **black** standard base; grey body, small gold "LMS" both sides (lhs of doors); green doors and roof
p172	1935-39	No. 1 CATTLE TRUCK; LMS, black standard base; grey body, small gold "LMS" both sides (lhs of doors); **grey doors, white roof**
p70	1939-41	No. 1 CATTLE TRUCK; LMS, black standard base; grey body, small **serif white "LMS"** both sides (lhs of doors); grey doors, white roof
p172	1924-25	**No. 1 CATTLE TRUCK; LNER**, olive green open axleguard base, "No. 1 Cattle Truck" one side on solebar; small gold "LNER" both sides on grey body; **dark grey-green roof**
p172	1925-26	No. 1 CATTLE TRUCK; LNER, olive green open axleguard base, **small gold "LNER" both solebars**; grey body; dark grey-green roof
-	1926	No. 1 CATTLE TRUCK; LNER, olive green open axleguard base; grey body, small gold "**LNER" both sides on body**, plain solebars; dark grey-green roof
-	1926-27	No. 1 CATTLE TRUCK; NE, olive green open axleguard base; grey body, small gold "NE" both sides on body; dark grey-green roof (PU)
p220	1927-30	No. 1 CATTLE TRUCK; NE, **blue** open axleguard base; **pale blue/grey body**, small gold "NE" both sides on body; **blue doors and roof**
p172	1930-32	No. 1 CATTLE TRUCK; NE, blue **standard base**; pale blue/grey body, small gold "NE" both sides; blue doors and roof
p48	1932-33	No. 1 CATTLE TRUCK; NE, **red** standard base; pale blue/grey body, small gold "NE" both sides (lhs of doors); blue doors and roof
-	1933	No. 1 CATTLE TRUCK; NE, red standard base; pale blue/grey body, small gold "NE" both sides (**rhs of doors**); blue doors and roof (PU)
-	1933-34	No. 1 CATTLE TRUCK; NE, **green** standard base; grey body, small gold "NE" both sides (lhs of doors); **green doors and roof**
-	1934-35	No. 1 CATTLE TRUCK; NE, **black** standard base; grey body, small gold "NE" both sides (lhs of doors); green doors and roof
-	1935-39	No. 1 CATTLE TRUCK; NE, black standard base; grey body, small gold "NE" both sides (lhs of doors); **grey doors, white roof**
-	1939-41	No. 1 CATTLE TRUCK; NE, black standard base; grey body, small **white "NE"** both sides (lhs of doors); grey doors, white roof
p26	1926	No. 1 CATTLE TRUCK; GW, olive green open axleguard base, small gold "GW" both sides on solebar; grey body; dark grey-green roof
-	1926-27	No. 1 CATTLE TRUCK; GW, olive green open axleguard base; grey body, small gold "**GW" both sides on body**, plain solebars; dark grey-green roof (PU)
p172	1927-30	No. 1 CATTLE TRUCK; GW, **blue** open axleguard base; **pale blue/grey body**, small gold "GW" both sides on body; **blue doors and roof**
-	1930-32	No. 1 CATTLE TRUCK; GW, blue **standard base**; pale blue/grey body, small gold "GW" both sides; blue doors and roof
-	1932-33	No. 1 CATTLE TRUCK; GW, **red** standard base; pale blue/grey body, small gold "GW" both sides (lhs of doors); blue doors and roof
p172	1933	No. 1 CATTLE TRUCK; GW, red standard base; pale blue/grey body, small gold "GW" both sides (**rhs of doors**); blue doors and roof (PU)
-	1933-34	No. 1 CATTLE TRUCK; GW, **green** standard base; grey body, small gold "GW" both sides (lhs of doors); **green doors and roof**
p172	1934-35	No. 1 CATTLE TRUCK; GW, **black** standard base; grey body, small gold "GW" both sides (lhs of doors); green doors and roof
-	1935-39	No. 1 CATTLE TRUCK; GW, black standard base; grey body, small gold "GW" both sides (lhs of doors); **grey doors, white roof**
p172	1939-41	No. 1 CATTLE TRUCK; GW, black standard base; grey body, small **white "GW"** both sides (lhs of doors); grey doors, white roof

p172	1928-30	**No. 1 CATTLE TRUCK**; **SR**, black open axleguard base; brown body and doors, small gold "SR" both sides on body; white roof
-	1930-33	**No. 1 CATTLE TRUCK**; SR, black **standard base**; brown body and doors, small gold "SR" both sides on body (lhs of doors); white roof
-	1933	**No. 1 CATTLE TRUCK**; SR, black standard base; brown body and doors, small gold "SR" both sides on body (**rhs of doors**); white roof
p172	1933-34	**No. 1 CATTLE TRUCK**; SR, **green** standard base; brown body, small gold "SR" both sides on body (lhs of doors); **green doors and roof**
-	1934-35	**No. 1 CATTLE TRUCK**; SR, **black** standard base; brown body, small gold "SR" both sides on body (lhs of doors); green doors and roof (PU)
-	1935-39	**No. 1 CATTLE TRUCK**; SR, black standard base; brown body, small gold "SR" both sides on body (lhs of doors); brown doors, **white roof**
p172	1939-41	**No. 1 CATTLE TRUCK**; SR, black standard base; brown body, small **white "SR"** both sides on body (lhs of doors); brown doors, white roof

| p173 | 1923-24 | **No. 2 CATTLE TRUCK**; **PLAIN**, olive green base, "No. 2 Cattle Truck" one side; grey body, white roof |

-	1924-25	**No. 2 CATTLE TRUCK**; **LMS**, olive green base, "No. 2 Cattle Truck" one side; white "LMS" on grey body, dark grey-green roof
-	1925-27	**No. 2 CATTLE TRUCK**; LMS, olive green base, **unlettered**; white "LMS" on grey body, dark grey-green roof
p173	1927-28	**No. 2 CATTLE TRUCK**; LMS, **blue base**; white "LMS" on pale blue/grey body; **blue roof**
p173	1928-30	**No. 2 CATTLE TRUCK**; LMS, blue base; **large gold "LMS"** on pale blue/grey body; blue roof
-	1930-33	**No. 2 CATTLE TRUCK**; LMS, blue base; large gold "LMS" on pale blue/grey body; blue roof; **lowered bogies**
-	1933-34	**No. 2 CATTLE TRUCK**; LMS, **green base**; large gold "LMS" on grey body; **green bogies and roof**
-	1934-35	**No. 2 CATTLE TRUCK**; LMS, green base; **smaller gold "LMS"** on grey body; green bogies and roof. Normal body pressing
p95	1935	**No. 2 CATTLE TRUCK**; LMS, green base; smaller gold "LMS" on grey body; green bogies and roof. **Luggage Van body pressing**
-	1935-36	**No. 2 CATTLE TRUCK**; LMS, **grey base**; **large gold "LMS"** on grey body; green bogies; **white roof**. Normal body pressing
p173	1936-38	**No. 2 CATTLE TRUCK**; LMS, grey base; **smaller gold "LMS"** on grey body; **black bogies**; white roof
-	1938-41	**No. 2 CATTLE TRUCK**; LMS, grey base; **white "LMS"** on grey body; black bogies; white roof
p173	1939	**No. 2 CATTLE TRUCK**; LMS, **black base**; white "LMS" on grey body; black bogies; white roof

p173	1924-25	**No. 2 CATTLE TRUCK**; **LNER**, olive green base, "No. 2 Cattle Truck" one side; white "LNER" on grey body, dark grey-green roof
-	1925-26	**No. 2 CATTLE TRUCK**; LNER, olive green base, **unlettered**; white "LNER" on grey body, dark grey-green roof
p173	1926-27	**No. 2 CATTLE TRUCK**; **NE**, olive green base, unlettered; white "**NE**" on grey body, dark grey-green roof
-	1927-28	**No. 2 CATTLE TRUCK**; NE, blue base; white "NE" on pale blue/grey body; **blue roof** (PU)
-	1928-30	**No. 2 CATTLE TRUCK**; NE, blue base; large **gold "NE"** on pale blue/grey body; blue roof
-	1930-33	**No. 2 CATTLE TRUCK**; NE, blue base; large gold "NE" on pale blue/grey body; blue roof; **lowered bogies**
-	1933-35	**No. 2 CATTLE TRUCK**; NE, **green base**; **smaller gold "NE"** on grey body; **green bogies and roof**. Normal body pressing
-	1935	**No. 2 CATTLE TRUCK**; NE, green base; smaller gold "NE" on grey body; green bogies and roof. **Luggage Van body pressing**
p173	1935-36	**No. 2 CATTLE TRUCK**; NE, **grey base**; smaller gold "NE" on grey body; green bogies; **white roof**. Normal body pressing
-	1936-38	**No. 2 CATTLE TRUCK**; NE, grey base; smaller gold "NE" on grey body; **black bogies**; white roof
-	1938-41	**No. 2 CATTLE TRUCK**; NE, grey base; **white "NE"** on grey body; black bogies; white roof
-	1939	**No. 2 CATTLE TRUCK**; NE, **black base**; white "NE" on grey body; black bogies; white roof

p173	1926-27	**No. 2 CATTLE TRUCK**; **GW**, olive green base, unlettered; white "**GW**" on grey body, dark grey-green roof
-	1927-28	**No. 2 CATTLE TRUCK**; GW, **blue base**; white "GW" on pale blue/grey body; **blue roof**
p32	1928-30	**No. 2 CATTLE TRUCK**; GW, blue base; **large gold "GW"** on pale blue/grey body; blue roof
-	1930-33	**No. 2 CATTLE TRUCK**; GW, blue base; **smaller gold "GW"** on pale blue/grey body; blue roof; **lowered bogies**
p173	1933-35	**No. 2 CATTLE TRUCK**; GW, **green base**; smaller gold "GW" on grey body; **green bogies and roof**. Normal body pressing
-	1935	**No. 2 CATTLE TRUCK**; GW, green base; smaller gold "GW" on grey body; green bogies and roof. **Luggage Van body pressing** (PU)
-	1935-36	**No. 2 CATTLE TRUCK**; GW, **grey base**; smaller gold "GW" on grey body; green bogies; **white roof**. Normal body pressing

-	1936-38	**No. 2 CATTLE TRUCK**; GW, grey base; smaller gold "GW" on grey body; **black bogies**; white roof
p173	1938-41	**No. 2 CATTLE TRUCK**; GW, grey base; **white "GW"** on grey body; black bogies; white roof
-	1939	**No. 2 CATTLE TRUCK**; GW, **black base**; white "GW" on grey body; black bogies; white roof

p31	1928-30	**No. 2 CATTLE TRUCK**; **SR**, black base; large gold "SR" on brown body; white roof
-	1930-33	**No. 2 CATTLE TRUCK**; SR, black base; large gold "SR" on brown body; white roof; **lowered bogies**
-	1933-34	**No. 2 CATTLE TRUCK**; SR, **green base**; large gold "SR" on brown body; **green roof; green bogies** (PU)
-	1934-35	**No. 2 CATTLE TRUCK**; SR, **black base**; large gold "SR" on brown body; **white roof**; green bogies. (Normal body pressing)
-	1935	**No. 2 CATTLE TRUCK**; SR, black base; gold "SR" on brown body; white roof; black bogies. **Luggage Van body pressing** (PU)
p173	1935-39	**No. 2 CATTLE TRUCK**; SR, black base; **smaller gold "SR"** on brown body; white roof; black bogies. **(Normal body pressing)**
p60	1937?	**No. 2 CATTLE TRUCK**; SR, **brown base**; smaller gold "SR" on brown body; white roof; black bogies
-	1939-41	**No. 2 CATTLE TRUCK**; SR, **black base; white "SR"** on brown body; white roof; black bogies

p174	1922-23	CEMENT WAGON, PLAIN, black open axleguard base, grey body, white "Cement" both sides
p174	1923-24	CEMENT WAGON, PLAIN, black open axleguard base, grey body, **gold "Cement"** both sides

-	1924-25	CEMENT WAGON, LMS, black open axleguard base, "LMS" one solebar; grey body, white "Cement" both sides
p174	1924-25	CEMENT WAGON, LMS, black open axleguard base, "LMS" one solebar; grey body, **gold "Cement"** both sides
-	1925-27	CEMENT WAGON, LMS, black open axleguard base, **unlettered solebar**; grey body, gold **"Cement" one side, large gold "LMS" other**
p174	1927-30	CEMENT WAGON, LMS, red open axleguard base, **red body**, gold "Cement" one side, large gold "LMS" other

p174	1924-25	CEMENT WAGON, LNER, black open axleguard base, "LNER" one solebar; grey body, white "Cement" both sides
-	1924-25	CEMENT WAGON, LNER, black open axleguard base, "LNER" one solebar; grey body, **gold "Cement"** both sides
p174	1925-27	CEMENT WAGON, LNER, black open axleguard base, **unlettered solebar**; grey body, gold **"Cement" one side, large gold "LNER" other**
-	1927-30	CEMENT WAGON, LNER, red open axleguard base, **red body**, gold "Cement" one side, large gold "LNER" other

-	1926-27	CEMENT WAGON, GW, black open axleguard base; grey body, gold "Cement" one side, large gold "GW" other (PU)
p174	1927-30	CEMENT WAGON, GW, red open axleguard base, **red body**, gold "Cement" one side, large gold "GW" other

p174	1928-30	CEMENT WAGON, **SR**, red open axleguard base, red body, gold "Cement" one side, large gold "SR" other

-	1930	CEMENT WAGON, PLAIN, red open axleguard base, red body, gold "Cement" one side (PU)
p174	1930-37	CEMENT WAGON, PLAIN, red **standard base**, red body, gold "Cement" one side
p174	1937-41	CEMENT WAGON, **PORTLAND CEMENT**, black standard base, yellow body, "Blue Circle" transfer

Chocolate Van... see CADBURY'S

p174	1931-36	**COAL WAGON**, red body, gold "MECCANO" transfer
p174	1936-40	**COAL WAGON**, red body, gold "HORNBY RAILWAY COMPANY" transfer
p174	1940-41	**COAL WAGON**, maroon body, white "HORNBY RAILWAY COMPANY" transfer
p174	1940?	**COAL WAGON**, maroon body, gold "MECCANO" transfer

p169	1929-30	**COLAS BITUMEN TANK WAGON**; blue open axleguard base and tank
p44	1930-33	**COLAS BITUMEN TANK WAGON**; blue **standard base** and tank
p278	1933-36	**COLAS BITUMEN TANK WAGON**; **lighter blue** standard base and tank
p169	1936-39	**COLAS BITUMEN TANK WAGON**; lighter blue standard base, **red tank**
p169	1939-41	**COLAS BITUMEN TANK WAGON**; **black** standard base, red tank

p192 1923-24 **COLMAN'S MUSTARD VAN**; black open axleguard base, yellow body, white roof

Covered Wagon, French Type... see French Type Covered Wagon

p175	1923	**CRANE TRUCK**; PLAIN, black open axleguard base; grey unstrengthened jib, unlined "To lift.." one side
-	1923-24	**CRANE TRUCK**; PLAIN, black open axleguard base; grey unstrengthened jib, **white lined "To lift.." both sides** (PU)

-	1924	**CRANE TRUCK**; LMS, black open axleguard base; grey unstrengthened jib, **unlined "To lift.."**
-	1924	**CRANE TRUCK**; LMS, black open axleguard base; grey unstrengthened jib, **white lined "To lift.."** both sides (PU)
p175	1924-27	**CRANE TRUCK**; LMS, black open axleguard base; grey **strengthened jib**, white lined "To lift.." both sides
-	1927-30	**CRANE TRUCK**; LMS, **blue** open axleguard base; **brown** strengthened jib, **gold "To lift.."** both sides

-	1924	**CRANE TRUCK**; LNER, black open axleguard base; grey unstrengthened jib, **unlined "To lift.."** (PU)
-	1924	**CRANE TRUCK**; LNER, black open axleguard base; grey unstrengthened jib, **white lined "To lift.."** both sides
p175	1924-26	**CRANE TRUCK**; LNER, black open axleguard base; grey **strengthened jib**, white lined "To lift.." both sides
p29	1926-27	**CRANE TRUCK**; NE, black open axleguard base; grey strengthened jib, white lined "To lift.." both sides
p175	1927-30	**CRANE TRUCK**; NE, **blue** open axleguard base; **brown** strengthened jib, **gold "To lift.."** both sides

-	1926-27	**CRANE TRUCK**; GW, black open axleguard base; grey strengthened jib, white lined "To lift.." both sides
p36	1927-30	**CRANE TRUCK**; GW, **blue** open axleguard base; **brown** strengthened jib, **gold "To lift.."** both sides

p31 1928-30 **CRANE TRUCK**; SR, **blue** open axleguard base; **brown** strengthened jib, gold "To lift.." both sides

p175	1930	**CRANE TRUCK**; **PLAIN**, blue open axleguard base; brown strengthened jib, gold "To lift.." both sides
p175	1930-31	**CRANE TRUCK**; PLAIN, blue **standard base**; brown jib, gold "To lift.." both sides
p175	1931-33	**CRANE TRUCK**; PLAIN, blue standard base; brown jib, **red-lined**
p175	1933-34	**CRANE TRUCK**; PLAIN, **yellow standard base**; **blue jib, yellow-lined**
p175	1934-35	**CRANE TRUCK**; PLAIN, yellow standard base; blue jib, **red-lined**
p175	1935-38	**CRANE TRUCK**; PLAIN, **black standard base**; blue jib, red-lined
p175	1937	**CRANE TRUCK**; PLAIN, black standard base; blue jib, **green-lined**
p175	1938-41	**CRANE TRUCK**; PLAIN, black standard base; **grey jib, dark grey lined**

p193	1924-25	**CRAWFORD'S BISCUIT VAN**; open axleguard base; red body, white roof
p193	1925-30	**CRAWFORD'S BISCUIT VAN**; open axleguard base; red body, **red roof**
-	1930-32	**CRAWFORD'S BISCUIT VAN**; **standard base**; red body, red roof, hinged door, early transfer (PU)
p193	1932-33	**CRAWFORD'S BISCUIT VAN**; standard base; red body, red roof, **sliding door**, early transfer
p193	1933-34	**CRAWFORD'S BISCUIT VAN**; standard base; red body, red roof, **hinged door**, early transfer
p193	1934-38	**CRAWFORD'S BISCUIT VAN**; standard base; red body, red roof, **sliding door, revised transfer**, "By appointment"

p193   1938-41   **CRAWFORD'S BISCUIT VAN**; standard base; red body, red roof, sliding door, revised transfer, **"By appointment to the late King.."**

p190   1936-41   **ESSO PETROL TANK WAGON**; cream; standard base; pressed filler, embossed top; narrow flanges on ends

p175   1931-33   **FIBRE WAGON**; **red** standard wagon base
p175   1933-39   **FIBRE WAGON**; **blue** standard wagon base
p259   (also with no buffers, for M11 Complete Model Railway Set)
p175   1939-41   **FIBRE WAGON**; **black** standard wagon base
-                  (also with no buffers, for M11 Complete Model Railway Set)

p202   1931-33   **NO. O FISH VAN, NE**; black standard base, grey body, sliding doors
p202   1933-35   **NO. O FISH VAN, NE**; **green** standard base, grey body, sliding doors
p203   1935-41   **NO. O FISH VAN, NE**; **black** standard base, brown body, fixed doors
-         1937   **NO. O FISH VAN, LMS**; black standard base, red body, fixed doors, white roof
p203   1937-41   **NO. O FISH VAN, LMS**; **black standard base, red body, fixed doors, grey roof**
p203   1937-41   **NO. O FISH VAN, GW**; black standard base, brown body, fixed doors, white roof

p51   1934-41   **FLAT TRUCK**; grey, **LMS**
-        1934-41   **FLAT TRUCK; grey, NE**
-        1934-41   **FLAT TRUCK**; grey, **GW**
-        1934-41   **FLAT TRUCK**; brown, **SR**

p176   1934-37   **FLAT TRUCK and CABLE DRUM**; grey LMS truck; BI Cables drum, black stained
p176   1937-39   **FLAT TRUCK and CABLE DRUM; grey LMS truck; Liverpool Cables drum, green stained**
p176   1939-41   **FLAT TRUCK and CABLE DRUM**; grey LMS truck; BI Cables drum, not stained

p176   1934-37   **FLAT TRUCK and CABLE DRUM**; grey **NE** truck; BI Cables drum, black stained
-        1937-39   **FLAT TRUCK and CABLE DRUM**; grey NE truck; Liverpool Cables drum, green stained
p176   1939-41   **FLAT TRUCK and CABLE DRUM**; grey NE truck; BI Cables drum, not stained

p176   1934-37   **FLAT TRUCK and CABLE DRUM**; grey **GW** truck; BI Cables drum, black stained
p176   1937-39   **FLAT TRUCK and CABLE DRUM**; grey GW truck; Liverpool Cables drum, green stained
-        1939-41   **FLAT TRUCK and CABLE DRUM; grey GW truck; BI Cables drum, not stained**

p176   1934-37   **FLAT TRUCK and CABLE DRUM**; brown **SR** truck; BI Cables drum, black stained
-        1937-39   **FLAT TRUCK and CABLE DRUM**; brown SR truck; Liverpool Cables drum, green stained
-        1939-41   **FLAT TRUCK and CABLE DRUM**; brown SR truck; BI Cables drum, not stained

p176   1936-41   **FLAT TRUCK and CONTAINER**; **LMS** grey truck, **LMS** container
p176   1936-41   **FLAT TRUCK and CONTAINER**; **NE** grey truck, **NE** container
p176   1936-41   **FLAT TRUCK and CONTAINER**; **GW** grey truck, **GW** container
p176   1936-41   **FLAT TRUCK and CONTAINER**; **SR** brown truck, **SR** container

p177	1927-30	**FRENCH-TYPE BRAKE VAN**; NORD, blue open axleguard base, pale blue body, small gold "NORD"; blue roof
-	1930-33	**FRENCH-TYPE BRAKE VAN**; NORD, blue **standard** base, pale blue body, small gold "NORD"; blue roof
p145	1933-35	**FRENCH-TYPE BRAKE VAN**; NORD, **dark blue** standard base, **blue body**, small gold "NORD"; **red roof**
p177	1935-36	**FRENCH-TYPE BRAKE VAN**; NORD, **black** standard base, blue body, small gold "NORD"; **white roof**
p177	1927-28	**FRENCH-TYPE WAGON**; NORD, blue open axleguard base; pale blue/grey body, white "NORD"
p177	1928-30	**FRENCH-TYPE WAGON**; NORD, blue open axleguard base; pale blue/grey body, **large gold "NORD"**
-	1930-33	**FRENCH-TYPE WAGON**; NORD, blue **standard base**; pale blue/grey body, large gold "NORD"
p177	1933-36	**FRENCH-TYPE WAGON**; NORD, **red** standard base; **blue body**, large gold "NORD"
p177	1936-38	**FRENCH-TYPE WAGON**; NORD, red standard base; blue body, **smaller gold "NORD"**
-	1938-39	**FRENCH-TYPE WAGON**; NORD, **black** standard base; **grey body**, smaller gold "NORD"
p177	1929-30	**FRENCH-TYPE COVERED WAGON**; NORD, black open axleguard base; grey body, large gold "NORD"
p177	1930-33	**FRENCH-TYPE COVERED WAGON**; NORD, black **standard base**; grey body, large gold "NORD"
p177	1933-36	**FRENCH-TYPE COVERED WAGON**; NORD, black standard base; **lighter grey body**, large gold "NORD"
-	1936-39	**FRENCH-TYPE COVERED WAGON**; NORD, black standard base; lighter grey body, **smaller gold "NORD"**
p177	1939-41	**FRENCH-TYPE COVERED WAGON**; NORD, black standard base; lighter grey body, **white "NORD"**
p194	1931-32	**FYFFES BANANA VAN**; green standard base; yellow body; white roof; **hinged doors**
p194	1932-33	**FYFFES BANANA VAN**; green standard base; yellow body; white roof; **sliding doors**
p194	1933-39	**FYFFES BANANA VAN**; **red standard base**; yellow body; **red roof**; sliding doors
p194	1939-41	**FYFFES BANANA VAN**; **black standard base**; yellow body; red roof; sliding doors
p178	1923-24	**GAS CYLINDER**; PLAIN, black open axleguard base; red cylinders, gold "Gas Cylinder" both sides
p178	1924	**GAS CYLINDER**; LMS, black open axleguard base, "LMS" one side of base; red cylinders, gold "Gas Cylinder" both sides
-	1924-25	**GAS CYLINDER**; LMS, black open axleguard base, **"LMS" both sides** of base; red cylinders, gold "Gas Cylinder" both sides (PU)
p178	1925-30	**GAS CYLINDER**; LMS, black **unlettered** open axleguard base; red cylinders, **"LMS" one side, "Gas Cylinder" other**
p18	1924	**GAS CYLINDER**; L&NER, black open axleguard base, "L&NER" one side of base; red cylinders, gold "Gas Cylinder" both sides
p178	1924-25	**GAS CYLINDER**; LNER, black open axleguard base, **"LNER" both sides** of base; red cylinders, gold "Gas Cylinder" both sides
p178	1925-26	**GAS CYLINDER**; LNER, black **unlettered** open axleguard base; red cylinders, **"LNER" one side, "Gas Cylinder" other**
p178	1926-30	**GAS CYLINDER**; NE, black open axleguard base; red cylinders, **"NE"** one side, "Gas Cylinder" other
p178	1926-30	**GAS CYLINDER**; GW, black open axleguard base; red cylinders, **"GW"** one side, "Gas Cylinder" other
p178	1928-30	**GAS CYLINDER**; SR, black open axleguard base; green cylinders, **"SR"** one side, "Gas Cylinder" other
p178	1930	**GAS CYLINDER**; PLAIN, black open axleguard base; red cylinders, "Gas Cylinder" one side
p178	1930-32	**GAS CYLINDER**; PLAIN, black **standard base**; red cylinders, "Gas Cylinder" one side
-	1932-33	**GAS CYLINDER**; PLAIN, black standard base; **unlettered** red cylinders, separate black straps
p178	1933-39	**GAS CYLINDER**; PLAIN, **blue** standard base; unlettered red cylinders, embossed **blue-finished straps**
p178	1939-41	**GAS CYLINDER**; PLAIN, **black** standard base; unlettered red cylinders, embossed **black-finished straps**

-	1922	**GUNPOWDER VAN**; **LNWR**, black early wagon base, red body, black "Gunpowder Van" on doors
p179	1922	**GUNPOWDER VAN**; LNWR, black early wagon base, red body, **white "Gunpowder Van"** on doors
p179	1922-24	**GUNPOWDER VAN**; LNWR, black **open axleguard base**, red body, white "Gunpowder Van" on doors
p179	1924-25	**GUNPOWDER VAN**; **LMS**, black open axleguard base; red body, white "LMS"; white **"Gunpowder Van" on base**
-	1925-26	**GUNPOWDER VAN**; LMS, black open axleguard base; red body, white "LMS"; **not lettered "Gunpowder Van"**
-	1926-27	**GUNPOWDER VAN**; LMS, black open axleguard base; red body, white "LMS"; white **"Gunpowder Van" on doors**
p179	1927-29	**GUNPOWDER VAN**; LMS, black open axleguard base; red body, **large gold "LMS"**; white "Gunpowder Van" and **embossed crossed straps on doors**
-	1929-30	**GUNPOWDER VAN**; LMS, black open axleguard base; red body, large gold "LMS"; white "Gunpowder Van" and **embossed single strap on doors**
p179	1930-32	**GUNPOWDER VAN**; LMS, black **standard base**; red body, large gold "LMS"; white "Gunpowder Van" on hinged doors
-	1932-34	**GUNPOWDER VAN**; LMS, black standard base; red body, large gold "LMS"; white "Gunpowder Van" on **sliding doors**
p179	1934-39	**GUNPOWDER VAN**; LMS, black standard base; red body, **smaller gold "LMS"**; white "Gunpowder Van" on sliding doors
p179	1939-41	**GUNPOWDER VAN**; LMS, black standard base; red body, **white "LMS"**; white "Gunpowder Van" on sliding doors
p179	1924-25	**GUNPOWDER VAN**; **LNER**, black open axleguard base; red body, white "LNER"; white **"Gunpowder Van" on base**
p179	1925-26	**GUNPOWDER VAN**; LNER, black open axleguard base; red body, white "LNER"; **not lettered "Gunpowder Van"**
-	1926	**GUNPOWDER VAN**; LNER, black open axleguard base; red body, white "LNER"; white **"Gunpowder Van" on doors**
p29	1926-27	**GUNPOWDER VAN**; **NE**, black open axleguard base; red body, white **"NE"**; white "Gunpowder Van" on doors
-	1927-29	**GUNPOWDER VAN**; NE, black open axleguard base; red body, **large gold "NE"**; white "Gunpowder Van" and **embossed crossed straps on doors** (PU)
p179	1929-30	**GUNPOWDER VAN**; NE, black open axleguard base; red body, large gold "NE"; white "Gunpowder Van" and **embossed single strap on doors**
p179	1930-32	**GUNPOWDER VAN**; NE, black **standard base**; red body, large gold "NE"; white "Gunpowder Van" on hinged doors
-	1932-34	**GUNPOWDER VAN**; NE, black standard base; red body, large gold "NE"; white "Gunpowder Van" on **sliding doors** (PU)
p179	1934-39	**GUNPOWDER VAN**; NE, black standard base; red body, **smaller gold "NE"**; white "Gunpowder Van" on sliding doors
p179	1939-41	**GUNPOWDER VAN**; NE, black standard base; red body, **white "NE"**; white "Gunpowder Van" on sliding doors
p179	1926-27	**GUNPOWDER VAN**; **GW**, black open axleguard base; red body, white **"GW"**; white "Gunpowder Van" on doors
p179	1927-28	**GUNPOWDER VAN**; GW, black open axleguard base; red body, **large gold "GW"**; white "Gunpowder Van" on doors
p179	1928-29	**GUNPOWDER VAN**; GW, black open axleguard base; **grey body**, large gold "GW"; **red "GPV"**, **red-painted embossed crossed straps on doors**
p179	1929-30	**GUNPOWDER VAN**; GW, black open axleguard base; **dark grey body**, large gold "GW"; red "GPV", red-painted embossed crossed straps on doors
p179	1930-32	**GUNPOWDER VAN**; GW, black **standard base**; dark grey body, **smaller gold "GW"**; red "GPV", red-painted embossed crossed straps on doors
-	1932-33	**GUNPOWDER VAN**; GW, black standard base; grey body, smaller gold "GW"; red "GPV"; **sliding doors**, stencil-sprayed cross (PU)
p179	1933-39	**GUNPOWDER VAN**; GW, black standard base; **lighter grey** body, smaller gold "GW"; red "GPV"; sliding doors, stencil-sprayed cross
p179	1939-41	**GUNPOWDER VAN**; GW, black standard base; lighter grey body, **white "GW"**; red "GPV"; sliding doors, stencil-sprayed cross
p179	1928-29	**GUNPOWDER VAN**; **SR**, black open axleguard base; red body, large gold "SR"; white "Gunpowder Van" and embossed crossed straps on doors
-	1929-30	**GUNPOWDER VAN**; SR, black open axleguard base; red body, large gold "SR"; white "Gunpowder Van" and **embossed single strap on doors** (PU)
-	1930-32	**GUNPOWDER VAN**; SR, black **standard base**; red body, large gold "SR"; white "Gunpowder Van" on hinged doors
p179	1932-34	**GUNPOWDER VAN**; SR, black standard base; red body, large gold "SR"; white "Gunpowder Van" on **sliding doors**
p179	1934-39	**GUNPOWDER VAN**; SR, black standard base; red body, **smaller gold "SR"**; white "Gunpowder Van" on sliding doors
p179	1939-41	**GUNPOWDER VAN**; SR, black standard base; red body, **white "SR"**; white "Gunpowder Van" on sliding doors

p180	1936-41	**No. 2 HIGH CAPACITY WAGON; LMS coal**
p180	1936-41	**No. 2 HIGH CAPACITY WAGON; NE brick**
p180	1936-41	**No. 2 HIGH CAPACITY WAGON; GW coal**

| p181 | 1923-24 | **HOPPER WAGON; PLAIN**, black open axleguard base, "HOPPER WAGON" one side; grey unlettered body |

-	1924-25	**HOPPER WAGON; LMS**, black open axleguard base, "HOPPER WAGON" one side; grey body, gold "LMS" both sides
p181	1925-27	**HOPPER WAGON; LMS**, black **unlettered** open axleguard base; grey body, gold "LMS" both sides
p181	1927-30	**HOPPER WAGON; LMS**, **green** unlettered open axleguard base; **green body**, gold "LMS" both sides
p181	1930-33	**HOPPER WAGON; LMS**, green **standard base**; green body, gold "LMS" both sides
p181	1933-39	**HOPPER WAGON; LMS**, **lighter green** standard base and body, gold "LMS" both sides
p181	1939-40	**HOPPER WAGON; LMS**, **black** standard base; lighter green body, gold "LMS" both sides
-	1940-41	**HOPPER WAGON; LMS**, black standard base; lighter green body, **serif white "LMS"** both sides

p181	1924-25	**HOPPER WAGON; LNER**, black open axleguard base, "HOPPER WAGON" one side; grey body, gold "LNER" both sides
p217	1925-26	**HOPPER WAGON; LNER**, black **unlettered** open axleguard base; grey body, gold "LNER" both sides
-	1926-27	**HOPPER WAGON; LNER**, **green** unlettered open axleguard base; **green body**, gold "LNER" both sides
-	1927-30	**HOPPER WAGON; NE**, green unlettered open axleguard base; green body, gold "NE" both sides
p181	1930-33	**HOPPER WAGON; NE**, green **standard base**; green body, gold "NE" both sides
p181	1933-39	**HOPPER WAGON; NE**, **lighter green** standard base and body, gold "NE" both sides
-	1939-40	**HOPPER WAGON; NE**, **black** standard base; lighter green body, gold "NE" both sides (PU)
p181	1940-41	**HOPPER WAGON; NE**, black standard base; lighter green body, **white "NE"** both sides

p181	1926-27	**HOPPER WAGON; GW**, black unlettered open axleguard base; grey body, gold "GW" both sides
p181	1927-30	**HOPPER WAGON; GW**, **green** unlettered open axleguard base; **green body**, gold "GW" both sides
p181	1930-33	**HOPPER WAGON; GW**, green **standard base**; green body, gold "GW" both sides
p181	1933-39	**HOPPER WAGON; GW**, **lighter green** standard base and body, gold "GW" both sides
-	1939-40	**HOPPER WAGON; GW**, **black** standard base; lighter green body, gold "GW" both sides (PU)
p67	1940-41	**HOPPER WAGON; GW**, black standard base; lighter green body, **white "GW"** both sides

p181	1928-30	**HOPPER WAGON; SR**, black open axleguard base; red body, gold "SR" both sides
p181	1930-40	**HOPPER WAGON; SR**, black **standard base**; red body, gold "SR" both sides
-	1940-41	**HOPPER WAGON; SR**, black standard base; red body, **white "SR"** both sides

p194	1924-25	**JACOB'S BISCUIT VAN**; open axleguard base; maroon body, white roof
p195	1925-30	**JACOB'S BISCUIT VAN**; open axleguard base; maroon body, **maroon roof**
-	1930-32	**JACOB'S BISCUIT VAN**; **standard base**; maroon body, maroon roof, hinged door, early transfer
-	1932-33	**JACOB'S BISCUIT VAN**; standard base; maroon body, maroon roof, **sliding door**, early transfer (PU)
p194	1933-34	**JACOB'S BISCUIT VAN**; standard base; maroon body, maroon roof, **hinged door**, early transfer
p195	1934-40	**JACOB'S BISCUIT VAN**; standard base; maroon body, maroon roof, **sliding door, revised transfer**
-	1940-41	**JACOB'S BISCUIT VAN**; standard base; **brown body**, maroon roof, sliding door, revised transfer

p182	1921-23	No. 1 LUGGAGE VAN; **MR**, early wagon base; grey body, unlettered doors; clip-on "MR"
-	1923	No. 1 LUGGAGE VAN; MR, early wagon base; grey body, **"Luggage Van" on doors**; clip-on "MR" (PU)
p182	1923-24	No. 1 LUGGAGE VAN; MR, **open axleguard base**; grey body, **"Luggage Van" on doors**; clip-on "MR"
p182	1924-25	No. 1 LUGGAGE VAN; **LMS**, open axleguard base; grey body, white transfer "LMS"; **"Luggage Van" on base**
-	1925-27	No. 1 LUGGAGE VAN; LMS, open axleguard base; grey body, white "LMS"; **no "Luggage Van" lettering**
p33	1927-30	No. 1 LUGGAGE VAN; LMS, open axleguard base; grey body, large **gold "LMS"**
p182	1930-32	No. 1 LUGGAGE VAN; LMS, **standard base**; grey body, large gold "LMS"; hinged doors
-	1932-33	No. 1 LUGGAGE VAN; LMS, standard base; grey body, large gold "LMS"; **sliding doors**
p182	1933-34	No. 1 LUGGAGE VAN; LMS, standard base; **lighter grey body**, large gold "LMS"; sliding doors
p57	1934-39	No. 1 LUGGAGE VAN; LMS, standard base; lighter grey body, **smaller gold "LMS"**; sliding doors
p70	1939-41	No. 1 LUGGAGE VAN; LMS, standard base; lighter grey body, **white "LMS"**; sliding doors
p24	1924-25	No. 1 LUGGAGE VAN; **LNER**, open axleguard base; grey body, white transfer "LNER"; **"Luggage Van" on base**
p182	1925-26	No. 1 LUGGAGE VAN; LNER, open axleguard base; grey body, white "LNER"; **no "Luggage Van" lettering**
p29	1926-27	No. 1 LUGGAGE VAN; **NE**, open axleguard base; grey body, white **"NE"**
p182	1927-30	No. 1 LUGGAGE VAN; NE, open axleguard base; grey body, large **gold "NE"**
-	1930-32	No. 1 LUGGAGE VAN; NE, **standard base**; grey body, large gold "NE"; hinged doors (PU)
-	1932-33	No. 1 LUGGAGE VAN; NE, standard base; grey body, large gold "NE"; **sliding doors**
-	1933-34	No. 1 LUGGAGE VAN; NE, standard base; **lighter grey body**, large gold "NE"; sliding doors
p182	1934-39	No. 1 LUGGAGE VAN; NE, standard base; lighter grey body, **smaller gold "NE"**; sliding doors
-	1939-41	No. 1 LUGGAGE VAN; NE, standard base; lighter grey body, **white "NE"**; sliding doors
p205	1926-27	No. 1 LUGGAGE VAN; **GW**, open axleguard base; grey body, white "GW"
-	1927-30	No. 1 LUGGAGE VAN; GW, open axleguard base; grey body, large **gold "GW"**
-	1930-32	No. 1 LUGGAGE VAN; GW, **standard base**; grey body, **smaller gold "GW"**; hinged doors
p182	1932-33	No. 1 LUGGAGE VAN; GW, standard base; grey body, smaller gold "GW"; **sliding doors**
p210	1933-39	No. 1 LUGGAGE VAN; GW, standard base; **lighter grey body**, smaller gold "GW"; sliding doors
p182	1939-41	No. 1 LUGGAGE VAN; GW, standard base; lighter grey body, **white "GW"**; sliding doors
p182	1928-30	No. 1 LUGGAGE VAN; **SR**, open axleguard base; brown body, large gold "SR"
p45	1930-32	No. 1 LUGGAGE VAN; SR, **standard base**; brown body, large gold "SR"; hinged doors
-	1932-34	No. 1 LUGGAGE VAN; SR, standard base; brown body, large gold "SR"; **sliding doors**
p182	1934-39	No. 1 LUGGAGE VAN; SR, standard base; brown body, **smaller gold "SR"**; sliding doors
p67	1939-41	No. 1 LUGGAGE VAN; SR, standard base; brown body, **white "SR"**; sliding doors
p183	1923-24	No. 2 LUGGAGE VAN; **PLAIN**, olive green base; "No. 2 Luggage Van" on grey body; white roof
p183	1924	No. 2 LUGGAGE VAN; **LMS**, olive green unlettered base; "No. 2 Luggage Van" on grey body, white "LMS"; white roof
p183	1924-25	No. 2 LUGGAGE VAN; LMS, olive green base, **"No. 2 Luggage Van" one side of base**; grey body, white "LMS"; **dark grey-green roof**
-	1925-27	No. 2 LUGGAGE VAN; LMS, olive green **unlettered** base; grey body, white "LMS"; dark grey-green roof
-	1927-28	No. 2 LUGGAGE VAN; LMS, **blue base**; pale blue/grey body, white "LMS"; **blue roof**
-	1928-30	No. 2 LUGGAGE VAN; LMS, blue base; pale blue/grey body, **large gold "LMS"**; blue roof
p183	1930-33	No. 2 LUGGAGE VAN; LMS, blue base; pale blue/grey body, large gold "LMS"; blue roof; **lowered bogies**

A52

-	1933-34	No. 2 LUGGAGE VAN; LMS, **black base**; **light grey body**, large gold "LMS"; **white roof**
-	1934-36	No. 2 LUGGAGE VAN; LMS, black base; light grey body, **smaller gold "LMS"**; white roof; normal body pressing
-	1935?	No. 2 LUGGAGE VAN; LMS, black base; light grey body, smaller gold "LMS"; white roof; **Cattle Truck body pressing**
-	1936-38	No. 2 LUGGAGE VAN; LMS, **light grey base** and body, smaller gold "LMS"; white roof; normal body pressing
-	1939	No. 2 LUGGAGE VAN; LMS, **black base**, light grey body, **white "LMS"**; white roof
p183	1938-41	No. 2 LUGGAGE VAN; LMS, **light grey base** and body, white "LMS"; white roof

-	1924-25	No. 2 LUGGAGE VAN; LNER, olive green base, "No. 2 Luggage Van" one side of base; grey body, white "LNER"; dark grey-green roof
p183	1925-26	No. 2 LUGGAGE VAN; LNER, olive green **unlettered** base; grey body, white "LNER"; dark grey-green roof
p29	1926-27	No. 2 LUGGAGE VAN; NE, olive green unlettered base; grey body, white "NE"; dark grey-green roof
-	1927-28	No. 2 LUGGAGE VAN; NE, **blue base**; pale blue/grey body, white "NE"; **blue roof** (PU)
-	1928-30	No. 2 LUGGAGE VAN; NE, blue base; pale blue/grey body, **large gold "NE"**; blue roof
-	1930-33	No. 2 LUGGAGE VAN; NE, blue base; pale blue/grey body, large gold "NE"; blue roof; **lowered bogies**
-	1933-34	No. 2 LUGGAGE VAN; NE, **black base**; **light grey body**, large gold "NE"; **white roof**
p183	1934-36	No. 2 LUGGAGE VAN; NE, black base; light grey body, **smaller gold "NE"**; white roof; normal body pressing
-	1935	No. 2 LUGGAGE VAN; NE, black base; light grey body, smaller gold "NE"; white roof; **Cattle Truck body pressing** (PU)
p62	1936-38	No. 2 LUGGAGE VAN; NE, **light grey base** and body, smaller gold "NE"; white roof; normal body pressing
-	1939	No. 2 LUGGAGE VAN; NE, **black base**, light grey body, **white "NE"**; white roof (PU)
-	1938-41	No. 2 LUGGAGE VAN; NE, **light grey base** and body, white "NE"; white roof

-	1926-27	No. 2 LUGGAGE VAN; GW, olive green unlettered base; grey body, white **"GW"**; dark grey-green roof (PU)
p183	1927-28	No. 2 LUGGAGE VAN; GW, **blue base**; pale blue/grey body, white "GW"; **blue roof**
-	1928-30	No. 2 LUGGAGE VAN; GW, blue base; pale blue/grey body, **large gold "GW"**; blue roof
p183	1930-33	No. 2 LUGGAGE VAN; GW, blue base; pale blue/grey body, **smaller gold "GW"**; blue roof; **lowered bogies**
p183	1933-34	No. 2 LUGGAGE VAN; GW, **black base**; **light grey body**, smaller gold "GW"; **white roof**; normal body pressing; **green bogies**
-	1934-36	No. 2 LUGGAGE VAN; GW, black base; light grey body, smaller gold "GW"; white roof; normal body pressing; **black bogies**
p95	1935?	No. 2 LUGGAGE VAN; GW, black base; light grey body, smaller gold "GW"; white roof; **Cattle Truck body pressing**
p183	1936-38	No. 2 LUGGAGE VAN; GW, **light grey base** and body, smaller gold "GW"; white roof; normal body pressing
-	1939	No. 2 LUGGAGE VAN; GW, **black base**; light grey body, **white "GW"**; white roof
-	1938-41	No. 2 LUGGAGE VAN; GW, **light grey base** and body, white "GW"; white roof (PU)

p31	1928-30	No. 2 LUGGAGE VAN; SR, black base; brown body, large gold "SR"; white roof
-	1930-35	No. 2 LUGGAGE VAN; SR, black base; brown body, large gold "SR"; white roof; **lowered bogies**; normal body pressing
p95	1935	No. 2 LUGGAGE VAN; SR, black base; brown body, large gold "SR"; white roof; **lowered bogies**; **Cattle Truck body pressing**
p183	1935-39	No. 2 LUGGAGE VAN; SR, black base; brown body, **smaller gold "SR"**; white roof; normal body pressing
		(Brown-base versions may possibly have been produced)
-	1939-41	No. 2 LUGGAGE VAN; SR, black base; brown body, **white "SR"**; white roof; normal body pressing

| - | 1923 | No. 1 LUMBER WAGON; **PLAIN**, olive green open axleguard base; black bolsters |
| p184 | 1923-24 | No. 1 LUMBER WAGON; **PLAIN**, olive green open axleguard base; **red bolsters** |

p184	1924	No. 1 LUMBER WAGON; **LMS**, olive green open axleguard base, "LMS" both sides; **black bolsters**
p184	1924-25	No. 1 LUMBER WAGON; LMS, olive green open axleguard base; **"LMS" one side, "No. 1 Lumber Wagon" other; red bolsters**
p184	1925-30	No. 1 LUMBER WAGON; LMS, olive green open axleguard base; **"LMS" both sides**; red bolsters

-	1924	**No. 1 LUMBER WAGON; L&NER**, olive green open axleguard base, "L&NER" both sides; **black bolsters (PU)**
p184	1924	**No. 1 LUMBER WAGON; L&NER**, olive green open axleguard base, "L&NER" both sides; **red bolsters**
-	1924-25	**No. 1 LUMBER WAGON; LNER**, olive green open axleguard base; **"LNER" one side, "No. 1 Lumber Wagon" other; red bolsters**
p184	1925-26	**No. 1 LUMBER WAGON; LNER**, olive green open axleguard base; **"LNER" both sides**; red bolsters
p184	1926-30	**No. 1 LUMBER WAGON; NE**, olive green open axleguard base; **"NE" both sides**; red bolsters
p184	1926-30	**No. 1 LUMBER WAGON; GW**, olive green open axleguard base; **"GW" both sides**; red bolsters
p184	1928-30	**No. 1 LUMBER WAGON; SR**, light brown open axleguard base; **"SR" both sides**; blue bolsters
p40	1930	**No. 1 LUMBER WAGON; PLAIN**, light brown open axleguard base; blue bolsters (no lettering, but in SR colours)
-	1930	**No. 1 LUMBER WAGON; PLAIN**, olive green open axleguard base; red bolsters
p184	1930-33	**No. 1 LUMBER WAGON; PLAIN**, olive green **standard base**; red bolsters
p184	1933-39	**No. 1 LUMBER WAGON; PLAIN**, **light green** standard base; **yellow bolsters**
p184	1939-41	**No. 1 LUMBER WAGON; PLAIN**, **black** standard base; **red bolsters**
p19	1923	**No. 2 LUMBER WAGON; PLAIN**, olive green base, black bolsters
p184	1923-24	**No. 2 LUMBER WAGON; PLAIN**, olive green base, **red bolsters**
p184	1924-25	**No. 2 LUMBER WAGON; LMS**, olive green base, "LMS" one side, "No. 2 Lumber Wagon" other; red bolsters
p184	1925-30	**No. 2 LUMBER WAGON; LMS**, olive green base, **"LMS" both sides**; red bolsters
-	1924-25	**No. 2 LUMBER WAGON; LNER**, olive green base, "LNER" one side, "No. 2 Lumber Wagon" other; red bolsters
p184	1925-26	**No. 2 LUMBER WAGON; LNER**, olive green base, **"LNER" both sides**; red bolsters
-	1926-30	**No. 2 LUMBER WAGON; NE**, olive green base, **"NE" both sides**; red bolsters
p184	1926-30	**No. 2 LUMBER WAGON; GW**, olive green base, **"GW" both sides**; red bolsters
p184	1928-29	**No. 2 LUMBER WAGON; SR**, light brown base, "SR" both sides; blue bolsters
p35	1929-30	**No. 2 LUMBER WAGON; SR**, **dark brown** base, "SR" both sides; blue bolsters
-	1930	**No. 2 LUMBER WAGON; PLAIN**, olive green base; red bolsters; high bogies (PU)
-	1930-31	**No. 2 LUMBER WAGON; PLAIN**, olive green base; red bolsters; **lowered bogies (PU)**
p184	1931-33	**No. 2 LUMBER WAGON; PLAIN**, olive green base; red bolsters; lowered bogies **repositioned** for automatic couplings
p184	1933-35	**No. 2 LUMBER WAGON; PLAIN**, **yellow base; green bolsters; green bogies**
p184	1935-39	**No. 2 LUMBER WAGON; PLAIN**, yellow base; green bolsters; **black bogies**
-	1939	**No. 2 LUMBER WAGON; PLAIN**, yellow base; **red bolsters**; black bogies
p184	1939-41	**No. 2 LUMBER WAGON; PLAIN**, **grey base**; red bolsters; black bogies
p202	1931-33	**NO. O MEAT VAN; LMS**, black base; grey body, sliding doors; white roof
p202	1933-35	**NO. O MEAT VAN; LMS**, **green base**; grey body, sliding doors; white roof
p202	1935-37	**NO. O MEAT VAN; LMS**, **black base**; grey body, **fixed doors**; white roof
p203	1937-41	**NO. O MEAT VAN; LMS**, black base; grey body, fixed doors; **grey roof**

A54

| p203 | 1937-41 | **NO. O MEAT VAN; NE** perishables, black base; bauxite body, fixed doors; white roof |
| p203 | 1937-41 | **NO. O MEAT VAN; GW** Mica, black base; grey body, fixed doors; white roof |

p185	1929-30	**MILK TANK WAGON, UNITED DAIRIES**; grey-blue open axleguard base, white tank
p44	1930-33	**MILK TANK WAGON, UNITED DAIRIES**; blue **standard base,** white tank
p185	1933-34	**MILK TANK WAGON, UNITED DAIRIES**; **lighter blue** standard base, white tank; with drain cocks
p185	1934-37	**MILK TANK WAGON, UNITED DAIRIES**; lighter blue standard base, white tank; **no drain cocks**
p186	1936-39	**MILK TANK WAGON, NESTLES**; **green** standard base, ladder and ends; white tank
p186	1936-39	**MILK TANK WAGON, NESTLES**; **light blue** standard base, ladder and ends; white tank
p186	1939-41	**MILK TANK WAGON, NESTLES**; **black** standard base, light blue ladder and ends; white tank

p202	1931-33	**No. O MILK TRAFFIC VAN; GW**, black base; grey body, sliding doors
p202	1933-35	**No. O MILK TRAFFIC VAN; GW**, **green base**; grey body, sliding doors
p203	1935-41	**No. O MILK TRAFFIC VAN; GW**, **black base; brown body, fixed doors**

| p187 | 1923 | **No. 1 MILK TRAFFIC VAN: PLAIN**, olive green open axleguard base, "Milk Traffic" one side; grey body; white roof; internal clips for cans |
| p187 | 1923-24 | **No. 1 MILK TRAFFIC VAN: PLAIN**, olive green open axleguard base, "Milk Traffic" one side; grey body; **dark grey-green roof; no clips for cans** |

-	1924-25	**No. 1 MILK TRAFFIC VAN: LMS**, olive green open axleguard base, **"Milk Traffic" one side, "LMS" other**; grey body; dark grey-green roof
p187	1925-27	**No. 1 MILK TRAFFIC VAN: LMS**, olive green open axleguard base, **"LMS" both sides**; grey body; dark grey-green roof
-	1927	**No. 1 MILK TRAFFIC VAN: LMS**, olive green open axleguard base, "LMS" both sides; **blue body and roof**
p187	1927-30	**No. 1 MILK TRAFFIC VAN: LMS**, **green** open axleguard base, "LMS" both sides; blue body and roof

-	1924-25	**No. 1 MILK TRAFFIC VAN: LNER**, olive green open axleguard base, **"Milk Traffic" one side, "LNER" other**; grey body; dark grey-green roof
p187	1925-26	**No. 1 MILK TRAFFIC VAN: LNER**, olive green open axleguard base, **"LNER" both sides**; grey body; dark grey-green roof
p187	1926-27	**No. 1 MILK TRAFFIC VAN: NE**, olive green open axleguard base, **"NE"** both sides; grey body; dark grey-green roof (PU)
p29	1927	**No. 1 MILK TRAFFIC VAN: NE**, olive green open axleguard base, "NE" both sides; **blue body and roof**
-	1927-30	**No. 1 MILK TRAFFIC VAN: NE**, **green** open axleguard base, "NE" both sides; blue body and roof

p187	1926-27	**No. 1 MILK TRAFFIC VAN: GW**, olive green open axleguard base, **"GW"** both sides; grey body; dark grey-green roof
-	1927	**No. 1 MILK TRAFFIC VAN: GW**, olive green open axleguard base, "GW" both sides; **blue body and roof**
p36	1927-30	**No. 1 MILK TRAFFIC VAN: GW**, **green** open axleguard base, "GW" both sides; blue body and roof

| p187 | 1928-30 | **No. 1 MILK TRAFFIC VAN: SR**, black open axleguard base, "SR" both sides; green body; white roof |
| p187 | 1930 | **No. 1 MILK TRAFFIC VAN: PLAIN**, black **standard base**; green body; white roof (no lettering, but in SR colours) |

p187	1930	**No. 1 MILK TRAFFIC VAN: PLAIN**, green open axleguard base; blue body and roof
p187	1930	**No. 1 MILK TRAFFIC VAN: PLAIN**, green **standard base**, green buffer beams; blue body and roof
p187	1930-33	**No. 1 MILK TRAFFIC VAN: PLAIN**, green standard base, **blue buffer beams**; blue body and roof
p187	1933-35	**No. 1 MILK TRAFFIC VAN: PLAIN**, **red** standard base; **lighter blue body**; cream roof
p187	1935-40	**No. 1 MILK TRAFFIC VAN: PLAIN**, **black** standard base; lighter blue body; cream roof; normal planking
p187	1936	**No. 1 MILK TRAFFIC VAN: PLAIN**, black standard base; lighter blue body; cream roof; **not planked**
p187	1940-41	**No. 1 MILK TRAFFIC VAN: PLAIN**, black standard base; lighter blue body; **lighter blue roof**; normal planking

| p190 | 1931-34 | **MOBILOIL OIL TANK WAGON**; grey; standard base; pressed filler, cast top; narrow flanges on ends |
| p190 | 1934-41 | **MOBILOIL OIL TANK WAGON**; grey; standard base; pressed filler, **embossed top**; narrow flanges on ends |

| p247 | 1935-36 | **MO CRANE TRUCK**; black MO base; blue crane |
| p247 | 1936-41 | **MO CRANE TRUCK**; **green MO base**; blue crane |

p247	1935-36	**MO PETROL TANK WAGON**; black MO base, "Shellmex and BP"
p247	1936-38	**MO PETROL TANK WAGON**; **red MO base**, "Shellmex and BP"
p247	1938-41	**MO PETROL TANK WAGON**; red MO base, **"Shell" one side, "BP" other**

p247	1935-36	**MO ROTARY TIPPING WAGON**; black MO base; green centre and tipper
p247	1936-41	**MO ROTARY TIPPING WAGON**; **red MO base**; green centre and tipper
p247	1936?	**MO ROTARY TIPPING WAGON**; red MO base, **blue centre and tipper**
-	1936?	**MO ROTARY TIPPING WAGON**; red MO base, **green centre,** blue tipper

| - | 1935-36 | **MO SIDE TIPPING WAGON**; black MO base, yellow top |
| p247 | 1936-41 | **MO SIDE TIPPING WAGON**; **green MO base**, yellow top |

p246	1930-41	**MO WAGON**; black MO base, red top
-	1933-41	**MO WAGON**; black MO base, green top
-	1932-36	**BRITISH EXPRESS WAGON (PU)**

p190	1923-24	**NATIONAL BENZOLE TANK TANK WAGON**; yellow; open axleguard base; early cast filler
p190	1924-27	**NATIONAL BENZOLE TANK TANK WAGON**; yellow; open axleguard base; **pressed filler, cast top**; black buffers
-	1927-29	**NATIONAL BENZOLE TANK TANK WAGON**; yellow; open axleguard base; pressed filler, cast top; **yellow buffers** (PU)

Oil Tank Wagon... see Castrol, Mobiloil, Royal Daylight

p190	1931-33	**OPEN WAGON B**; **LMS**, green standard base; black body, white "LMS"; black rail
p190	1933-35	**OPEN WAGON B**; LMS, green standard base; **blue body**, white "LMS"; blue rail
p190	1935-38	**OPEN WAGON B**; LMS, **black** standard base; blue body, white "LMS"; blue rail
-	1938-39	**OPEN WAGON B**; LMS, black standard base; blue body, white "LMS"; **black rail**
-	1939-41	**OPEN WAGON B**; LMS, black standard base; blue body, white **serif "LMS"**; black rail

p190	1931-33	**OPEN WAGON B**; **NE**, green standard base; black body, white "NE"; black rail
p190	1933-35	**OPEN WAGON B**; NE, green standard base; **blue body**, white "NE"; blue rail
p190	1935-38	**OPEN WAGON B**; NE, **black** standard base; blue body, white "NE"; blue rail
-	1938-41	**OPEN WAGON B**; NE, black standard base; blue body, white "NE"; **black rail**

p190	1931-33	**OPEN WAGON B**; **GW**, green standard base; black body, white "GW"; black rail
p190	1933-35	**OPEN WAGON B**; GW, green standard base; **blue body**, white "GW"; blue rail
p190	1935-38	**OPEN WAGON B**; GW, **black** standard base; blue body, white "GW"; blue rail
-	1938-41	**OPEN WAGON B**; GW, black standard base; blue body, white "GW"; **black rail**

p190	1931-33	**OPEN WAGON B**; **SR**, green standard base; black body, white "SR"; black rail
p190	1933-35	**OPEN WAGON B**; SR, green standard base; **blue body**, white "SR"; blue rail
p190	1935-38	**OPEN WAGON B**; SR, **black** standard base; blue body, white "SR"; blue rail
-	1938-41	**OPEN WAGON B**; SR, black standard base; blue body, white "SR"; **black rail**

p15	1920-23	**OPEN WAGON**; **LNWR**, early wagon base; grey body, clip-on "LNWR"
	1922-23	**OPEN WAGON**; LNWR, **open axleguard base**; grey body, clip-on "LNWR"
p15	1920-23	**OPEN WAGON**; **MR**, early wagon base; grey body, clip-on "MR"
-	1922-23	**OPEN WAGON**; MR, **open axleguard base**; grey body, clip-on "MR"
p15	1920-23	**OPEN WAGON**; **GN**, early wagon base; grey body, clip-on "GN"
-	1922-23	**OPEN WAGON**; GN, **open axleguard base**; grey body, clip-on "GN"
p117	1921-22	**OPEN WAGON**; **CR**, early wagon base; grey body, clip-on "CR"
p188	1921-22	**OPEN WAGON**; **LBSC**, early wagon base; grey body, clip-on "LBSC"
-	1921-22	**OPEN WAGON**; **GE**, early wagon base; grey body, clip-on "GE"
-	1921-22	**OPEN WAGON**; **SECR**, early wagon base; grey body, clip-on "SECR" (PU)

p17	1922-23	**ZULU WAGON**; **LNW**, early wagon base; grey body secured by eyelets, stencil sprayed "LNW"

-	1923-24	**OPEN WAGON**; **LMS**, early wagon base; grey body, white "LMS", cast buffers (no slots for pregroup letters; No. 1 and No. 2 Sets)
p115	1923-24	**OPEN WAGON**;LMS, early wagon base; grey body, white "LMS", cast buffers (**with slots** for pregroup letters; Zulu Wagons c1923-24)
-	1923-24	**OPEN WAGON**; LMS, **open axleguard base**; grey body, white "LMS", cast buffers (for No. 1 set)
p188	1923-24	**OPEN WAGON**; LMS, open axleguard base; grey body, white "LMS", **brass buffers** (for No. 2 set)
p188	1924-25	**OPEN WAGON**; LMS, **long thin base**; grey body, white "LMS", brass buffers (for No. 2 set)
p188	1924-25	**OPEN WAGON**; LMS, long thin base; grey body, white "LMS", **cast buffers** (for No. 1 set)
p188	1925-26	**OPEN WAGON**; LMS, **early wagon base**; grey body, white "LMS", cast buffers (slots for pregroup letters)
p188	1925-26	**OPEN WAGON**; LMS, **open axleguard base**; grey body, white "LMS", cast buffers (slots for pregroup letters)
p188	1926-27	**OPEN WAGON**; LMS, open axleguard base; grey body, white "LMS", cast buffers (no slots)
p189	1927-30	**OPEN WAGON**; LMS, open axleguard base; enamelled grey body, **large gold "LMS"**
p189	1930	**No. 1 OPEN WAGON**; LMS, **standard base**; enamelled grey body, **large gold "LMS"**
-	1930?	**No. 1 (?) OPEN WAGON**; LMS, **open axleguard base**; **plain grey enamelled, white "LMS"** (smaller letters than 1926-27)
p189	1930-32	**No. 1 OPEN WAGON**; LMS, **standard base**; enamelled grey body, **white "LMS"**
p50	1933	**No. 1 OPEN WAGON**; LMS, **green** standard base; enamelled **lighter grey** body, white "LMS" (supplied in certain sets)
p189	1932-41	**No. 1 OPEN WAGON**; LMS, black standard base; detailed **tinprinted "LMS"** (many tinprinting variants)

p189	1929-30	**No. O OPEN WAGON**; LMS, open axleguard base; plain grey **tinprinted "LMS"**
p189	1930	**No. O OPEN WAGON**; LMS, open axleguard base; **detailed** tinprinted "LMS"
p189	1930-41	**No. O OPEN WAGON**; LMS, **standard base**; detailed tinprinted "LMS" (many tinprinting variants)

p255	1926-27	**M WAGON**; **LMS**, black long thin base; enamelled grey body, white "LMS" with buffers (for M3 trains)
-	1927	**M WAGON**; LMS, black long thin base; enamelled grey body, white "LMS" **without buffers** (for M3 trains)
p256	1927-29	**M WAGON**; LMS, black long thin base; enamelled grey body, **large gold "LMS"**, without buffers (for M3 trains)

p252	1929-30	M WAGON; LMS, black long thin base; plain grey **tinprinted "LMS"** (for M1 trains)
-	1929?	M WAGON; LMS, black long thin base; **plain grey enamelled, white "LMS"** (for M1 trains) (PU)
p252	1930-33	**M1** WAGON; LMS, black long thin base; **detailed tinprinted** "LMS" (for M1 trains)
p252	1933-35	**M1** WAGON; LMS, **green** long thin base; detailed tinprinted "LMS" (for M1 trains)
p252	1935-41	**M1** WAGON; LMS, **black** long thin base; detailed tinprinted "LMS" (for M1 trains)
-	1931-33	**M3** WAGON; LMS, black crimped long thin base; **detailed** tinprinted "LMS" (for M3 Tank Goods Sets)
-	1933-35	**M3** WAGON; LMS, **green** crimped long thin base; detailed tinprinted "LMS" (for M3 Tank Goods Sets)
p259	1935-41	**M3** WAGON; LMS, **black** crimped long thin base; detailed tinprinted "LMS" (for M3 Tank Goods Sets)
p188	1923-24	**OPEN WAGON; LNER,** early wagon base; grey body, white "LNER", cast buffers (no slots for pregroup letters)
p188	1923-24	**OPEN WAGON;** LNER, **open axleguard base**; grey body, white "LNER", cast buffers (for No. 1 set)
p188	1923-24	**OPEN WAGON;** LNER, open axleguard base; grey body, white "LNER", **brass buffers** (for No. 2 set)
p188	1924-25	**OPEN WAGON;** LNER, **long thin base**; grey body, white "LNER", brass buffers (for No. 2 set)
p188	1924-25	**OPEN WAGON;** LNER, long thin base; grey body, white "LNER", **cast buffers** (for No. 1 set)
p188	1925-26	**OPEN WAGON;** LNER, **early wagon base**; grey body, white "LNER", cast buffers (slots for pregroup letters)
p188	1925-26	**OPEN WAGON;** LNER, **open axleguard base**; grey body, white "LNER", cast buffers (slots for pregroup letters)
p188	1926	**OPEN WAGON;** LNER, open axleguard base; grey body, white "LNER", cast buffers (no slots)
p188	1926-27	**OPEN WAGON; NE**, open axleguard base; grey body, white "NE", cast buffers (no slots)
p189	1927-30	**OPEN WAGON;** NE, open axleguard base; enamelled grey body, **large gold "NE"**
p189	1930	**No. 1 OPEN WAGON;** NE, **standard base**; enamelled grey body, **large gold "NE"**
-	1930?	**No. 1 (?) OPEN WAGON;** NE, **open axleguard base; plain grey enamelled, white "NE"** (smaller letters than 1926-27)
p189	1930-32	**No. 1 OPEN WAGON;** NE, **standard base**; enamelled grey body, **white "NE"**
-	1933	**No. 1 OPEN WAGON;** NE, **green** standard base; enamelled **lighter grey** body, white "NE" (supplied in certain sets) (PU)
p189	1932-41	**No. 1 OPEN WAGON;** NE, black standard base; detailed **tinprinted "NE"** (many tinprinting variants)
p189	1929-30	**No. O OPEN WAGON; NE**, open axleguard base; plain grey **tinprinted "NE"**
p189	1930	**No. O OPEN WAGON;** NE, open axleguard base; **detailed** tinprinted "NE"
p189	1930-41	**No. O OPEN WAGON;** NE, **standard base**; detailed tinprinted "NE" (many tinprinting variants)
p252	1929-30	**M** WAGON; NE, black long thin base; plain grey **tinprinted "NE"** (for M1 trains)
-	1929?	**M** WAGON; NE, black long thin base; **plain enamelled grey, white "NE"** (for M1 trains)
p252	1930-33	**M1** WAGON; NE, black long thin base; **detailed tinprinted** "NE" (for M1 trains)
-	1933-35	**M1** WAGON; NE, **green** long thin base; detailed tinprinted "NE" (for M1 trains)
p252	1935-41	**M1** WAGON; NE, **black** long thin base; detailed tinprinted "NE" (for M1 trains)
-	1931-33	**M3** WAGON; NE, black crimped long thin base; **detailed** tinprinted "NE" (for M3 Tank Goods Sets)
p252	1933-35	**M3** WAGON; NE, **green** crimped long thin base; detailed tinprinted "NE" (for M3 Tank Goods Sets)
-	1935-41	**M3** WAGON; NE, **black** crimped long thin base; detailed tinprinted "NE" (for M3 Tank Goods Sets)
-	1926	**OPEN WAGON; GW, early wagon base;** grey body, white "GW", cast buffers (slots for pregroup letters) (PU)
-	1926	**OPEN WAGON;** GW, **open axleguard base**; grey body, white "GW", cast buffers (slots for pregroup letters)
p26	1926-27	**OPEN WAGON;** GW, open axleguard base; grey body, white "GW", cast buffers (no slots)
p189	1927-30	**OPEN WAGON;** GW, open axleguard base; enamelled grey body, **large gold "GW"**

A58

p189	1930	No. 1 OPEN WAGON; GW, **standard base**; enamelled grey body, **large gold "GW"**
-	1930?	No. 1 (?) OPEN WAGON; GW, **open axleguard base**; **plain grey enamelled, white "GW"**, smaller letters than 1926-27 (PU)
p189	1930-32	No. 1 OPEN WAGON; GW, **standard base**; enamelled grey body, **white "GW"**
p49	1933	No. 1 OPEN WAGON; GW, **green** standard base; enamelled **lighter grey** body, white "GW" (supplied in certain sets)
p189	1932-41	No. 1 OPEN WAGON; GW, black standard base; detailed **tinprinted "GW"** (many tinprinting variants)
p189	1929-30	No. O OPEN WAGON; **GW**, open axleguard base; plain grey **tinprinted "GW"**
p189	1930	No. O OPEN WAGON; GW, open axleguard base; **detailed** tinprinted "GW"
p189	1930-41	No. O OPEN WAGON; GW, **standard base**; detailed tinprinted "GW" (many tinprinting variants)
-	1926-27	M WAGON; **GW**, black long thin base; enamelled grey body, white "GW", cast buffers (for M3 trains)
-	1926-27	M WAGON; GW, black long thin base; enamelled grey body, white "GW", **without buffers** (for M3 trains)
p256	1927-29	M WAGON; GW, black long thin base; enamelled grey body, **large gold "GW"**, without buffers (for M3 trains)
p252	1929-30	M WAGON; GW, black long thin base; plain grey **tinprinted "GW"** (for M1 trains)
-	1929?	M WAGON; GW, black long thin base; **plain enamelled grey, white "GW"** (for M1 trains) (PU)
p252	1930-33	M1 WAGON; GW, black long thin base; **detailed tinprinted** "GW" (for M1 trains)
p252	1933-35	M1 WAGON; GW, **green** long thin base; detailed tinprinted "GW" (for M1 trains)
p252	1935-41	M1 WAGON; GW, **black** long thin base; detailed tinprinted "GW" (for M1 trains)
-	1931-33	M3 WAGON; GW, black crimped long thin base; **detailed** tinprinted "GW" (for M3 Tank Goods Sets)
-	1933-35	M3 WAGON; GW, **green** crimped long thin base; detailed tinprinted "GW" (for M3 Tank Goods Sets)
-	1935-41	M3 WAGON; GW, **black** crimped long thin base; detailed tinprinted "GW" (for M3 Tank Goods Sets)
p189	1928-30	OPEN WAGON; **SR**, open axleguard base; enamelled brown body, **large gold "SR"**
p189	1930	No. 1 OPEN WAGON; SR, **standard base**; enamelled brown body, **large gold "SR"**
-	1930?	No. 1 (?) OPEN WAGON; SR, **open axleguard base**; **plain enamelled, white "SR"** (PU)
p189	1930-32	No. 1 OPEN WAGON; SR, **standard base**; enamelled brown body, **white "SR"**
-	1933	No. 1 OPEN WAGON; SR, **green** standard base; enamelled brown body, white "SR" (supplied in certain sets) (PU)
p189	1932-41	No. 1 OPEN WAGON; SR, black standard base; detailed brown **tinprinted "SR"** (many tinprinting variants)
p189	1929-30	No. O OPEN WAGON; **SR**, open axleguard base; plain grey **tinprinted "SR"**
p189	1930	No. O OPEN WAGON; SR, open axleguard base; **detailed** brown tinprinted "SR"
p189	1930-41	No. O OPEN WAGON; SR, **standard base**; detailed brown tinprinted "SR" (many tinprinting variants)
p252	1929-30	M WAGON; SR, black long thin base; plain grey **tinprinted "SR"** (for M1 trains)
-	1929?	M WAGON; SR, black long thin base; **plain enamelled, white "SR"** (for M1 trains) (PU)
p251	1930-33	M1 WAGON; SR, black long thin base; **detailed grey tinprinted** "SR" (for M1 trains)
p252	1933-35	M1 WAGON; SR, **green** long thin base; detailed grey tinprinted "SR" (for M1 trains)
p252	1935-41	M1 WAGON; SR, **black** long thin base; detailed tinprinted "SR" (colours as for LMS etc., not brown; for M1 trains)
p252	1931-33	M3 WAGON; SR, black crimped long thin base; **detailed** grey tinprinted "SR" (for M3 Tank Goods Sets)
-	1933-35	M3 WAGON; SR, **green** crimped long thin base; detailed grey tinprinted "SR" (for M3 Tank Goods Sets)
-	1935-41	M3 WAGON; SR, **black** crimped long thin base; detailed tinprinted "SR" (colours as for LMS etc., not brown; for M3 Tank Goods Sets)

p196	1938-41	**PALETHORPE'S SAUSAGE VAN**; black standard base; maroon body; grey roof
		Petrol Tank Wagon... see company name
p190	1940-41	**POOL PETROL TANK WAGON**; grey; standard base; pressed filler, embossed top; narrow flanges on ends
p190	1938-41	**POWER ETHYL PETROL TANK WAGON**; green; standard base; pressed filler, embossed top; narrow flanges on ends
p190	1925-27	**PRATTS PETROL TANK WAGON; green, "ANGLOCO"**; open axleguard base; pressed filler, cast top; black buffers
-	1927-30	**PRATTS PETROL TANK WAGON**; green, "ANGLOCO"; open axleguard base; pressed filler, cast top; **green buffers**
p190	1930-31	**PRATTS PETROL TANK WAGON; orange, "HIGH TEST"; standard base**; pressed filler, cast top; wide flanges on ends
p190	1931-33	**PRATTS PETROL TANK WAGON**; orange, "HIGH TEST" **(round logo)**; standard base; pressed filler, cast top; narrow flanges on ends
p190	1933-34	**PRATTS PETROL TANK WAGON; lighter orange**, "HIGH TEST" (round logo); standard base; pressed filler, cast top; narrow flanges on ends
p190	1934-36	**PRATTS PETROL TANK WAGON**; lighter orange, "HIGH TEST" (round logo); standard base; pressed filler, **embossed top**; narrow flanges on ends
p190	1928-30	**REDLINE PETROL TANK WAGON**; blue; open axleguard base; pressed filler, cast top
p190	1930-31	**REDLINE PETROL TANK WAGON**; blue; **standard base**; pressed filler, cast top; wide flanges on ends
p190	1931-32	**REDLINE PETROL TANK WAGON**; blue; standard base; pressed filler, cast top; **narrow flanges on ends**
-	1932-34	**REDLINE GLICO PETROL TANK WAGON**; blue; standard base; pressed filler, cast top; narrow flanges on ends
p190	1934-41	**REDLINE GLICO PETROL TANK WAGON**; blue; standard base; pressed filler, **pressed top**; narrow flanges on ends
p203	1937-41	**No. O REFRIGERATOR VAN; LMS**; black standard base; grey body; grey roof; fixed doors
p203	1937-41	**No. O REFRIGERATOR VAN; NE**; black standard base; white body; white roof; fixed doors
p203	1937-41	**No. O REFRIGERATOR VAN; GW Mica B**; black standard base; white body; white roof; fixed doors
p203	1937-41	**No. O REFRIGERATOR VAN; SR**; black standard base; buff body; white roof; fixed doors
p196	1923	**REFRIGERATOR VAN; MR**, early wagon base; white body, "MR" clip on letters; not lettered "Refrigerator Van"
p196	1923	**REFRIGERATOR VAN; MR**, early wagon base; white body, "MR" clip on letters; **"Refrigerator Van" on doors**
p196	1923-24	**REFRIGERATOR VAN; MR, open axleguard base**; white body, "MR" clip on letters; "Refrigerator Van" on doors
p196	1924-25	**REFRIGERATOR VAN; LMS**, black open axleguard base; white body, large black "LMS" transfer; **"Refrigerator Van" on base**
p196	1925-30	**REFRIGERATOR VAN; LMS**, black open axleguard base; white body, large black "LMS"; black-outline white lettered **"Refrigerator Van" on doors**
-	1930	**REFRIGERATOR VAN; LMS**, black open axleguard base; white body, large black "LMS"; **all-black lettered** "Refrigerator Van" on doors (PU)
-	1930-32	**REFRIGERATOR VAN; LMS, black standard base**; white body, large black "LMS"; "Refrigerator Van" on hinged doors
-	1932-33	**REFRIGERATOR VAN; LMS**, black standard base; white body, large black "LMS"; "Refrigerator Van" on **sliding doors** (same as 1934-39)
-	1933-34	**REFRIGERATOR VAN; LMS, blue** standard base; white body, large black "LMS"; "Refrigerator Van" on sliding doors; **blue roof**
-	1934-39	**REFRIGERATOR VAN; LMS, black** standard base; white body, large black "LMS"; "Refrigerator Van" on sliding doors; **white roof**
p196	1939-41	**REFRIGERATOR VAN; LMS**, black standard base; white body, **smaller black "LMS"**; "Refrigerator Van" on sliding doors; white roof
-	1924-25	**REFRIGERATOR VAN; LNER**, black open axleguard base; white body, large black "LNER" transfer; **"Refrigerator Van" on base**
p196	1925-27	**REFRIGERATOR VAN; LNER**, black open axleguard base; white body, large black "LNER"; **"Refrigerator Van" on doors**
p196	1927-30	**REFRIGERATOR VAN; NE**, black open axleguard base; white body, large black "**NE**"; black-outline white lettered "Refrigerator Van" on doors

-	1930	**REFRIGERATOR VAN**; NE, black open axleguard base; white body, large black "NE"; **all-black lettered** "Refrigerator Van" on doors (PU)
p196	1930-32	**REFRIGERATOR VAN**; NE, **black standard base**; white body, large black "NE"; "Refrigerator Van" on hinged doors
-	1932-33	**REFRIGERATOR VAN**; NE, black standard base; white body, large black "NE"; "Refrigerator Van" on **sliding doors** (same as 1934-39)
-	1933-34	**REFRIGERATOR VAN**; NE, **blue** standard base; white body, large black "NE"; "Refrigerator Van" on sliding doors; **blue roof**
p196	1934-39	**REFRIGERATOR VAN**; NE, **black** standard base; white body, large black "NE"; "Refrigerator Van" on sliding doors; **white roof**
p196	1939-41	**REFRIGERATOR VAN**; NE, black standard base; white body, **smaller black "NE"**; "Refrigerator Van" on sliding doors; white roof
p196	1926-30	**REFRIGERATOR VAN**; **GW**, black open axleguard base; white body, large black "GW"; black-outline white lettered "Refrigerator Van" on doors
-	1930	**REFRIGERATOR VAN**; GW, black open axleguard base; white body, large black "GW"; **all-black lettered** "Refrigerator Van" on doors
-	1930-32	**REFRIGERATOR VAN**; GW, **black standard base**; white body, large black "GW"; "Refrigerator Van" on hinged doors
-	1932-33	REFRIGERATOR VAN; GW, black standard base; white body, large black "GW"; "Refrigerator Van" on sliding doors; white roof (same as 1934-39)
p196	1933-34	**REFRIGERATOR VAN**; GW, **blue** standard base; white body, large black "GW"; "Refrigerator Van" on sliding doors; **blue roof**
p196	1934-39	**REFRIGERATOR VAN**; GW, **black** standard base; white body, large black "GW"; "Refrigerator Van" on sliding doors; white roof
p67	1939-41	**REFRIGERATOR VAN**; GW, black standard base; white body, **smaller black "GW"**; "Refrigerator Van" on sliding doors; white roof
p31	1928-29	**REFRIGERATOR VAN**; **SR**, black open axleguard base; pink body, large gold "SR"; "Refrigerator Van" on doors
-	1929-30	**REFRIGERATOR VAN**; SR, black open axleguard base; **white** body, **large black "SR"**; black-outline white lettered "Refrigerator Van" on doors
-	1930	**REFRIGERATOR VAN**; SR, black open axleguard base; white body, large black "SR"; **all-black lettered** "Refrigerator Van" on doors (PU)
-	1930-32	**REFRIGERATOR VAN**; SR, **black standard base**; white body?, large black "SR"; "Refrigerator Van" on hinged doors (PU)
-	1932-34	**REFRIGERATOR VAN**; SR, black standard base; white body, large black "SR"; "Refrigerator Van" on **sliding doors; white roof**
p196	1934-39	**REFRIGERATOR VAN**; SR, black standard base; **pink body**, large black "SR"; "Refrigerator Van" on sliding doors; white roof
p196	1939-41	**REFRIGERATOR VAN**; SR, black standard base; pink body, **smaller black "SR"**; "Refrigerator Van" on sliding doors; white roof
		(The Southern Railway pink varied erratically from pale to dark)
p197	1934-35	**No. O ROTARY TIPPING WAGON**; red open axleguard base; blue body, "MECCANO" one side
p197	1935-39	**No. O ROTARY TIPPING WAGON**; red open axleguard base; **plain blue body, red lining**
-	1939	**No. O ROTARY TIPPING WAGON**; **black** open axleguard base; plain blue body, red lining
p197	1939-41	**No. O ROTARY TIPPING WAGON**; black open axleguard base; plain blue body, **dark blue lining**
-	1923	**No. 1 ROTARY TIPPING WAGON**; **black open axleguard base**; grey top, **plain one side, "Rotary Tipper" other**
-	1923-24	**No. 1 ROTARY TIPPING WAGON**; black open axleguard base; grey top, **"McALPINE" one side, "Rotary Tipper" other**
p197	1923-26	**No. 1 ROTARY TIPPING WAGON**; black open axleguard base; grey top, **"McALPINE" both sides** (unvarnished top 1923-24)
p197	1923-25	**No. 1 ROTARY TIPPING WAGON**; **olive green open axleguard base**; grey top, **"McALPINE" one side, "Rotary Tipper" other** (unvarn. top 1923-24)
p197	1923-26	**No. 1 ROTARY TIPPING WAGON**; olive green open axleguard base; grey top, **"McALPINE" both sides** (unvarnished top 1923-24)
p197	1926-29	**No. 1 ROTARY TIPPING WAGON**; **orange open axleguard base and top**, "McALPINE" both sides
p197	1929-30	**No. 1 ROTARY TIPPING WAGON**; orange open axleguard base and top, **"MECCANO"** both sides
p197	1930-32	**No. 1 ROTARY TIPPING WAGON**; orange **standard base** and top, "MECCANO" both sides
p197	1932-36	**No. 1 ROTARY TIPPING WAGON**; **blue standard base; yellow top**, "MECCANO" both sides
p197	1936-39	**No. 1 ROTARY TIPPING WAGON**; blue standard base; yellow top, **"TRINIDAD LAKE ASPHALT"** both sides
p197	1939-41	**No. 1 ROTARY TIPPING WAGON**; **black standard base**; yellow top, "TRINIDAD LAKE ASPHALT" both sides
p190	1936-41	**ROYAL DAYLIGHT OIL TANK WAGON**; red; standard base; pressed filler, **pressed top**; narrow flanges on ends
p190		(also M3 Tank Goods Set version with no buffers)

Sausage Van... see Palethorpes

p192	1924-30	**SECCOTINE VAN**; black open axleguard base; blue body; orange roof
p25	1925	**SECCOTINE VAN**; black **early wagon base**; blue body; orange roof
-	1930-32	**SECCOTINE VAN**; black **standard base**; blue body; orange roof; hinged doors (PU)
-	1932-33	**SECCOTINE VAN**; black standard base; blue body; orange roof; **sliding doors** (PU)
p50	1933-34	**SECCOTINE VAN**; black standard base; blue body; **red roof**; **hinged doors**

p190	1922-23	**SHELL PETROL TANK WAGON**; red; early wagon base; early cast filler
p190	1923-24	**SHELL PETROL TANK WAGON**; red; **open axleguard base**; early cast filler
p190	1924-27	**SHELL PETROL TANK WAGON**; red; open axleguard base; **pressed filler, cast top**; black buffers
-	1927-30	**SHELL PETROL TANK WAGON**; red; open axleguard base; pressed filler, cast top; **red buffers**
p190	1930-31	**SHELL PETROL TANK WAGON**; red; **standard base**; pressed filler, cast top; wide flanges on ends
p190	1931-34	**SHELL PETROL TANK WAGON**; red; standard base; pressed filler, cast top; **narrow flanges on ends**
-		(also M3 Tank Goods Set version with no buffers)
p190	1934-36	**SHELL PETROL TANK WAGON**; red; standard base; pressed filler, **pressed top**; narrow flanges on ends
p259		(also M3 Tank Goods Set version with no buffers)

p190	1936-38	**SHELLMEX and BP PETROL TANK WAGON**; cream; standard base; pressed filler, pressed top; narrow flanges on ends

-	1923	**SIDE TIPPING WAGON**; black open axleguard base, "TILTING WAGON" on top of base; grey tipper, **black stencilled lining**
p19	1923	**SIDE TIPPING WAGON**; black open axleguard base, "TILTING WAGON" on top of base; grey tipper, **red stencilled lining**
p18	1923-24	**SIDE TIPPING WAGON**; black open axleguard base, "TIPPING WAGON" on top of base; grey tipper, red stencilled lining
p198	1924	**SIDE TIPPING WAGON**; black open axleguard base, "TIPPING WAGON" on top of base; grey tipper, red stencilled lining, **"McALPINE" both sides**
-	1924-25	**SIDE TIPPING WAGON**; black open axleguard base, "TIPPING WAGON" on top of base; grey tipper, **transfer lining**, "McALPINE" both sides
p198	1925-27	**SIDE TIPPING WAGON**; black open axleguard base, **unlettered on top of base**; grey tipper, transfer lining, "McALPINE" both sides
p198	1927-30	**SIDE TIPPING WAGON**; **blue open axleguard base and tipper**, "McALPINE" both sides
p198	1929-30	**SIDE TIPPING WAGON**; blue open axleguard base and tipper, **"ROBERT HUDSON"** both sides
p198	1930-33	**SIDE TIPPING WAGON**; blue **standard base** and tipper, "ROBERT HUDSON" both sides
p198	1933-38	**SIDE TIPPING WAGON**; **lighter blue standard base; yellow tipper**, "ROBERT HUDSON" both sides
p198	1938-39	**SIDE TIPPING WAGON**; lighter blue standard base; yellow tipper, **"McALPINE"** both sides
p198	1939-41	**SIDE TIPPING WAGON**; **black standard base**; yellow tipper, "McALPINE" both sides

p199	1923-24	**SNOWPLOUGH; PLAIN**; black open axleguard base; grey body, black-lined corner straps and plough; "SNOW PLOUGH" on doors

p199	1924-25	**SNOWPLOUGH**; LMS; black open axleguard base; **"LMS" on base**; grey body, black-lined corner straps and plough; "SNOW PLOUGH" on doors
p199	1925-26	**SNOWPLOUGH**; LMS; black open axleguard base; "LMS" on base; grey body **and corner straps**, black lined plough; "SNOW PLOUGH" on doors
-	1925	**SNOWPLOUGH**; LMS; black open axleguard base; "LMS" on base; grey body and corner straps, black lined plough; **plain doors**
p199	1926	**SNOWPLOUGH**; LMS; black open axleguard base; "LMS" on base; grey body, **red lined plough**; "SNOW PLOUGH" on **grey enamelled doors**
p199	1926	**SNOWPLOUGH**; LMS; black open axleguard base; "LMS" on base; grey body, red lined plough; "SNOW PLOUGH" on **dark grey tinprinted doors**
-	1926-27	**SNOWPLOUGH**; LMS; black open axleguard base; **"LMS" on body**; grey body, red lined plough; "SNOW PLOUGH" on dark grey tinprinted doors (PU)
p199	1927-28	**SNOWPLOUGH**; LMS; **green** open axleguard base; "LMS" on body; grey body, **green lined plough**; "SNOW PLOUGH" on dark grey tinprinted doors

-	1928-29	**SNOWPLOUGH**; LMS; green open axleguard base; "LMS" on body; grey body, green lined plough; "SNOW PLOUGH" on **green tinprinted doors**; rh throw
p199	1929-30	**SNOWPLOUGH**; LMS; green open axleguard base; "LMS" on body; grey body, green lined plough; "SNOW PLOUGH" on green tinprinted doors; **lh throw**
-	1924	**SNOWPLOUGH**; **LNER**; black open axleguard base; "LNER" on base; grey body, black-lined corner straps and plough; "SNOW PLOUGH" on doors (PU)
p199	1924-26	**SNOWPLOUGH**; LNER; black open axleguard base; "LNER" on base; grey body **and corner straps**, black lined plough; "SNOW PLOUGH" on doors
-	1925	**SNOWPLOUGH**; LNER; black open axleguard base; "LNER" on base; grey body and corner straps, black lined plough; **plain doors** (PU)
-	1926	**SNOWPLOUGH**; LNER; black open axleguard base; "LNER" on base; grey body, **red lined plough**; "SNOW PLOUGH" on grey enamelled doors
-	1926	**SNOWPLOUGH**; LNER; black open axleguard base; "LNER" on base; grey body, red lined plough; "SNOW PLOUGH" on **dark grey tinprinted doors** (PU)
-	1926-27	**SNOWPLOUGH**; **NE**; black open axleguard base; **"NE" on body**; grey body, red lined plough; "SNOW PLOUGH" on dark grey tinprinted doors
-	1927-28	**SNOWPLOUGH**; NE; **green** open axleguard base; "NE" on body; grey body, **green lined plough**; "SNOW PLOUGH" on dark grey tinprinted doors
-	1928-29	**SNOWPLOUGH**; NE; green open axleguard base; "NE" on body; grey body, green lined plough; "SNOW PLOUGH" on **green tinprinted doors**; rh throw
-	1929-30	**SNOWPLOUGH**; NE; green open axleguard base; "NE" on body; grey body, green lined plough; "SNOW PLOUGH" on green tinprinted doors; **lh throw**
-	1926	**SNOWPLOUGH**; **GW**; black open axleguard base; "GW" on base; grey body and corner straps, black lined plough; "SNOW PLOUGH" on doors
p205	1926	**SNOWPLOUGH**; GW; black open axleguard base; "GW" on base; grey body, **red lined plough**; "SNOW PLOUGH" on grey enamelled doors
-	1926	**SNOWPLOUGH**; GW; black open axleguard base; "GW" on base; grey body, red lined plough; "SNOW PLOUGH" on **dark grey tinprinted doors** (PU)
-	1926-27	**SNOWPLOUGH**; GW; black open axleguard base; **"GW" on body**; grey body, red lined plough; "SNOW PLOUGH" on dark grey tinprinted doors (PU)
-	1927-28	**SNOWPLOUGH**; GW; **green** open axleguard base; "GW" on body; grey body, **green lined plough**; "SNOW PLOUGH" on dark grey tinprinted doors
-	1928-29	**SNOWPLOUGH**; GW; green open axleguard base; "GW" on body; grey body, green lined plough; "SNOW PLOUGH" on **green tinprinted doors**; rh throw
p36	1929-30	**SNOWPLOUGH**; GW; green open axleguard base; "GW" on body; grey body, green lined plough; "SNOW PLOUGH" on green tinprinted doors; **lh throw**
p31	1928-29	**SNOWPLOUGH**; **SR**; green open axleguard base; "SR" on body; grey body, green lined plough; "SNOW PLOUGH" on **green tinprinted doors**; rh throw
-	1929-30	**SNOWPLOUGH**; SR; green open axleguard base; "SR" on body; grey body, green lined plough; "SNOW PLOUGH" on green tinprinted doors; **lh throw**
p41	1930	**SNOWPLOUGH**; **PLAIN**; green open axleguard base; grey body, green lined plough; "SNOW PLOUGH" on green tinprinted doors; lh throw
p199	1930-32	**SNOWPLOUGH**; PLAIN; green **standard base**; grey body, green lined plough; "SNOW PLOUGH" on green tinprinted doors; lh throw
p199	1932-33	**SNOWPLOUGH**; PLAIN; **red** standard base; grey body, green lined plough; "SNOW PLOUGH" on green tinprinted doors; lh throw
-	1933	**SNOWPLOUGH**; PLAIN; **light green** standard base; **yellow body**, blue lined plough, lamp and windows; green roof; green fan; "SNOW PLOUGH" on green tinprinted doors; lh throw
p199	1933-34	**SNOWPLOUGH**; PLAIN; **blue** standard base; yellow body, **blue** lined plough and lamp; **blue roof**; "SNOW PLOUGH" on green tinprinted doors; lh throw

A63

p199	1934-36	**SNOWPLOUGH**; PLAIN; blue standard base; yellow body, blue lined plough; **no lamp**; blue roof; **fixed doors**
-	1936-40	**SNOWPLOUGH**; PLAIN; **black** standard base; yellow body, blue lined plough; no lamp; blue roof; fixed doors; lh throw
p199	1940-41	**SNOWPLOUGH**; PLAIN; black standard base; yellow body, blue lined plough; no lamp; blue roof; fixed doors; **rh throw** (but chute on left)

p167	1930-33	**TANK CAR**; black US base; red tank, red filler
p167	1933-36	**TANK CAR**; **green** US base; red tank, **green** filler
p167	1936-41	**TANK CAR**; **black** US base; red tank, green filler

| p200 | 1922-24 | **No. 1 TIMBER WAGON**; **PLAIN**; olive green open axleguard base and stanchions |

p200	1924-25	**No. 1 TIMBER WAGON**; **LMS**; olive green open axleguard base and stanchions; "LMS" one side, "No. 1 TIMBER WAGON" other
-	1925-26	**No. 1 TIMBER WAGON**; **LMS**; olive green open axleguard base and stanchions; **"LMS" both sides**
p200	1926-30	**No. 1 TIMBER WAGON**; **LMS**; olive green open axleguard base; **red stanchions**; "LMS" both sides

-	1924-25	**No. 1 TIMBER WAGON**; **LNER**; olive green open axleguard base and stanchions; "LNER" one side, "No. 1 TIMBER WAGON" other
p200	1925-26	**No. 1 TIMBER WAGON**; **LNER**; olive green open axleguard base and stanchions; **"LNER" both sides**
-	1926	**No. 1 TIMBER WAGON**; **NE**; olive green open axleguard base and stanchions; **"NE" both sides** (PU)
p200	1926-30	**No. 1 TIMBER WAGON**; **NE**; olive green open axleguard base; **red stanchions**; "NE" both sides

| p200 | 1926 | **No. 1 TIMBER WAGON**; **GW**; olive green open axleguard base and stanchions; "GW" both sides |
| - | 1926-30 | **No. 1 TIMBER WAGON**; **GW**; olive green open axleguard base; **red stanchions**; "GW" both sides |

| p200 | 1928-30 | **No. 1 TIMBER WAGON**; **SR**; light brown open axleguard base; red stanchions; "SR" both sides |
| p41 | 1930 | **No. 1 TIMBER WAGON**; **PLAIN**; light brown open axleguard base; red stanchions (no lettering, but in SR colours) |

p41	1930	**No. 1 TIMBER WAGON**; **PLAIN**; olive green open axleguard base; red stanchions
p200	1930-31	**No. 1 TIMBER WAGON**; **PLAIN**; olive green **standard base**; red stanchions
p200	1931-32	**No. 1 TIMBER WAGON**; **PLAIN**; red standard base; **yellow** stanchions
p200	1931-39	**No. 1 TIMBER WAGON**; **PLAIN**; red standard base; **green** stanchions (2 planks only from 1934)
p259		(also M3 Tank Goods Set version with no buffers)
p200	1939-41	**No. 1 TIMBER WAGON**; **PLAIN**; **black** standard base; **red** stanchions
-		(also M3 Tank Goods Set version with no buffers)

p200	1922	**No. 2 TIMBER WAGON**; **PLAIN**; olive green base and stanchions, plain both sides; early style with rivetted stanchions; 5 planks
p200	1922-23	**No. 2 TIMBER WAGON**; **PLAIN**; olive green base and stanchions, plain both sides; later style with pressed stanchions; 3 planks
p200	1923-24	**No. 2 TIMBER WAGON**; **PLAIN**; olive green base and stanchions, "**No. 2 TIMBER WAGON**" **both sides**; later style with pressed stanchions; 3 planks

-	1924-25	**No. 2 TIMBER WAGON**; **LMS**; olive green base and stanchions, "No. 2 TIMBER WAGON" one side, "LMS" other; 3 planks
-	1925-27	**No. 2 TIMBER WAGON**; **LMS**; olive green base and stanchions, **"LMS" both sides**; 3 planks
p200	1927-30	**No. 2 TIMBER WAGON**; **LMS**; olive green base; **red stanchions**, "LMS" both sides; 3 planks

p18	1924	**No. 2 TIMBER WAGON; L&NER**; olive green base and stanchions, "No. 2 TIMBER WAGON" one side, "L&NER" other; 3 planks
-	1924-25	**No. 2 TIMBER WAGON; LNER**; olive green base and stanchions, "No. 2 TIMBER WAGON" one side, "LNER" other; 3 planks (PU)
p200	1925-26	**No. 2 TIMBER WAGON; LNER**; olive green base and stanchions, "LNER" both sides; 3 planks
-	1926-27	**No. 2 TIMBER WAGON; NE**; olive green base and stanchions, "NE" both sides; 3 planks (PU)
p37	1927-30	**No. 2 TIMBER WAGON; NE**; olive green base; **red stanchions**, "NE" both sides; 3 planks
-	1926-27	**No. 2 TIMBER WAGON; GW**; olive green base and stanchions, **"GW"** both sides; 3 planks (PU)
p36	1927-30	**No. 2 TIMBER WAGON; GW**; olive green base; **red stanchions**, "GW" both sides; 3 planks
p200	1928-30	**No. 2 TIMBER WAGON; SR**; light brown base; red stanchions, "SR" both sides; 3 planks
-	1930-31	**No. 2 TIMBER WAGON; PLAIN**; olive green base; red stanchions, plain both sides; 3 planks; sides of base still turned up (PU)
p200	1931-33	**No. 2 TIMBER WAGON; PLAIN**; olive green base; red stanchions, plain both sides; 3 planks; **sides of base turned down**; bogies repositioned for auto couplings
p200	1933-34	**No. 2 TIMBER WAGON; PLAIN; red base; green stanchions**, plain both sides; 3 planks; **green bogies**
-	1934-36	**No. 2 TIMBER WAGON; PLAIN**; red base; green stanchions, plain both sides; **2 planks**; green bogies
p200	1936-39	**No. 2 TIMBER WAGON; PLAIN**; red base; green stanchions, plain both sides; 2 planks; **black bogies**
p200	1939-41	**No. 2 TIMBER WAGON; PLAIN; grey base; red stanchions**, plain both sides; 2 planks; black bogies
p201	1923	**TROLLEY WAGON; NE**, grey base, **black bolsters**; white "NE", white "50 TON TROLLEY"
p201	1923-24	**TROLLEY WAGON; NE**, grey base, **red bolsters**; white "NE", white "50 TON TROLLEY" ("NE" on lhs of well)
-	1923-24	**TROLLEY WAGON; NE**, grey base, red bolsters; white "NE", white "50 TON TROLLEY" (**"NE" on rhs** of well)
-	1924	**TROLLEY WAGON; LNER**, grey base, red bolsters; gold **"LNER"** both sides, white "50 TON TROLLEY"
-	1924-25	**TROLLEY WAGON; LNER**, grey base, red bolsters; gold "LNER" both sides, **gold "50 TON TROLLEY"**
p201	1925-26	**TROLLEY WAGON; LNER**, grey base, red bolsters; gold "LNER" both sides, **no "50 TON TROLLEY"**; black buffers
p29	1926-27	**TROLLEY WAGON; NE**, grey base, red bolsters; gold **"NE"** both sides; **grey buffers**
p201	1927-30	**TROLLEY WAGON; NE, brown base, blue bolsters**; gold "NE" both sides
p22	1924	**TROLLEY WAGON; LMS**, grey base, red bolsters; gold **"LMS"** both sides, white "50 TON TROLLEY"
-	1924-25	**TROLLEY WAGON; LMS**, grey base, red bolsters; gold "LMS" both sides, **gold "50 TON TROLLEY"**
-	1925-26	**TROLLEY WAGON; LMS**, grey base, red bolsters; gold "LMS" both sides, **no "50 TON TROLLEY"**; black buffers
-	1926-27	TROLLEY WAGON; LMS, grey base, red bolsters; gold "LMS" both sides, no "50 TON TROLLEY"; **grey buffers**
-	1927-30	**TROLLEY WAGON; LMS, brown base, blue bolsters**; gold "LMS" both sides
p201	1926	**TROLLEY WAGON; GW**, grey base, red bolsters; gold "GW" both sides, **no "50 TON TROLLEY"**; black buffers
-	1926-27	**TROLLEY WAGON; GW**, grey base, red bolsters; gold "GW" both sides, no "50 TON TROLLEY"; **grey buffers**
-	1927-30	**TROLLEY WAGON; GW, brown base, blue bolsters**; gold "GW" both sides
p31	1928-30	**TROLLEY WAGON; SR**, dark brown base, blue bolsters; gold "SR" both sides

-	1930	**TROLLEY WAGON**; **PLAIN**, brown base, blue bolsters; black bogies; buffers high on small buffer beam (PU)
p201	1930-33	**TROLLEY WAGON**; PLAIN, brown base, blue bolsters; black bogies; **lowered buffers on enlarged buffer beam**
p201	1933-35	**TROLLEY WAGON**; PLAIN, **red base, green bolsters**; **green bogies**
p201	1935-39	**TROLLEY WAGON**; PLAIN, red base, green bolsters; **black bogies**
p201	1939-41	**TROLLEY WAGON**; PLAIN, **grey base, red bolsters**; black bogies
p60	1936-37	**TROLLEY WAGON with CABLE DRUMS**; red base, green bolsters; black bogies; **"BI CABLES"**
-	1937-39	**TROLLEY WAGON with CABLE DRUMS**; red base, green bolsters; black bogies; **"LIVERPOOL CABLES"**
-	1939-41	**TROLLEY WAGON with CABLE DRUMS**; **grey base, red bolsters**; black bogies; **"BI CABLES"**
p177	1928-30	**DOUBLE WINE WAGON**; green long thin base, red barrels; with drain cocks and cast fillers
p177		(also circa 1935 with auto couplings)
-	1930-31	**DOUBLE WINE WAGON**; green **crimped axleguard French base**, red barrels; with drain cocks and cast fillers
p156	1932?	**DOUBLE WINE WAGON**; green **long thin base**, red barrels; with drain cocks, **no cast fillers**
p177	1936-39	**DOUBLE WINE WAGON**; green **French base**, red barrels; no drain cocks, no cast fillers
p177	1939-41	**DOUBLE WINE WAGON**; **black** French base, red barrels; no drain cocks, no cast fillers
p177	1929-30	**SINGLE WINE WAGON**; green open-axleguard base, red barrel
-		(also circa 1935 with auto couplings)
-	1930-33	**SINGLE WINE WAGON**; green **standard base**, red barrel (PU)
p177	1933-35	**SINGLE WINE WAGON**; **lighter green** standard base, red barrel

Wagon, see Open Wagon

Wagon, French Type... see French Type Wagon

p180	1937-41	**BRICKS** for High Capacity Wagon
p205	1922-23	**No. 1 BUFFERS**; **grey**, unpainted sleepers; holes for wire clips
p205	1923-27	**No. 1 BUFFERS**; **olive green**, unpainted sleepers; holes for wire clips
p205	1927-29	**No. 1 BUFFERS**; **green** overall, with **base for rail connecting plates**; red stocks, unpainted rails; high buffer beam
p205	1929-30	**No. 1 BUFFERS**; green overall, with base for rail connecting plates; red stocks, unpainted rails; **lowered buffer beam**
p205	1930-33	**No. 1 BUFFERS**; **blue** overall, with base for rail connecting plates; red stocks, unpainted rails
p205	1933-37	**No. 1 BUFFERS**; **lighter blue**, with base for rail connecting plates; red stocks, unpainted rails; no clip for Lighting Accessory
-	1937-39	**No. 1 BUFFERS**; lighter blue, with base for rail connecting plates; red stocks, unpainted rails; **clip for Lighting Accessory**
p205	1939-40	**No. 1 BUFFERS**; **grey**, with base for rail connecting plates; **red beam, red buffer heads**, unpainted rails; clip for Lighting Accessory
p205	1940-41	**No. 1 BUFFERS**; **grey**, with base for rail connecting plates; red beam, **plain buffer heads**, unpainted rails; clip for Lighting Accessory
p47	1932-33	**No. 1E BUFFERS**; **blue**
p156	1933-39	**No. 1E BUFFERS**; **lighter blue**
p205	1924	**No. 2 BUFFERS**; **dark grey**, black lined; base for wire clips; silver rails
p205	1924-27	**No. 2 BUFFERS**; dark grey-green, **gold lined**; base for wire clips; silver rails
p205	1927-30	**No. 2 BUFFERS**; **green**, gold lined; base for wire clips; high buffer beam; silver rails
-	1930	**No. 2 BUFFERS**; **blue**, gold lined; base for wire clips; **lowered buffer beam**; silver rails
p205	1930-31	**No. 2 BUFFERS**; blue, gold-lined; **base for rail connecting plates**; lowered buffer beam; silver rails
-	1931-33	**No. 2 BUFFERS**; blue, gold-lined; base for rail connecting plates; lowered buffer beam; **blue rails and braces**
p205	1933-37	**No. 2 BUFFERS**; **lighter blue**, gold lined; base for rail connecting plates; lighter blue rails and braces; no clip for Lighting Accessory
-	1937-39	**No. 2 BUFFERS**; lighter blue, gold lined; base for rail connecting plates; lighter blue rails and braces; **clip for Lighting Accessory**
-	1932-33	**No. 2E BUFFERS**; **blue**, gold lined; blue rails and braces
p64	1933-38	**No. 2E BUFFERS**; **lighter blue**, gold lined; lighter blue rails and braces
p205	1937-39	**No. 2A BUFFERS**; **blue**; red buffer beam, stocks etc; plain buffer heads
p205	1939-41	**No. 2A BUFFERS**; **grey**; red buffer heads and beam only
-	1938-39	**No. 3A BUFFERS**; **blue**; red buffer beam, stocks etc; plain buffer heads
-	1939-41	**No. 3A BUFFERS**; **grey**; red buffer heads and beam only (PU)
p176	1934-36	**CABLE DRUM**; **"BI CABLES"**; wood stained black; narrow black bands on rim
-	1936-37	**CABLE DRUM**; **"BI CABLES"**; wood stained **green**; narrow black bands on rim
-	1937-38	**CABLE DRUM**; **"LIVERPOOL CABLES"**; wood stained green; **broad bands with rivets** on rim; not marked "Regd. Trade Mark" under birds
p176	1938-39	**CABLE DRUM**; **"LIVERPOOL CABLES"**; wood stained green; broad bands with rivets on rim; **marked "Regd. Trade Mark"** under birds
p176	1939-40	**CABLE DRUM**; **"BI CABLES"**; **wood not stained**; broad bands with rivets on rim
p180	1937-41	**COAL** for High Capacity Wagon

p176	1936-41	**CONTAINER, LMS** Furniture
p176	1936-41	**CONTAINER, LNER** Goods
p176	1936-41	**CONTAINER, GW** Insulated, white
p176	1936-41	**CONTAINER, SR** Ventilated, silver.
p210	1932-36	**COUNTRYSIDE SECTION F**, square field
-	1932-36	**COUNTRYSIDE SECTION J1**, rectangular field
-	1932-36	**COUNTRYSIDE SECTION J2**, rectangular field
-	1932-36	**COUNTRYSIDE SECTION J3**, half rectangular field
p210	1932-36	**COUNTRYSIDE SECTION G1**, inside curved section
p210	1932-36	**COUNTRYSIDE SECTION G2**, inside curved section
p139	1932-36	**COUNTRYSIDE SECTION H**, road
p210	1932-36	**COUNTRYSIDE SECTION K1**, triangular section
p210	1932-36	**COUNTRYSIDE SECTION K2**, triangular section
p50	1932-36	**COUNTRYSIDE SECTION L1**, outside curved section
p50	1932-36	**COUNTRYSIDE SECTION L2**, outside curved section
p50	1932-36	**COUNTRYSIDE SECTION M1**, outside corner section
p50	1932-36	**COUNTRYSIDE SECTION M2**, outside corner section
-	1932-36	**COUNTRYSIDE SECTION R**, support for Level Crossing
p116	1932-40	**No. O CUTTING**
p211	1932-39	**No. 1 CUTTING**; end section
p211	1932-39	**No. 2 CUTTING**; straight section
p211	1932-39	**No. 3 CUTTING**; curved section
p211	1932-37	**No. 4 CUTTING**
p213	1931-38	**DINKY TOYS No. 1 STATION STAFF, STATIONMASTER**; large figure, red base
-	1938	**DINKY TOYS No. 1 STATION STAFF,** STATIONMASTER; large figure, **buff base**
p214	1938-40	**DINKY TOYS No. 1 STATION STAFF,** STATIONMASTER; **smaller figure**, buff base
-	1940-41	**DINKY TOYS No. 1 STATION STAFF,** STATIONMASTER; smaller figure, buff base; **plainer finish**
p213	1931-38	**DINKY TOYS No. 1 STATION STAFF, GUARD**; large figure, red base
p214	1938	**DINKY TOYS No. 1 STATION STAFF,** GUARD; **smaller figure**, red base
p214	1938-40	**DINKY TOYS No. 1 STATION STAFF,** GUARD; smaller figure, **buff base**
-	1940-41	**DINKY TOYS No. 1 STATION STAFF,** GUARD; smaller figure, buff base; **plainer finish**
p213	1931-38	**DINKY TOYS No. 1 STATION STAFF, TICKET COLLECTOR**; large figure, red base
p214	1938-40	**DINKY TOYS No. 1 STATION STAFF,** TICKET COLLECTOR; **smaller figure, buff base**
-	1940-41	**DINKY TOYS No. 1 STATION STAFF,** TICKET COLLECTOR; smaller figure, buff base; **plainer finish**
p213	1931-38	**DINKY TOYS No. 1 STATION STAFF, DRIVER**; large figure, red base
p214	1938-40	**DINKY TOYS No. 1 STATION STAFF,** DRIVER; **smaller figure, buff base**
-	1940-41	**DINKY TOYS No. 1 STATION STAFF,** DRIVER; smaller figure, buff base; **plainer finish**
p213	1931-38	**DINKY TOYS No. 1 STATION STAFF, PORTER WITH LUGGAGE**; large figure, red base
p214	1938-40	**DINKY TOYS No. 1 STATION STAFF,** PORTER WITH LUGGAGE; **smaller figure, buff base**
-	1940-41	**DINKY TOYS No. 1 STATION STAFF,** PORTER WITH LUGGAGE; smaller figure, buff base; **plainer finish**

p213	1931-35	**DINKY TOYS No. 1 STATION STAFF, PORTER**; large figure, red base; buttons wrong side
p214	1935-38	**DINKY TOYS No. 1 STATION STAFF, PORTER**; large figure, red base; **buttons correct side**
p214	1938-40	**DINKY TOYS No. 1 STATION STAFF, PORTER**; **smaller figure, buff base**
-	1940-41	**DINKY TOYS No. 1 STATION STAFF, PORTER**; smaller figure, buff base; **plainer finish**

p213	1932-41	**DINKY TOYS No. 2 FARMYARD ANIMALS, HORSE**; white
p213	1932-41	**DINKY TOYS No. 2 FARMYARD ANIMALS, HORSE**; brown
p213	1932-41	**DINKY TOYS No. 2 FARMYARD ANIMALS, COW**; black and white
p213	1932-41	**DINKY TOYS No. 2 FARMYARD ANIMALS, COW**; brown
p213	1932-41	**DINKY TOYS No. 2 FARMYARD ANIMALS, PIG**
p213	1932-41	**DINKY TOYS No. 2 FARMYARD ANIMALS, SHEEP**, white with black detail

p213	1932-38	**DINKY TOYS No. 3 PASSENGERS, WOMAN and CHILD**; large figure, cream base
-	1938	**DINKY TOYS No. 3 PASSENGERS, WOMAN and CHILD**; **smaller figure**, cream base
p214	1938-40	**DINKY TOYS No. 3 PASSENGERS, WOMAN and CHILD**; smaller figure, **buff base**
p214	1940-41	**DINKY TOYS No. 3 PASSENGERS, WOMAN and CHILD**; smaller figure, buff base; **plainer finish**
p213	1932-38	**DINKY TOYS No. 3 PASSENGERS, BUSINESS MAN**; large figure, cream base
p214	1938-40	**DINKY TOYS No. 3 PASSENGERS, BUSINESS MAN**; **smaller figure, buff base**
p214	1940-41	**DINKY TOYS No. 3 PASSENGERS, BUSINESS MAN**; smaller figure, buff base; **plainer finish**
p213	1932-38	**DINKY TOYS No. 3 PASSENGERS, MALE HIKER**; large figure, cream base
p214	1938-40	**DINKY TOYS No. 3 PASSENGERS, MALE HIKER**; **smaller figure, buff base**
p214	1940-41	**DINKY TOYS No. 3 PASSENGERS, MALE HIKER**; smaller figure, buff base; **plainer finish**
p213	1932-38	**DINKY TOYS No. 3 PASSENGERS, FEMALE HIKER**; large figure, cream base
p214	1938-40	**DINKY TOYS No. 3 PASSENGERS, FEMALE HIKER**; **smaller figure, buff base**, white blouse
p214	1940-41	**DINKY TOYS No. 3 PASSENGERS, FEMALE HIKER**; smaller figure, buff base; **plainer finish, blue blouse**
p213	1932-38	**DINKY TOYS No. 3 PASSENGERS, NEWSBOY**; large running figure, cream base
p214	1938	**DINKY TOYS No. 3 PASSENGERS, NEWSBOY**; **smaller standing figure**, cream base
p214	1938-40	**DINKY TOYS No. 3 PASSENGERS, NEWSBOY**; smaller standing figure, **buff base**
p214	1940-41	**DINKY TOYS No. 3 PASSENGERS, NEWSBOY**; smaller standing figure, buff base; **plainer finish**
p213	1932-38	**DINKY TOYS No. 3 PASSENGERS, WOMAN**; large figure, cream base
p214	1938	**DINKY TOYS No. 3 PASSENGERS, WOMAN**; **smaller figure**, cream base
p214	1938-40	**DINKY TOYS No. 3 PASSENGERS, WOMAN**; smaller figure, **buff base**
p214	1940-41	**DINKY TOYS No. 3 PASSENGERS, WOMAN**; smaller figure, buff base; **plainer finish**

p213	1932-38	**DINKY TOYS No. 4 ENGINEERING STAFF, ELECTRICIAN**; large figure, cream base
p214	1938-40	**DINKY TOYS No. 4 ENGINEERING STAFF, ELECTRICIAN**; **smaller figure, buff base**
p214	1940-41	**DINKY TOYS No. 4 ENGINEERING STAFF, ELECTRICIAN**; smaller figure, buff base; **plainer finish**
p213	1932-35	**DINKY TOYS No. 4 ENGINEERING STAFF, FITTER**; dark blue large figure, cream base; buttons wrong side
p214	1935-38	**DINKY TOYS No. 4 ENGINEERING STAFF, FITTER**; **light blue** large figure, cream base; **buttons correct side**
p214	1938-40	**DINKY TOYS No. 4 ENGINEERING STAFF, FITTER**; light blue **smaller figure, buff base**
p214	1940-41	**DINKY TOYS No. 4 ENGINEERING STAFF, FITTER**; light blue smaller figure, buff base; **plainer finish**
p213	1932-35	**DINKY TOYS No. 4 ENGINEERING STAFF, FITTER**; brown large figure, cream base; buttons wrong side
-	1935-38	**DINKY TOYS No. 4 ENGINEERING STAFF, FITTER**; brown large figure, cream base; **buttons correct side**
p214	1938-40	**DINKY TOYS No. 4 ENGINEERING STAFF, FITTER**; brown **smaller figure, buff base**

p214	1940-41	**DINKY TOYS No. 4 ENGINEERING STAFF, FITTER**; brown smaller figure, buff base; **plainer finish**
p213	1932-38	**DINKY TOYS No. 4 ENGINEERING STAFF, STOREKEEPER**; large figure, cream base
p214	1938-40	**DINKY TOYS No. 4 ENGINEERING STAFF, STOREKEEPER**; **smaller figure, buff base**
p214	1940-41	**DINKY TOYS No. 4 ENGINEERING STAFF, STOREKEEPER**; smaller figure, buff base; **plainer finish**
p213	1932-38	**DINKY TOYS No. 4 ENGINEERING STAFF, GREASER**; brown large figure, cream base
p214	1938-40	**DINKY TOYS No. 4 ENGINEERING STAFF, GREASER**; brown **smaller figure, buff base**
p214	1940-41	**DINKY TOYS No. 4 ENGINEERING STAFF, GREASER**; brown smaller figure, buff base; **plainer finish**
-	1932	**DINKY TOYS No. 4 ENGINEERING STAFF, ENGINE ROOM ATTENDANT**; large dark blue figure, cream base
p213	1932-38	**DINKY TOYS No. 4 ENGINEERING STAFF, ENGINE ROOM ATTENDANT**; large **blue figure**, cream base
p214	1938-40	**DINKY TOYS No. 4 ENGINEERING STAFF, ENGINE ROOM ATTENDANT**; **smaller figure, buff base**
p214	1940-41	**DINKY TOYS No. 4 ENGINEERING STAFF, ENGINE ROOM ATTENDANT**; smaller figure, buff base; **plainer finish**

p213	1932-38	**DINKY TOYS No. 5 TRAIN AND HOTEL STAFF, PULLMAN CAR CONDUCTOR**; large figure
p214	1938-40	**DINKY TOYS No. 5 TRAIN AND HOTEL STAFF, PULLMAN CAR CONDUCTOR**; **smaller figure**
p214	1940-41	**DINKY TOYS No. 5 TRAIN AND HOTEL STAFF, PULLMAN CAR CONDUCTOR**; smaller figure; **plainer finish**
p213	1932-35	**DINKY TOYS No. 5 TRAIN AND HOTEL STAFF, PULLMAN CAR WAITER**; large figure; buttons wrong side
-	1935-38	**DINKY TOYS No. 5 TRAIN AND HOTEL STAFF, PULLMAN CAR WAITER**; large figure; **buttons correct side**
p214	1938-40	**DINKY TOYS No. 5 TRAIN AND HOTEL STAFF, PULLMAN CAR WAITER**; **smaller figure**
p214	1940-41	**DINKY TOYS No. 5 TRAIN AND HOTEL STAFF, PULLMAN CAR WAITER**; smaller figure; **plainer finish**
p213	1932-38	**DINKY TOYS No. 5 TRAIN AND HOTEL STAFF, HOTEL PORTER**; **red**, large figure
p214	1938-40	**DINKY TOYS No. 5 TRAIN AND HOTEL STAFF, HOTEL PORTER**; red, **smaller figure**, blue and red cases
p214	1940-41	**DINKY TOYS No. 5 TRAIN AND HOTEL STAFF, HOTEL PORTER**; red, smaller figure; **plainer finish**, red and buff cases
p213	1932-38	**DINKY TOYS No. 5 TRAIN AND HOTEL STAFF, HOTEL PORTER**; **green**, large figure
p214	1938-40	**DINKY TOYS No. 5 TRAIN AND HOTEL STAFF, HOTEL PORTER**; green, **smaller figure**, orange and red cases
p214	1940-41	**DINKY TOYS No. 5 TRAIN AND HOTEL STAFF, HOTEL PORTER**; green, smaller figure; **plainer finish**, green and buff cases

p217	1934-38	**DINKY TOYS No. 6 SHEPHERD SET; SHEPHERD**, blue figure
p213	1938-41	**DINKY TOYS No. 6 SHEPHERD SET**; SHEPHERD, **brown figure**
p213	1934-41	**DINKY TOYS No. 6 SHEPHERD SET; DOG**
p213	1934-41	**DINKY TOYS No. 6 SHEPHERD SET; SHEEP**, white with black detail (identical to No. 2 Set Sheep)
p213	1934-41	**DINKY TOYS No. 6 SHEPHERD SET; SHEEP**, black

| p48 | 1932-41 | **DINKY TOYS No. 13 HALL'S DISTEMPER ADVERTISEMENT** |

Double Arm Signal.... see SIGNAL, DOUBLE ARM

Engineering Staff.... see DINKY TOYS

p35	1928-33	**ENGINE SHED No. 1**; **yellow-cream base**, yellow ridge tiles, inside of doors printed
-	1933-35	**ENGINE SHED No. 1**; **green base, blue ridge tiles**, inside of doors printed
-	1935-41	**ENGINE SHED No. 1**; green base, **yellow ridge tiles, inside of doors plain**

| - | 1934-35 | **ENGINE SHED No. 1A**; green base, blue ridge tiles, inside of doors printed |
| p214 | 1935-41 | **ENGINE SHED No. 1A**; green base, **yellow ridge tiles, inside of doors plain** |

A70

-	1932-33	**ENGINE SHED No. E1E; yellow-cream base**, yellow ridge tiles, inside of doors printed
-	1933-35	**ENGINE SHED No. E1E; green base, blue ridge tiles**, inside of doors printed (PU)
p60	1935-41	**ENGINE SHED No. E1E;** green base, **yellow ridge tiles, inside of doors plain**

p34	1928-33	**ENGINE SHED No. 2; yellow-cream base**, yellow ridge tiles, inside of doors printed
-	1933-35	**ENGINE SHED No. 2; green base, blue ridge tiles**, inside of doors printed
-	1935-41	**ENGINE SHED No. 2;** green base, **yellow ridge tiles, inside of doors plain**

p52	1934-35	**ENGINE SHED No. 2A;** green base, blue ridge tiles, inside of doors printed
-	1935-41	**ENGINE SHED No. 2A;** green base, **yellow ridge tiles, inside of doors plain**

-	1932-33	**ENGINE SHED No. E2E; yellow-cream base**, yellow ridge tiles, inside of doors printed
-	1933-35	**ENGINE SHED No. E2E; green base**, blue ridge tiles, inside of doors printed (PU)
p239	1935-41	**ENGINE SHED No. E2E;** green base, **yellow ridge tiles, inside of doors plain**

(No. 1, No. 2, No. 1A and No. 2A Engine Sheds could be obtained to special order with electric rails but without lights)

Farmyard Animals.... see DINKY TOYS

Fencing.... see PALED FENCING

-	1932-41	**FENCING WITH FOUR TREES**

-	1924-27	**FOOTBRIDGE No. 1, WITHOUT SIGNALS;** white with blue lining, pale grey bases
-	1927-29	**FOOTBRIDGE No. 1, WITHOUT SIGNALS;** white with **grey-blue lining, grey-blue bases**
-	1929-33	**FOOTBRIDGE No. 1, WITHOUT SIGNALS;** white with **blue lining, blue bases**
-	1933-41	**FOOTBRIDGE No. 1, WITHOUT SIGNALS; cream with green lining, green bases**
-	1933-39	**FOOTBRIDGE No. 1, WITHOUT SIGNALS; cream with lighter blue lining, lighter blue bases**
-	1933-39	**FOOTBRIDGE No. 1, WITHOUT SIGNALS; cream with red lining, red bases**

p23	1924-27	**FOOTBRIDGE No. 2, WITH SIGNALS;** white with blue lining, pale grey bases
p32	1927-29	**FOOTBRIDGE No. 2, WITH SIGNALS;** white with **grey-blue lining, grey-blue bases**
-	1929-33	**FOOTBRIDGE No. 2, WITH SIGNALS;** white with **blue lining, blue bases**
-	1933-34	**FOOTBRIDGE No. 2, WITH SIGNALS; cream with green lining, green bases**
-	1933-34	**FOOTBRIDGE No. 2, WITH SIGNALS; cream with lighter blue lining, lighter blue bases**
p49	1933-34	**FOOTBRIDGE No. 2, WITH SIGNALS; cream with red lining, red bases**
		See "SIGNALS for FOOTBRIDGE" for No. 2 Footbridge signal variations.

No. 1A Footbridge signals were: blue and white striped M-type signals 1933-34; No. 1 type signals with short red "levers", and top colour matching footbridge bases, 1933-39; yellow distant arms from 1936; black top/black lever 1939-41

p251	1930-33	**FOOTBRIDGE No. 1A, WITH TINPRINTED SIGNALS**; white with blue lining, **blue bases**; diagonal-lattice M-type signals
p251	1933-41	**FOOTBRIDGE No. 1A, WITH SIGNALS; cream with green lining, green bases**
p52	1933-39	**FOOTBRIDGE No. 1A, WITH SIGNALS; cream with lighter blue lining, lighter blue bases**
-	1933-39	**FOOTBRIDGE No. 1A, WITH SIGNALS; cream with red lining, red bases**
p13	1921-22	**LATTICE GIRDER BRIDGE**; greenish-brown wooden pillars and bricks, brownish-red mortar (5 rows) and reverse side, white girders
p126	1922-23	**LATTICE GIRDER BRIDGE; brownish-green** wooden pillars and bricks, **red** mortar (5 rows) and reverse, **cream** girders
-	1923-24	**LATTICE GIRDER BRIDGE; olive green** wooden pillars and bricks, red mortar (**9 rows**) and reverse, **pale greenish-grey** girders
p217	1924-27	**LATTICE GIRDER BRIDGE**; olive green **tin** pillars and bricks, red mortar (9 rows) and reverse, pale greenish-grey girders
-	1927-33	**LATTICE GIRDER BRIDGE; white** tin pillars, **grey** bricks, **dark blue** mortar (9 rows) and reverse, **white blue-lined** girders
-		(side walls tinprinted grey/dark blue-grey, not enamelled, on later versions)
p157	1933-34	**LATTICE GIRDER BRIDGE; cream** tin pillars, grey bricks, dark blue-grey mortar (9 rows) and reverse, **cream lighter-blue lined** girders

Gantry.... see SIGNAL GANTRY

-	1934-35	**GOODS PLATFORM No. 1; green** platform, pale grey-blue roof
p217	1935-37	**GOODS PLATFORM No. 1**; green platform, **blue roof**
p168	1937-41	**GOODS PLATFORM No. 1; tinprinted speckled** platform
p29	1926-28	**GOODS PLATFORM No. 2**; grey platform, simple tinprinted canopy; red crane with red base, free rotation
p31	1928-29	**GOODS PLATFORM No. 2**; grey platform, **tinprinted building**; red crane with **grey base, worm drive**
p37	1929-30	**GOODS PLATFORM No. 2; dark green** platform, tinprinted building; **grey crane** with **dark red base**
p41	1930-33	**GOODS PLATFORM No. 2; yellow-cream** platform, tinprinted building; **blue crane** with **red base**
-	1933-34	**GOODS PLATFORM No. 2; green platform**, tinprinted building with pale blue-grey roof; **green crane** with red base
p53	1934-37	**GOODS PLATFORM No. 2**; green platform, tinprinted building with **light blue roof**; green crane with red base
p218	1937-38	**GOODS PLATFORM No. 2; tinprinted speckled platform**, tinprinted building with light blue roof; green crane with red base
p70	1938-40	**GOODS PLATFORM No. 2**; tinprinted speckled platform, tinprinted building with light blue roof; **grey crane** with red base
p47	1932-33	**GOODS PLATFORM No. 2E; yellow-cream** platform, tinprinted building; **blue crane** with **red base**
-	1933-34	**GOODS PLATFORM No. 2E; green platform**, tinprinted building with pale blue-grey roof; **green crane** with red base
-	1934-37	**GOODS PLATFORM No. 2E**; green platform, tinprinted building with **light blue roof**; green crane with red base
-	1937-38	**GOODS PLATFORM No. 2E; tinprinted speckled** platform, tinprinted building with light blue roof; green crane with red base; blue lamps
p67	1938-40	**GOODS PLATFORM No. 2E**; tinprinted speckled platform, tinprinted building with light blue roof; **grey crane** with red base; **green lamps**

Hall's Distemper.... see DINKY TOYS

p220	1933-35	**HEDGES**; wide base
p275	1935-41	**HEDGES; narrow** base (late versions had dark stain, as shown on p275; earlier as p274)

Hoarding.... see STATION OR FIELD HOARDING

p30	1926-29	**ISLAND PLATFORM; WINDSOR**, grey platform; long canopy
-	1929-33	**ISLAND PLATFORM; WINDSOR, yellow-cream** platform; **shorter** canopy
p49	1933-34	**ISLAND PLATFORM; WINDSOR, green** platform; **long pale blue-grey** canopy
-	1934-36	**ISLAND PLATFORM; WINDSOR**, green platform; long **blue** canopy
-	1936-37	**ISLAND PLATFORM; WEMBLEY**, green platform; long blue canopy
-	1937-38	**ISLAND PLATFORM; WEMBLEY**, green platform; long **green canopy (PU)**
-	1938-41	**ISLAND PLATFORM; WEMBLEY, tinprinted speckled platform**; long green canopy
-	1936-37	**ISLAND PLATFORM; RIPON**, green platform; long blue canopy
-	1937-38	**ISLAND PLATFORM; RIPON**, green platform; long **green canopy (PU)**
-	1938-41	**ISLAND PLATFORM; RIPON, tinprinted speckled platform**; long green canopy (PU)
p59	1936-37	**ISLAND PLATFORM; BRISTOL**, green platform; long blue canopy
-	1937-38	**ISLAND PLATFORM; READING**, green platform; long **green canopy (PU)**
p67	1938-41	**ISLAND PLATFORM; READING, tinprinted speckled platform**; long green canopy
-	1936-37	**ISLAND PLATFORM; MARGATE**, green platform; long blue canopy
-	1937-38	**ISLAND PLATFORM; MARGATE**, green platform; long **green canopy (PU)**
-	1938-41	**ISLAND PLATFORM; MARGATE, tinprinted speckled platform**; long green canopy (PU)
p47	1932-33	**ISLAND PLATFORM E; WINDSOR, yellow-cream** platform; **short** canopy
-	1933-34	**ISLAND PLATFORM E; WINDSOR, green** platform; **long pale blue-grey** canopy (PU)
-	1934-36	**ISLAND PLATFORM E; WINDSOR**, green platform; long **blue** canopy
p57	1936-37	**ISLAND PLATFORM E; WEMBLEY**, green platform; long blue canopy
-	1937-38	**ISLAND PLATFORM E; WEMBLEY**, green platform; long **green canopy (PU)**
p66	1938-41	**ISLAND PLATFORM E; WEMBLEY, tinprinted speckled platform**; long green canopy
-	1936-37	**ISLAND PLATFORM E; RIPON**, green platform; long blue canopy (PU)
p62	1937-38	**ISLAND PLATFORM E; RIPON**, green platform; long **green canopy**
-	1938-41	**ISLAND PLATFORM E; RIPON**, tinprinted speckled platform; long green canopy (PU)
-	1936-37	**ISLAND PLATFORM E; BRISTOL**, green platform; long blue canopy (PU)
-	1937-38	**ISLAND PLATFORM E; READING**, green platform; long **green canopy (PU)**
-	1938-41	**ISLAND PLATFORM E; READING, tinprinted speckled platform**; long green canopy (PU)
-	1936-37	**ISLAND PLATFORM E; MARGATE**, green platform; long blue canopy (PU)
-	1937-38	**ISLAND PLATFORM E; MARGATE**, green platform; long **green canopy (PU)**
-	1938-41	**ISLAND PLATFORM E; MARGATE, tinprinted speckled platform**; long green canopy (PU)

Junction Signal.... see SIGNAL, JUNCTION

-	1923-24	**LAMP STANDARD No. 1**; black base and finial, black ratchet panel; unstrengthened bracket
p219	1924-27	**LAMP STANDARD No. 1**; black base and finial, black ratchet panel; **strengthened bracket**
-	1927-29	**LAMP STANDARD No. 1; grey-blue** base and finial, **grey-blue** ratchet panel
-	1929-32	**LAMP STANDARD No. 1; blue** base and finial, **blue** ratchet panel
-	1932	**LAMP STANDARD No. 1**; blue base and finial, **black** ratchet panel
-	1932-39	**LAMP STANDARD No. 1; lighter blue** base and finial, black ratchet panel

(It is possible that No. 1 and No. 2 green-base versions may have been produced in 1938)

-	1923-24	**LAMP STANDARD No. 2**; black base and finial, black ratchet panel; unstrengthened brackets
p19	1924-27	**LAMP STANDARD No. 2**; black base and finial, black ratchet panel; **strengthened brackets**
-	1927-29	**LAMP STANDARD No. 2**; **grey-blue** base and finial, **grey-blue** ratchet panel
-	1929-32	**LAMP STANDARD No. 2**; **blue** base and finial, **blue** ratchet panel
p219	1932	**LAMP STANDARD No. 2**; blue base and finial, **black** ratchet panel
p219	1932-39	**LAMP STANDARD No. 2**; **lighter blue** base and finial, black ratchet panel
p219	1931-33	**LAMP STANDARD No. 1E**; blue base, lamp and finial
p61	1933-38	**LAMP STANDARD No. 1E**; **lighter blue** base, lamp and finial
p219	1938-41	**LAMP STANDARD No. 1E**; **green** base and lamp, **red finial**
p45	1931-33	**LAMP STANDARD No. 2E**; blue base, lamps and finial
p219	1933-38	**LAMP STANDARD No. 2E**; **lighter blue** base, lamps and finial
p215	1938-41	**LAMP STANDARD No. 2E**; **green** base and lamps, **red finial**

Lattice Girder Bridge.... see FOOTBRIDGE

p219	1928-30	**LEVEL CROSSING No. 1**; **white** gateposts
p219	1930-33	**LEVEL CROSSING No. 1**; **green** gateposts
p219	1933-38	**LEVEL CROSSING No. 1**; **lighter green** gateposts
-	1938-41	**LEVEL CROSSING No. 1**; **light brown** gateposts
		(there were many changes in the tinprinting of the road pattern)
-	1931-33	**LEVEL CROSSING No. E1**; **green** gateposts
p139	1933-38	**LEVEL CROSSING No. E1**; **lighter green** gateposts
-	1938-41	**LEVEL CROSSING No. E1**; **light brown** gateposts
p47	1932-33	**LEVEL CROSSING No. E1E**; **green** gateposts
p149	1933-38	**LEVEL CROSSING No. E1E**; **lighter green** gateposts
p65	1938-41	**LEVEL CROSSING No. E1E**; **light brown** gateposts
p115	1924-25	**LEVEL CROSSING**; white gateposts, narrow track spacing; sans-serif "Beware of the Trains"
p29	1925-28	**LEVEL CROSSING**; white gateposts, narrow track spacing; **serif "Beware of the Trains"** (with quotation marks after 1926)
p37	1928-30	**LEVEL CROSSING No. 2**; white gateposts, **standard double track spacing; unlettered gates**
p44	1930-33	**LEVEL CROSSING No. 2**; **green** gateposts, standard double track spacing
-	1933-38	**LEVEL CROSSING No. 2**; **lighter green** gateposts, standard double track spacing
-	1938-41	**LEVEL CROSSING No. 2**; **light brown** gateposts, standard double track spacing
-	1930-33	**LEVEL CROSSING No. E2**; **green** gateposts, standard double track spacing (red insulator 1930, black thereafter)
-	1933-38	**LEVEL CROSSING No. E2**; **lighter green** gateposts, standard double track spacing
-	1938-41	**LEVEL CROSSING No. E2**; **light brown** gateposts, standard double track spacing

-	1932-33	**LEVEL CROSSING No. E2E; green** gateposts, standard double track spacing
p220	1933-38	**LEVEL CROSSING No. E2E; lighter green** gateposts, standard double track spacing
-	1938-41	**LEVEL CROSSING No. E2E; light brown** gateposts, standard double track spacing
p18	1923-27	**LOADING GAUGE**; round black base, black finial
-	1927	**LOADING GAUGE**; round **grey-blue** base, **grey-blue** finial
p31	1927-29	**LOADING GAUGE; rectangular** grey-blue base, grey-blue finial; revised design
p220	1929-33	**LOADING GAUGE**; rectangular **blue base, blue finial**; revised design
-	1933-34	**LOADING GAUGE**; rectangular **lighter blue** base, **lighter blue** finial
-	1934-38	**LOADING GAUGE**; rectangular lighter blue base, lighter blue flat top
-	1938-39	**LOADING GAUGE**; rectangular **green** base, **red** flat top
p67	1939-41	**LOADING GAUGE**; rectangular green base, **black** flat top
p247	1933-41	**M FOOTBRIDGE**; tinprinted sides, yellow steps
p259	1933?	**M FOOTBRIDGE**; tinprinted sides, **blue** steps
p247	1931-33	**M LEVEL CROSSING**; black posts
-	1933-41	**M LEVEL CROSSING; light green** posts
p56	1933-41	**M LEVEL CROSSING; yellow** posts
p247	1931-33	**M LOADING GAUGE**; blue base and top, white post
p247	1933-38	**M LOADING GAUGE; lighter blue** base and top, white post
p247	1938-41	**M LOADING GAUGE; green** base and top, white post
p246	1930-33	**M SIGNAL BOX**; blue/black roof, woodwork brown and cream
p248	1933-41	**M SIGNAL BOX**; blue/white roof, woodwork orange and yellow
p249	1932-36	**BRITISH EXPRESS SIGNAL BOX**
p246	1930-33	**M SIGNAL**; diagonal lattice post
p247	1933-38	**M SIGNAL; blue and white striped** post
p260	1938-41	**M SIGNAL; red and white striped** post
p249	1932-36	**BRITISH EXPRESS SIGNAL** (no trademark)
p246	1930-33	**M STATION**; brown canopy, round-tiled roof
p247	1933-36	**M STATION; red canopy**, round-tiled roof
p247	1936-41	**M STATION; green canopy, square-tiled** roof
p249		Also in late versions incorporating obsolete British Express printings
-	1932-36	**BRITISH EXPRESS STATION**
p247	1930-41	**M WAYSIDE STATION**; green hut
p249		Also in late versions incorporating obsolete British Express printings
-	1932-36	**BRITISH EXPRESS WAYSIDE STATION**; red hut
-	1930-41	**M STATION SET**; two M Telegraph Poles, two M Signals, M Station, M Wayside Station, M Signal Box

p246	1930-33	**M TELEGRAPH POLE No. 1**; diagonal lattice post
-	1933-38	**M TELEGRAPH POLE No. 1**; **blue and white striped** post
p257	1938-41	**M TELEGRAPH POLE No. 1**; **red and white striped** post

p247	1931-33	**M TELEGRAPH POLE No. 2**; diagonal lattice post
-	1933-41	**M TELEGRAPH POLE No. 2**; **blue and white striped** post
		(Version with red and white striped post not known)

| p56 | 1934-41 | **M TUNNEL** (for M8 Complete Model Railway Set) |

p26	1926-27	**PALED FENCING**; **white**, solid base
p29	1927-29	**PALED FENCING**; **green**, solid base
-	1929-31	**PALED FENCING**; **white**, solid base
p59	1931-41	**PALED FENCING**; white, **cut-out base**
p50	1933	**PALED FENCING**; **brighter green**, cut-out base

Passengers.... see DINKY TOYS

p26	1926-27	**PASSENGER PLATFORM**; **grey platform**, white fence
-	1927-29	**PASSENGER PLATFORM**; grey platform, **green fence**
p36	1929-33	**PASSENGER PLATFORM**; **yellow-cream platform**, white fence
p57	1933-37	**PASSENGER PLATFORM**; **green platform**, white fence
p63	1937-40	**PASSENGER PLATFORM**; **speckled platform**, white line both sides; white fence
p69	1940-41	**PASSENGER PLATFORM**; speckled platform, white line **one side**; white fence

p221	1930-34	**PLATELAYER'S HUT**; opening planked door
p221	1934-36	**PLATELAYER'S HUT**; **fixed plain green door**, painted handles
p221	1936-41	**PLATELAYER'S HUT**; fixed **planked door**

Platform Accessories.... see RAILWAY ACCESSORIES

p221	1928-29	**PLATFORM CRANE**; white-lined grey base, grey centre, red crane
p221	1929-30	**PLATFORM CRANE**; white-lined **dark green base, dark red centre, blue-grey crane**
p221	1930-33	**PLATFORM CRANE**; white-lined **yellow-cream base, red centre, dark blue crane**
p221	1933-38	**PLATFORM CRANE**; **green-lined yellow base**, red centre, **green crane**
p221	1938-39	**PLATFORM CRANE**; green-lined yellow base, red centre, **grey crane**
-	1939-41	**PLATFORM CRANE**; **white-lined buff base**, red centre, grey crane

p26	1926-29	**PLATFORM RAMPS**; grey
p47	1929-33	**PLATFORM RAMPS**; **yellow-cream**
p59	1933-37	**PLATFORM RAMPS**; **green**
p70	1937-41	**PLATFORM RAMPS**; **tinprinted, speckled**

POSTER Series 1 1931-41; Series 2 1934-41. There were several changes in the contents of the packets during these periods.

p223	**POSTER, large** Series 2 **ATORA** 'Make it with Hugon's..The good beef suet'
p223	**POSTER**, large Series 1 **BOVRIL** 'Prevents that sinking feeling'
p223	**POSTER**, large Series 2 **BOVRIL** 'Take..and develop strength'
p223	**POSTER**, large Series 1 **BP Ethyl** 'Banishes Pinking'
p223	**POSTER**, large Series 1 **BP Plus** 'Gives you more, costs no more'
p223	**POSTER**, large Series 1 **CHERRY BLOSSOM** Boot Polish
p223	**POSTER**, large Series 2 **CHIVERS'** Jellies 'Where the rainbow ends'
p223	**POSTER**, large Series 1 **CLARK'S** Creamed Barley 'A meal in a moment'
p223	**POSTER**, large Series 1 **COLAS** '..makes perfect drives and paths'
p223	**POSTER**, large Series 2 **COLAS** 'the perfect surface for drives & paths'
-	**POSTER**, large Series 2 **ELEKTRON** Electrical Outfits
p223	**POSTER**, large Series 1 **ESSO and ESSOLUBE** 'When you buy these you buy quality'
p223	**POSTER**, large Series 2 **FRY'S** Chocolate Cream, 'The famous original'
p223	**POSTER**, large Series 1 **FRY'S** Milk and Hazel Bars, 'Thick bars for flavour'
p223	**POSTER**, large Series 1 **FRY'S** Sandwich 'I said you'd like it'
p223	**POSTER**, large Series 2 **HARTLEY'S** Table Jelly, 4d only
-	**POSTER**, large Series 2 **HORLICK'S** 'Guards against night starvation'
p223	**POSTER**, large Series 1 **HORLICK'S** 'Brings deep, sound sleep'
p223	**POSTER**, large Series 2 **HORNBY** SPEED BOATS
p223	**POSTER**, large Series 1 **HORNBY** TRAINS, 'British and guaranteed'
p223	**POSTER**, large Series 1 **JACOB & Co.'s** Jabisco Assorted Biscuits
-	**POSTER**, large Series 2 **KEMEX**
p223	**POSTER**, large Series 1 **LIBBY'S** 'The blue and white label'
p223	**POSTER**, large Series 1 **LYON'S** Coffee and Chicory Extract
p223	**POSTER**, large Series 2 **MARMITE** with Cook, Butler, Boots 'Good for soups......etc'
p223	**POSTER**, large Series 1 **MECCANO** 'Begin Meccano now..'
p223	**POSTER**, large Series 2 **MECCANO** Aeroplane Constructor
p223	**POSTER**, large Series 2 **MECCANO** Motor Car Constructor
p223	**POSTER**, large Series 1 **ODOL** 'The perfect British dentifrice'
p223	**POSTER**, large Series 1 **OXO** 'Beef in brief'
p223	**POSTER**, large Series 1 **PRATTS** High Test 'Hi! Test High Test!'
p223	**POSTER**, large Series 2 **ROBERTSON'S** Golden Shred
p223	**POSTER**, large Series 1 **SECCOTINE** 'In handy tubes. Sticks Everything'
p223	**POSTER**, large Series 1 **SECCOTINE** in red on yellow, red border 'Sticks everything'
p223	**POSTER**, large Series 2 **SECCOTINE** in white on red, yellow border 'Sticks everything'
p223	**POSTER**, large Series 2 **SECCOTINE** 'Sticks everything. Sold in handy tubes'
p223	**POSTER**, large Series 2 **SHELL** Lubricating Oil 'for reliability'
p223	**POSTER**, large Series 1 **SHELL** 'That's Shell..That was'
p223	**POSTER**, large Series 2 **SKIPPERS** 'The tastiest meal that ever came out of a tin'
p223	**POSTER**, large Series 1 **WAKEFIELD CASTROL** 'Sir Malcolm Cambell used..'
p223	**POSTER**, large Series 2 **WAKEFIELD CASTROL** '..patent..reduces cylinder wear'
-	**POSTER**, large Series 2 **WAKEFIELD CASTROL** ...272 mph
p223	**POSTER**, large Series 2 **WAVERLEY** Oats 'Better porridge'

p223	**POSTER**, large Series 2 **YARDLEY** Lavender 'the lovable fragrance'
p223	**POSTER**, **small** Series 1 **ATORA** 'The good beef suet', blue background
p223	**POSTER**, small Series 2 **ATORA** 'Make it with Hugon's Atora, the good beef suet'
-	**POSTER**, small Series 2 **BEEFEX** 'Best of the beef'
p223	**POSTER**, small Series 1 **BIRD'S** Custard, 'More sold than ever'
p223	**POSTER**, small Series 2 **BIRD'S** 'The quality custard. Quality counts!'
p223	**POSTER**, small Series 2 **BIRD'S** Custard Creams, 'Something to sing about'
p223	**POSTER**, small Series 2 **BOVRIL** '..promotes that singing feeling'
p223	**POSTER**, small Series 1 **BRASSO** 'for brightness'
p223	**POSTER**, small Series 2 **CADBURY'S** Bourn-Vita 'for sleep and energy'
p223	**POSTER**, small Series 1 **CAMP** Coffee 'is the best'
	('Don't be misled!!!' is in red on early printings)
p223	**POSTER**, small Series 1 **CARR'S** 'Pioneers of the biscuit industry'
p223	**POSTER**, small Series 1 **CHIVERS'** Jellies 'make a meal a banquet'
p223	**POSTER**, small Series 1 **CLARK'S** Creamed Barley
p223	**POSTER**, small Series 1 **COLMAN'S** Starch 'Nothing to touch it'
p223	**POSTER**, small Series 2 **ELEKTRON** Electrical Outfits
p223	**POSTER**, small Series 1 **FORCE** 'Whole wheat in flakes'
p223	**POSTER**, small Series 2 **GLO** 'The warming winter drink. Keeps you in tune'
p223	**POSTER**, small Series 2 **GOLDEN SHRED** Marmalade, 'Golly it's good'
p223	**POSTER**, small Series 1 **HARTLEY'S** Marmalade
p223	**POSTER**, small Series 2 **HARTLEY'S** Strawberry, 'Judge it by its flavour'
p223	**POSTER**, small Series 1 **HORLICK'S** 'for sound sleep'
p223	**POSTER**, small Series 2 **HORNBY** SPEED BOATS
p223	**POSTER**, small Series 1 **HORNBY** TRAINS
p223	**POSTER**, small Series 1 **HP** SAUCE 'Mary had a little lamb with lots of..'
p223	**POSTER**, small Series 1 **KARDOMAH** Tea 'Makes better tea'
p223	**POSTER**, small Series 2 **KEMEX** chemical outfits
p223	**POSTER**, small Series 2 **KLG** plugs 'Fit and forget'
p223	**POSTER**, small Series 1 **LIBBY'S** 'a whole sliced pineapple in a can'
p223	**POSTER**, small Series 1 **LIFEBUOY** Soap 'for health', red and blue triangle background
p223	**POSTER**, small Series 2 **LIFEBUOY** Soap 'for health', with boy's face
p223	**POSTER**, small Series 1 **LUX** 'If it's safe in water, it's safe in..'
p223	**POSTER**, small Series 2 **LUX** 'Prolongs the life of all lovely fabrics'
p223	**POSTER**, small Series 2 **LYONS'** Tea 'Huge sale tells own tale'
p223	**POSTER**, small Series 1 **LYONS'** Tea 'The best tea value'
p223	**POSTER**, small Series 1 **MARMITE** with Cook, 'is good for soups....etc'
p223	**POSTER**, small Series 2 **MARMITE**, with Cook, 'I must have Marmite for soups....etc'
	POSTER, small Series 2 **MARMITE** with Cook and Butler, 'good for soups....etc.'
p223	**POSTER**, small Series 1 **MECCANO** 'Begin Meccano now..'
p223	**POSTER**, small Series 2 **MECCANO** Aeroplane Constructor
p223	**POSTER**, small Series 2 **MECCANO** Motor Car Constructor
p223	**POSTER**, small Series 1 **MERIDIAN** Underwear, Slumber wear, Bathing wear

p223		**POSTER**, small Series 1 **NESTLE'S** Milk, 'Best for baby'
p223		**POSTER**, small Series 2 **NESTLE'S**, 'Thanks to..'
-		**POSTER**, small Series 2 **NESTLE'S**, 'Happy Days'
p223		**POSTER**, small Series 1 **OVALTINE** 'Country Health for you'
p223		**POSTER**, small Series 2 **OVALTINE** 'for radiant health'
p223		**POSTER**, small Series 2 **OXO** 'Beef in Brief'
p223		**POSTER**, small Series 1 **PEARS** Soap 'King of soaps, soap of Kings'
p223		**POSTER**, small Series 2 **PEARS** 'Golden Glory soap, 6d per cake'
p223		**POSTER**, small Series 1 **PERSIL** 'Used by over 2,000,000 housewives'
p223		**POSTER**, small Series 1 **QUAKER** Oats 'For health - Quick ...'
p223		**POSTER**, small Series 2 **SHELL** 'You can be sure of ...', with anchor
p223		**POSTER**, small Series 1 **SKIPPERS** 'are tasty for tea'
p223		**POSTER**, small Series 2 **SKIPPERS**, 'A feast of flavour, and no bones about it'
p223		**POSTER**, small Series 1 **SOUTHERN RAILWAY** 'South for Sunshine'
p223		**POSTER**, small Series 1 **SOUTHERN RAILWAY**, 'Sunny South Sam, still at your service'
p223		**POSTER**, small Series 2 **SPRATTS** Bonio 'A bone shaped biscuit for all breeds'
p223		**POSTER**, small Series 1 **SUNLIGHT** Soap, 'Don't worry, use..'
p223		**POSTER**, small Series 2 **SUNLIGHT** Soap 'for extra soapiness use..'
p223		**POSTER**, small Series 2 **SWAN** Ink 'for all pens'
p223		**POSTER**, small Series 1 **SWAN** Pens 'World Famous'
p223		**POSTER**, small Series 2 **SWAN** Pens (no slogan)
p223		**POSTER**, small Series 2 **SWAN VESTAS** 'British made by Bryant and May. See there's a swan on your box'
p223		**POSTER**, small Series 1 **TREX** 'for better cooking'
p223		**POSTER**, small Series 1 **VIM** 'Cleanser..Polisher'
p223		**POSTER**, small Series 2 **VIM** 'The double action cleanser. Loosens the dirt, then absorbs it'
p223		**POSTER**, small Series 2 **WAVERLEY** Oats 'Perfect Porridge'
p223		**POSTER**, small Series 2 **WILLS** Capstan Cigarettes 'They're good, they're Capstan'
p223		**POSTER**, small Series 2 **WILLS** Gold Flake Cigarettes, 'Always fresh'
p223		**POSTER**, small Series 2 **WINCARNIS** 'for glorious health, take..'
p223		**POSTER**, small Series 2 Young **WOLSEY**, 'finest woollen underwear'
p223		**POSTER**, small Series 2 **YARDLEY LAVENDER** 'The lovable fragrance'
-	1931-41	**POSTER BOARDS**; usually green, though other colours were occasionally used
-	1924-27	**RAILWAY ACCESSORIES No. 1, TRUCK**; green, tin wheels
p226	1927-31	**RAILWAY ACCESSORIES No. 1, TRUCK; darker green**, tin wheels
p226	1931-33	**RAILWAY ACCESSORIES No. 1, TRUCK**; darker green, **cast wheels**
p226	1933-41	**RAILWAY ACCESSORIES No. 1, TRUCK; lighter green**, cast wheels
p226	1924-31	**RAILWAY ACCESSORIES No. 1, LUGGAGE; trunk, round top**; dark blue with red and brown straps
p226		(usually folded body, but tabbed version circa 1928)
p226	1931-38	**RAILWAY ACCESSORIES No. 1, LUGGAGE**; trunk, round top; blue with red and **buff straps**; folded body
p226	1938-41	**RAILWAY ACCESSORIES No. 1, LUGGAGE**; trunk, round top; blue with **green and orange straps**; folded body
p226	1924-31	**RAILWAY ACCESSORIES No. 1, LUGGAGE; small suitcase, brown**
p226		(usually folded body, but tabbed version circa 1928)

p226	1931-38	**RAILWAY ACCESSORIES No. 1**, LUGGAGE; small suitcase, **green with green corners**; folded body
p226	1938-41	**RAILWAY ACCESSORIES No. 1**, LUGGAGE; small suitcase, **green with black corners**; folded body
p226	1924-26	**RAILWAY ACCESSORIES No. 1**, LUGGAGE; **hamper, "Carlisle"** label; black and brown on buff; folded body
-	1926-31	**RAILWAY ACCESSORIES No. 1**, LUGGAGE; hamper, **"London"** label; black and brown on buff; folded body
p226		(usually folded body, but tabbed version circa 1928)
p226	1931-38	**RAILWAY ACCESSORIES No. 1**, LUGGAGE; hamper, "London" label; black and brown on **lighter buff**; folded body
p226	1938-41	**RAILWAY ACCESSORIES No. 1**, LUGGAGE; hamper, "London" label; **black and orange on cream**; folded body
p226	1924-31	**RAILWAY ACCESSORIES No. 1**, LUGGAGE; **trunk, flat top**; **brown**
p226		(usually folded, but tabbed version circa 1928)
p226	1931-38	**RAILWAY ACCESSORIES No. 1**, LUGGAGE; trunk, flat top; **light brown**
p226	1938-41	**RAILWAY ACCESSORIES No. 1**, LUGGAGE; trunk, flat top; **orange**
p225	1924-41	**RAILWAY ACCESSORIES No. 2, MILK CANS**
p225	1924-25	**RAILWAY ACCESSORIES No. 2, TRUCK**; green, tin wheels
p225	1925-31	**RAILWAY ACCESSORIES No. 2, TRUCK**; **orange**, tin wheels
p225	1931-33	**RAILWAY ACCESSORIES No. 2, TRUCK**; orange, **cast wheels**
p225	1933-41	**RAILWAY ACCESSORIES No. 2, TRUCK**; **blue**, cast wheels
p225	1924-35	**RAILWAY ACCESSORIES No. 3, PLATFORM MACHINES ETC.**; **pillar box**, tinprinted
p225	1935-41	**RAILWAY ACCESSORIES No. 3, PLATFORM MACHINES ETC.**; pillar box, **Dinky Toy**
-	1924-27	**RAILWAY ACCESSORIES No. 3, PLATFORM MACHINES ETC.**; **seat**, green
p225	1927-33	**RAILWAY ACCESSORIES No. 3, PLATFORM MACHINES ETC.**; seat, **darker green**
p225	1933-41	**RAILWAY ACCESSORIES No. 3, PLATFORM MACHINES ETC.**; seat, **lighter green**
p225	1924-31	**RAILWAY ACCESSORIES No. 3, PLATFORM MACHINES ETC.**; **platform ticket machine**, black lining
p225	1931-41	**RAILWAY ACCESSORIES No. 3, PLATFORM MACHINES ETC.**; platform ticket machine, **black and white lining**
p225	1924-31	**RAILWAY ACCESSORIES No. 3, PLATFORM MACHINES ETC.**; **nametape machine**, brown
p225	1931-41	**RAILWAY ACCESSORIES No. 3, PLATFORM MACHINES ETC.**; nametape machine, **green**
p225	1936-41	**RAILWAY ACCESSORIES No. 3, PLATFORM MACHINES ETC.**; **fire hut**
p226	1927-41	**RAILWAY ACCESSORIES No. 4;** combined sets 1 to 3
p227	1928-41	**RAILWAY ACCESSORIES No. 5, GRADIENT AND MILE POSTS**; gradient, 1-130/level
p227	1928-41	**RAILWAY ACCESSORIES No. 5, GRADIENT AND MILE POSTS**; gradient, 1-210/1-250
p227	1928-41	**RAILWAY ACCESSORIES No. 5, GRADIENT AND MILE POSTS**; gradient, 1-300/1-210
p227	1928-41	**RAILWAY ACCESSORIES No. 5, GRADIENT AND MILE POSTS**; gradient, 1-165/1-189
p227	1928-41	**RAILWAY ACCESSORIES No. 5, GRADIENT AND MILE POSTS**; gradient, 1-147/1-260
p227	1928-41	**RAILWAY ACCESSORIES No. 5, GRADIENT AND MILE POSTS**; gradient, 1-120/level
p227	1928-41	**RAILWAY ACCESSORIES No. 5, GRADIENT AND MILE POSTS**; gradient, level/1-156 (uphill)
p227	1928-41	**RAILWAY ACCESSORIES No. 5, GRADIENT AND MILE POSTS**; gradient, level/1-156 (downhill)
p227	1928-41	**RAILWAY ACCESSORIES No. 5, GRADIENT AND MILE POSTS**; milepost, 1/4 mile
p227	1928-41	**RAILWAY ACCESSORIES No. 5, GRADIENT AND MILE POSTS**; milepost, 1/2 mile
p227	1928-41	**RAILWAY ACCESSORIES No. 5, GRADIENT AND MILE POSTS**; milepost, 3/4 mile
p227	1928-41	**RAILWAY ACCESSORIES No. 5, GRADIENT AND MILE POSTS**; milepost, 1 mile
		(1929-30 versions were tinprinted)

p227	1928-29	**RAILWAY ACCESSORIES No. 6, STATION NAMES & NOTICE BOARDS**; grey-blue bases; combined sets 8 and 9
p227	1928-40	**RAILWAY ACCESSORIES No. 7, WATCHMAN'S HUT, BRAZIER, SHOVEL & POKER**; brazier with red fire on black background
-	1940-41	**RAILWAY ACCESSORIES No. 7**, WATCHMAN'S HUT, BRAZIER, SHOVEL & POKER; brazier with **black dots on red background**
p227	1929-33	**RAILWAY ACCESSORIES No. 8, NOTICE BOARDS; "SHUT OFF STEAM"**, blue base
-	1933-39	**RAILWAY ACCESSORIES No. 8**, NOTICE BOARDS; "SHUT OFF STEAM", **lighter blue** base
-	1939-41	**RAILWAY ACCESSORIES No. 8**, NOTICE BOARDS; "SHUT OFF STEAM", **green base**
p227	1929-33	**RAILWAY ACCESSORIES No. 8**, NOTICE BOARDS; **"CATCH POINTS"**, blue base
-	1933-39	**RAILWAY ACCESSORIES No. 8**, NOTICE BOARDS; "CATCH POINTS", **lighter blue** base
p67	1939-41	**RAILWAY ACCESSORIES No. 8**, NOTICE BOARDS; "CATCH POINTS", **green base**
p227	1929-33	**RAILWAY ACCESSORIES No. 8**, NOTICE BOARDS; **"WHISTLE"**, blue base
-	1933-39	**RAILWAY ACCESSORIES No. 8**, NOTICE BOARDS; "WHISTLE", **lighter blue** base
p67	1939-41	**RAILWAY ACCESSORIES No. 8**, NOTICE BOARDS; "WHISTLE", **green base**
p227	1929-33	**RAILWAY ACCESSORIES No. 8**, NOTICE BOARDS; **"REPAIRS"**, blue base
-	1933-39	**RAILWAY ACCESSORIES No. 8**, NOTICE BOARDS; "REPAIRS", **lighter blue** base
-	1939-41	**RAILWAY ACCESSORIES No. 8**, NOTICE BOARDS; "REPAIRS", **green base**
p227	1929-33	**RAILWAY ACCESSORIES No. 8**, NOTICE BOARDS; **"CAUTION"**, blue base
-	1933-39	**RAILWAY ACCESSORIES No. 8**, NOTICE BOARDS; "CAUTION", **lighter blue** base
-	1939-41	**RAILWAY ACCESSORIES No. 8**, NOTICE BOARDS; "CAUTION", **green base**
p227	1929-33	**RAILWAY ACCESSORIES No. 8**, NOTICE BOARDS; **"TUNNEL 200 YDS"**, blue base
-	1933-39	**RAILWAY ACCESSORIES No. 8**, NOTICE BOARDS; "TUNNEL 200 YDS", **lighter blue** base
-	1939-41	**RAILWAY ACCESSORIES No. 8**, NOTICE BOARDS; "TUNNEL 200 YDS", **green base**
p227	1929-33	**RAILWAY ACCESSORIES No. 9, STATION NAMES; "KING'S CROSS"**, blue base
-	1933-39	**RAILWAY ACCESSORIES No. 9**, STATION NAMES; "KING'S CROSS", **lighter blue** base
-	1939-41	**RAILWAY ACCESSORIES No. 9**, STATION NAMES; "KING'S CROSS", **green base**
p227	1929-33	**RAILWAY ACCESSORIES No. 9**, STATION NAMES; **"GRANTHAM"**, blue base
-	1933-39	**RAILWAY ACCESSORIES No. 9**, STATION NAMES; "GRANTHAM", **lighter blue** base
-	1939-41	**RAILWAY ACCESSORIES No. 9**, STATION NAMES; "GRANTHAM", **green base**
p227	1929-33	**RAILWAY ACCESSORIES No. 9**, STATION NAMES; **"EDINBURGH"**, blue base
p149	1933-39	**RAILWAY ACCESSORIES No. 9**, STATION NAMES; "EDINBURGH", **lighter blue** base
-	1939-41	**RAILWAY ACCESSORIES No. 9**, STATION NAMES; "EDINBURGH", **green base**
p227	1929-33	**RAILWAY ACCESSORIES No. 9**, STATION NAMES; **"NEWCASTLE"**, blue base
-	1933-39	**RAILWAY ACCESSORIES No. 9**, STATION NAMES; "NEWCASTLE", **lighter blue** base
-	1939-41	**RAILWAY ACCESSORIES No. 9**, STATION NAMES; "NEWCASTLE", **green base**
p227	1929-33	**RAILWAY ACCESSORIES No. 9**, STATION NAMES; **"DONCASTER"**, blue base
-	1933-39	**RAILWAY ACCESSORIES No. 9**, STATION NAMES; "DONCASTER", **lighter blue** base
-	1939-41	**RAILWAY ACCESSORIES No. 9**, STATION NAMES; "DONCASTER", **green base**
p227	1929-33	**RAILWAY ACCESSORIES No. 9**, STATION NAMES; **"YORK"**, blue base
-	1933-39	**RAILWAY ACCESSORIES No. 9**, STATION NAMES; "YORK", **lighter blue** base
-	1939-41	**RAILWAY ACCESSORIES No. 9**, STATION NAMES; "YORK", **green base**

-	1932-41	**ROOF CLIPS No. 2**
-	1932-41	**ROOF CLIPS No. 2S**

Shepherd Set.... see DINKY TOYS

p33	1928-40	**SHUNTER'S POLE**

p228	1928-31	**SIGNAL CABIN No. 1**; red round-tiled roof; brown and cream building; printed dustbin on side
p228	1931-34	**SIGNAL CABIN No. 1; blue** round-tiled roof; brown and cream building; **revised window printing; no printed dustbin**
p228	1934-41	**SIGNAL CABIN No. 1; darker blue** round-tiled roof; **red, green and yellow building**; revised window printing; no printed dustbin

p228	1924-26	**SIGNAL CABIN No. 2**; blue-grey square-tiled roof; "WINDSOR" name panel; **light cream** steps
p29	1926-27	**SIGNAL CABIN No. 2**; blue-grey square-tiled roof; "WINDSOR" name panel; **yellow-cream** steps
-	1927-28	**SIGNAL CABIN No. 2**; blue-grey square-tiled roof; "WINDSOR" name panel; **cream** steps
p32	1928-29	**SIGNAL CABIN No. 2**; blue-grey square-tiled roof; **no name panel**; cream steps
p228	1929-31	**SIGNAL CABIN No. 2**; blue-grey **round-tiled** roof; no name panel; cream steps; cream and brown woodwork; white mortar
p228	1931-32	**SIGNAL CABIN No. 2**; blue-grey round-tiled roof; no name panel; **light cream steps**; cream and brown woodwork; **black mortar**
p228	1932-34	**SIGNAL CABIN No. 2; blue square-tiled roof; blank name panel;** light cream steps; **brown and yellow woodwork**
p51	1934-35	**SIGNAL CABIN No. 2**; blue square-tiled roof; blank name panel; light cream steps; **green and yellow** woodwork
p65	1935-39	**SIGNAL CABIN No. 2**; blue square-tiled roof; blank name panel; **yellow steps**; green and yellow woodwork
p228	1939-41	**SIGNAL CABIN No. 2**; blue square-tiled roof; blank name panel; **buff steps**; green and yellow woodwork

-	1932	**SIGNAL CABIN No. 2E**; blue-grey round-tiled roof; no name panel; light cream steps; cream and brown woodwork; black mortar
p47	1932-34	**SIGNAL CABIN No. 2E; blue square-tiled roof; blank name panel;** light cream steps; **brown and yellow** woodwork
-	1934-35	**SIGNAL CABIN No. 2E**; blue square-tiled roof; blank name panel; light cream steps; **green and yellow** woodwork (PU)
p57	1935-39	**SIGNAL CABIN No. 2E**; blue square-tiled roof; blank name panel; **yellow steps**; green and yellow woodwork
p66	1939-41	**SIGNAL CABIN No. 2E**; blue square-tiled roof; blank name panel; **buff steps**; green and yellow woodwork

p52	1934-35	**SIGNAL GANTRY No. 1**; green bridge, green tops, red levers, HOME & red DISTANT arms
-	1935-38	**SIGNAL GANTRY No. 1**; green bridge, green tops, red levers, **HOME** only
-	1938-39	**SIGNAL GANTRY No. 1**; green bridge, **red tops**, red levers, HOME
-	1939	**SIGNAL GANTRY No. 1; white bridge**, red tops, **black levers**, HOME
-	1939-41	**SIGNAL GANTRY No. 1**; white bridge, **black tops**, black levers, HOME

-	1935-36	**SIGNAL GANTRY No. 1**; green bridge, green tops, red levers, red **DISTANT** arms only (PU)
-	1936-38	**SIGNAL GANTRY No. 1**; green bridge, green tops, red levers, **yellow** DISTANT arms
-	1938-39	**SIGNAL GANTRY No. 1**; green bridge, **red tops**, red levers, yellow DISTANT arms
-	1939	**SIGNAL GANTRY No. 1; white bridge**, red tops, **black levers**, yellow DISTANT arms (PU)
p66	1939-41	**SIGNAL GANTRY No. 1**; white bridge, **black tops**, black levers, yellow DISTANT arms

-	1928	**SIGNAL GANTRY No. 2**; grey-blue bridge lining, grey-blue bases and ladder, grey-blue finials, grey-blue levers; HOME and red DISTANT (notched home) arms
p32	1928-29	**SIGNAL GANTRY No. 2**; grey-blue bridge lining, grey-blue bases and ladder, grey-blue finials, grey-blue levers; HOME and red DISTANT (**printed chevron**) arms

-	1929-33	**SIGNAL GANTRY No. 2**; **blue** bridge lining, **blue** bases and ladder, **blue** finials, **blue** levers; HOME and red DISTANT (printed chevron) arms
p51	1933-35	**SIGNAL GANTRY No. 2**; **green bridge lining, lighter blue bases and ladder, lighter blue finials, red levers**; HOME and red DISTANT arms
p57	1935-38	**SIGNAL GANTRY No. 2**; green bridge lining, lighter blue bases and ladder, lighter blue finials, red levers; **HOME** only
-	1938-39	**SIGNAL GANTRY No. 2**; green bridge lining, **green bases and ladder, red finials**, red levers; HOME
-	1939-41	**SIGNAL GANTRY No. 2**; **white bridge**, green bases, **black ladder, black finials, black levers**; HOME
-	1935-36	**SIGNAL GANTRY No. 2**; green bridge lining, lighter blue bases and ladder, lighter blue finials, red levers; red **DISTANT** arms only
-	1936-38	**SIGNAL GANTRY No. 2**; green bridge lining, lighter blue bases and ladder, lighter blue finials, red levers; **yellow** DISTANT arms
-	1938-39	**SIGNAL GANTRY No. 2**; green bridge lining, **green bases and ladder, red finials**, red levers; yellow DISTANT arms (PU)
-	1939-41	**SIGNAL GANTRY No. 2**; **white bridge**, green bases, **black ladder, black finials, black levers**; yellow DISTANT arms
-	1932-33	**SIGNAL GANTRY No. 2E**; blue bridge lining, blue bases and ladder, blue finials, blue levers; HOME and red DISTANT arms
-	1933-35	**SIGNAL GANTRY No. 2E**; **green bridge lining, lighter blue bases and ladder, lighter blue finials, red levers**; HOME and red DISTANT arms
p54	1935-38	**SIGNAL GANTRY No. 2E**; green bridge lining, lighter blue bases and ladder, lighter blue finials, red levers; **HOME** only
p65	1938-39	**SIGNAL GANTRY No. 2E**; green bridge lining, **green bases and ladder, red finials**, red levers; HOME
-	1939-41	**SIGNAL GANTRY No. 2E**; **white bridge**, green bases, **black ladder, black finials, black levers**; HOME
-	1935-36	**SIGNAL GANTRY No. 2E**; green bridge lining, lighter blue bases and ladder, lighter blue finials, red levers; red **DISTANT** arms
-	1936-38	**SIGNAL GANTRY No. 2E**; green bridge lining, lighter blue bases and ladder, lighter blue finials, red levers; **yellow** DISTANT arms
p230	1938-39	**SIGNAL GANTRY No. 2E**; green bridge lining, **green bases and ladder, red finials**, red levers; yellow DISTANT arms
-	1939-41	**SIGNAL GANTRY No. 2E**; **white bridge**, green bases, **black ladder, black finials, black levers**; yellow DISTANT arms (PU)
-	1928-29	**SIGNAL No. 1**; square grey-blue base, grey-blue flat top, grey-blue lever, HOME
p33	1929-33	**SIGNAL No. 1**; square **blue** base, **blue** flat top, **blue** lever, HOME
-	1933-34	**SIGNAL No. 1**; square **lighter blue base, lighter blue** flat top, **red lever**, HOME
p231	1933-34	**SIGNAL No. 1**; square **green base, green** flat top, **red lever**, HOME
-	1934-38	**SIGNAL No. 1**; **round** green base, green **pyramid top**, red lever, HOME
-	1938-39	**SIGNAL No. 1**; round green base, **red pyramid top**, red lever, HOME
-	1939	**SIGNAL No. 1**; round green base, red pyramid top, **black lever**, HOME (PU)
-	1939-41	**SIGNAL No. 1**; round green base, **black pyramid top**, black lever, HOME
		(No. 1 Single Arm and Double Arm Signals were available in a choice of colours only from 1933 to 1934)
-	1928-29	**SIGNAL No. 1**; square grey-blue base, grey-blue flat top, grey-blue lever, red **DISTANT** arm (printed chevron)
p231	1929-33	**SIGNAL No. 1**; square **blue** base, **blue** flat top, **blue** lever, red **DISTANT** arm
p231	1933-34	**SIGNAL No. 1**; square **lighter blue base, lighter blue** flat top, **red lever**, red DISTANT arm
-	1933-34	**SIGNAL No. 1**; square **green base, green** flat top, **red lever**, red DISTANT arm
p231	1934-36	**SIGNAL No. 1**; **round** green base, green **pyramid top**, red lever, red DISTANT arm
p231	1936-38	**SIGNAL No. 1**; round green base, green pyramid top, red lever, **yellow** DISTANT arm
p231	1938-39	**SIGNAL No. 1**; round green base, **red pyramid top**, red lever, yellow DISTANT arm
-	1939	**SIGNAL No. 1**; round green base, red pyramid top, **black lever**, yellow DISTANT arm (PU)
p231	1939-41	**SIGNAL No. 1**; round green base, **black pyramid top**, black lever, yellow DISTANT arm
p229	1923-27	**SIGNAL No. 2**; black base and ladder, black finial, black lever; **HOME**
p30	1927-29	**SIGNAL No. 2**; **grey-blue base and ladder, grey-blue finial, grey-blue lever**; HOME

-	1929-33	**SIGNAL No. 2; blue base and ladder, blue finial, blue lever;** HOME
-	1933-34	**SIGNAL No. 2; lighter blue base and ladder, lighter blue finial, red lever;** HOME
-	1933-34	**SIGNAL No. 2; green base and ladder, green finial, red lever;** HOME
-	1934-38	SIGNAL No. 2; lighter blue base and ladder, lighter blue **flat top**, red lever; HOME
-	1934-38	SIGNAL No. 2; green base and ladder, green **flat top**, red lever; HOME
p210	1938-39	SIGNAL No. 2; green base and ladder, **red flat top**, red lever; HOME
-	1939	SIGNAL No. 2; green base, **black ladder**, red flat top, **black lever**; HOME (PU)
-	1939-41	SIGNAL No. 2; green base, black ladder, **black flat top**, black lever; HOME

(No. 2/2E Single Arm, Double Arm and Junction Signals were available in a choice of colours from 1933 to 1938)

p229	1924-27	SIGNAL No. 2; black base and ladder, black finial, black lever; red **DISTANT** arm (notched home)
-	1927-28	**SIGNAL No. 2; grey-blue base and ladder, grey-blue finial, grey-blue lever;** red DISTANT arm (notched home)
p229	1928-29	SIGNAL No. 2; grey-blue base and ladder, grey-blue finial, grey-blue lever; red DISTANT arm **(printed chevron)**
-	1929-33	**SIGNAL No. 2; blue base and ladder, blue finial, blue lever;** red DISTANT arm (printed chevron)
-	1933-34	**SIGNAL No. 2; lighter blue base and ladder, lighter blue finial, red lever;** red DISTANT arm
p229	1933-34	**SIGNAL No. 2; green base and ladder, green finial, red lever;** red DISTANT arm
-	1934-36	SIGNAL No. 2; lighter blue base and ladder, lighter blue **flat top**, red lever; red DISTANT arm
p229	1934-36	SIGNAL No. 2; green base and ladder, green **flat top**, red lever; red DISTANT arm
-	1936-38	SIGNAL No. 2; lighter blue base and ladder, lighter blue flat top, red lever; **yellow** DISTANT arm
-	1936-38	SIGNAL No. 2; green base and ladder, green flat top, red lever; **yellow** DISTANT arm
-	1938-39	SIGNAL No. 2; green base and ladder, **red flat top**, red lever; yellow DISTANT arm
-	1939	SIGNAL No. 2; green base, **black ladder**, red flat top, **black lever**; yellow DISTANT arm (PU)
p229	1939-41	SIGNAL No. 2; green base, black ladder, **black flat top**, black lever; yellow DISTANT arm

-	1932-33	SIGNAL No. 2E; blue base and ladder, blue finial, blue lever; HOME
-	1933-38	**SIGNAL No. 2E; lighter blue base and ladder, lighter blue finial, red lever;** HOME
-	1933-38	**SIGNAL No. 2E; green base and ladder, green finial, red lever;** HOME
-	1938-39	SIGNAL No. 2E; green base and ladder, **red finial**, red lever; HOME
-	1939	SIGNAL No. 2E; green base, **black ladder**, red finial, **black lever**; HOME
-	1939-41	SIGNAL No. 2E; green base, black ladder, **black finial**, black lever; HOME

p229	1932-33	SIGNAL No. 2E; blue base and ladder, blue finial, blue lever; red DISTANT arm
p229	1933-36	**SIGNAL No. 2E; lighter blue base and ladder, lighter blue finial, red lever;** red DISTANT arm
-	1933-36	**SIGNAL No. 2E; green base and ladder, green finial, red lever;** red DISTANT arm
p229	1936-38	SIGNAL No. 2E; lighter blue base and ladder, lighter blue finial, red lever; **yellow** DISTANT arm
-	1936-38	SIGNAL No. 2E; green base and ladder, grccn finial, red lever; **yellow** DISTANT arm
p229	1938-39	SIGNAL No. 2E; green base and ladder, **red finial**, red lever; yellow DISTANT arm
-	1939	SIGNAL No. 2E; green base, **black ladder**, red finial, **black lever**; yellow DISTANT arm (PU)
-	1939-41	SIGNAL No. 2E; green base, black ladder, **black finial**, black lever; yellow DISTANT arm

-	1928-29	**SIGNAL, No. 1 DOUBLE ARM**; square grey-blue base, grey-blue flat top, grey-blue levers; HOME and red DISTANT (printed chevron) arms
p231	1929-33	**SIGNAL, No. 1 DOUBLE ARM**; square **blue** base, **blue** flat top, **blue** levers; HOME and red DISTANT arms
-	1933-34	**SIGNAL, No. 1 DOUBLE ARM**; square **lighter blue base, lighter blue flat top, red levers**; HOME and red DISTANT arms
p231	1933-34	**SIGNAL, No. 1 DOUBLE ARM**; square **green base, green flat top, red levers**; HOME and red DISTANT arms
-	1934-36	**SIGNAL, No. 1 DOUBLE ARM**; **round** green base, green **pyramid top**, red levers; HOME and red DISTANT arms
p231	1936-38	**SIGNAL, No. 1 DOUBLE ARM**; round green base, green pyramid top, red levers; HOME and **yellow DISTANT** arms
p231	1938-39	**SIGNAL, No. 1 DOUBLE ARM**; round green base, **red pyramid top**, red levers; HOME and yellow DISTANT arms
-	1939	**SIGNAL, No. 1 DOUBLE ARM**; round green base, red pyramid top, **black levers**; HOME and yellow DISTANT arms (PU)
p231	1939-41	**SIGNAL, No. 1 DOUBLE ARM**; round green base, **black pyramid top**, black levers; HOME and yellow DISTANT arms

-	1928	**SIGNAL, No. 2 DOUBLE ARM**; grey-blue base and ladder, grey-blue finial, grey-blue levers; HOME and red DISTANT (notched home) arms
-	1928-29	**SIGNAL, No. 2 DOUBLE ARM**; grey-blue base and ladder, grey-blue finial, grey-blue levers; HOME and red DISTANT **(printed chevron)** arms
-	1929-33	**SIGNAL, No. 2 DOUBLE ARM**; **blue** base and ladder, **blue** finial, **blue** levers; HOME and red DISTANT (printed chevron) arms
-	1933-34	**SIGNAL, No. 2 DOUBLE ARM**; **lighter blue base and ladder, lighter blue finial, red levers**; HOME and red DISTANT arms
p230	1933-34	**SIGNAL, No. 2 DOUBLE ARM**; **green base and ladder, green finial, red levers**; HOME and red DISTANT arms
p230	1934-36	**SIGNAL, No. 2 DOUBLE ARM**; lighter blue base and ladder, lighter blue **flat top**, red levers; HOME and red DISTANT arms
-	1934-36	**SIGNAL, No. 2 DOUBLE ARM**; green base and ladder, green **flat top**, red levers; HOME and red DISTANT arms
-	1936-38	**SIGNAL, No. 2 DOUBLE ARM**; lighter blue base and ladder, lighter blue flat top, red levers; HOME and **yellow DISTANT** arms
-	1936-38	**SIGNAL, No. 2 DOUBLE ARM**; green base and ladder, green flat top, red levers; HOME and **yellow DISTANT** arms
p230	1938-39	**SIGNAL, No. 2 DOUBLE ARM**; green base and ladder, **red flat top**, red levers; HOME and yellow DISTANT arms
-	1939	**SIGNAL, No. 2 DOUBLE ARM**; green base, **black ladder**, red flat top, **black levers**; HOME and yellow DISTANT arms (PU)
p67	1939-41	**SIGNAL, No. 2 DOUBLE ARM**; green base, black ladder, **black flat top**, black levers; HOME and yellow DISTANT arms

p230	1932-33	**SIGNAL, No. 2E DOUBLE ARM**; blue base and ladder, blue finial, blue levers; HOME and red DISTANT arms
-	1933-36	**SIGNAL, No. 2E DOUBLE ARM**; **lighter blue base and ladder, lighter blue finial, red levers**; HOME and red DISTANT arms
-	1933-36	**SIGNAL, No. 2E DOUBLE ARM**; **green base and ladder, green finial, red levers**; HOME and red DISTANT arms
p230	1936-38	**SIGNAL, No. 2E DOUBLE ARM**; lighter blue base and ladder, lighter blue finial, red levers; HOME and **yellow DISTANT** arms
p230	1936-38	**SIGNAL, No. 2E DOUBLE ARM**; green base and ladder, green finial, red levers; HOME and **yellow DISTANT** arms
-	1938-39	**SIGNAL, No. 2E DOUBLE ARM**; green base and ladder, **red finial**, red levers; HOME and yellow DISTANT arms
-	1939	**SIGNAL, No. 2E DOUBLE ARM**; green base, **black ladder,** red finial, **black levers**; HOME and yellow DISTANT arms (PU)
p230	1939-41	**SIGNAL, No. 2E DOUBLE ARM**; green base, black ladder, **black finial**, black levers; HOME and yellow DISTANT arms

p52	1934-38	**SIGNAL, No. 1 JUNCTION**; green bridge, round green base, green pyramid tops, red levers; HOME
-	1938-39	**SIGNAL, No. 1 JUNCTION**; green bridge, round green base, **red pyramid tops**, red levers; HOME
-	1939	**SIGNAL, No. 1 JUNCTION**; **white bridge**, round green base, red pyramid tops, **black levers**; HOME (PU)
p66	1939-41	**SIGNAL, No. 1 JUNCTION**; white bridge, round green base, **black pyramid tops**, black levers; HOME

-	1934-36	**SIGNAL, No. 1 JUNCTION**; green bridge, round green base, green pyramid tops, red levers; red **DISTANT** arms
-	1936-38	**SIGNAL, No. 1 JUNCTION**; green bridge, round green base, green pyramid tops, red levers; **yellow** DISTANT arms
-	1938-39	**SIGNAL, No. 1 JUNCTION**; green bridge, round green base, **red pyramid tops**, red levers; yellow DISTANT arms
-	1939	**SIGNAL, No. 1 JUNCTION**; **white bridge**, round green base, red pyramid tops, **black levers**; yellow DISTANT arms (PU)
-	1939-41	**SIGNAL, No. 1 JUNCTION**; white bridge, round green base, **black pyramid tops**, black levers; yellow DISTANT arms

-	1924-27	**SIGNAL, No. 2 JUNCTION**; black base and ladder, black finials, black levers; HOME
-	1927-29	**SIGNAL, No. 2 JUNCTION; grey-blue base and ladder, grey-blue finials, grey-blue levers;** HOME
p229	1929-33	**SIGNAL, No. 2 JUNCTION; blue base and ladder, blue finials, blue levers;** HOME
-	1933-34	**SIGNAL, No. 2 JUNCTION; lighter blue base and ladder, lighter blue finials, red levers;** HOME
-	1933-34	**SIGNAL, No. 2 JUNCTION; green base and ladder, green finials, red levers;** HOME
p57	1934-38	**SIGNAL, No. 2 JUNCTION;** lighter blue base and ladder, lighter blue **flat tops**, red levers; HOME
-	1934-38	**SIGNAL, No. 2 JUNCTION;** green base and ladder, green **flat tops**, red levers; HOME
p64	1938-39	**SIGNAL, No. 2 JUNCTION;** green base and ladder, **red flat tops**, red levers; HOME
-	1939	**SIGNAL, No. 2 JUNCTION;** green base, **black ladder,** red flat tops, **black levers;** HOME (PU)
p229	1939-41	**SIGNAL, No. 2 JUNCTION;** green base, black ladder, **black flat tops**, black levers; HOME
p229	1924-27	**SIGNAL, No. 2 JUNCTION**; black base and ladder, black finials, black levers; red DISTANT arms (notched home)
-	1927-28	**SIGNAL, No. 2 JUNCTION; grey-blue base and ladder, grey-blue finials, grey-blue levers;** red DISTANT arms (notched home)
-	1928-29	**SIGNAL, No. 2 JUNCTION;** grey-blue base and ladder, grey-blue finials, grey-blue levers; red DISTANT arms **(printed chevron)**
p45	1929-33	**SIGNAL, No. 2 JUNCTION; blue base and ladder, blue finials, blue levers;** red DISTANT arms (printed chevron)
p229	1933-34	**SIGNAL, No. 2 JUNCTION; lighter blue base and ladder, lighter blue finials, red levers;** red DISTANT arms
-	1933-34	**SIGNAL, No. 2 JUNCTION; green base and ladder, green finials, red levers;** red DISTANT arms
p229	1934-36	**SIGNAL, No. 2 JUNCTION;** lighter blue base and ladder, lighter blue **flat tops**, red levers; red DISTANT arms
-	1934-36	**SIGNAL, No. 2 JUNCTION;** green base and ladder, green **flat tops**, red levers; red DISTANT arms
-	1936-38	**SIGNAL, No. 2 JUNCTION;** lighter blue base and ladder, lighter blue flat tops, red levers; **yellow** DISTANT arms
-	1936-38	**SIGNAL, No. 2 JUNCTION;** green base and ladder, green flat tops, red levers; **yellow** DISTANT arms
p229	1938-39	**SIGNAL, No. 2 JUNCTION;** green base and ladder, **red flat tops**, red levers; yellow DISTANT arms
-	1939	**SIGNAL, No. 2 JUNCTION;** green base, **black ladder,** red flat tops, **black levers;** yellow DISTANT arms (PU)
-	1939-41	**SIGNAL, No. 2 JUNCTION;** green base, black ladder, **black flat tops**, black levers; yellow DISTANT arms
-	1932-33	**SIGNAL, No. 2E JUNCTION; blue base and ladder, blue finials, blue levers;** HOME
-	1933-38	**SIGNAL, No. 2E JUNCTION; lighter blue base and ladder, lighter blue finials, red levers;** HOME
-	1933-38	**SIGNAL, No. 2E JUNCTION; green base and ladder, green finials, red levers;** HOME
-	1938-39	**SIGNAL, No. 2E JUNCTION;** green base and ladder, **red finials,** red levers; HOME
p277	1939	**SIGNAL, No. 2E JUNCTION;** green base, **black ladder,** red finials, **black levers;** HOME
-	1939-41	**SIGNAL, No. 2E JUNCTION;** green base, black ladder, **black finials,** black levers; HOME
-	1932-33	**SIGNAL, No. 2E JUNCTION; blue base and ladder, blue finials, blue levers;** red DISTANT arms
-	1933-36	**SIGNAL, No. 2E JUNCTION; lighter blue base and ladder, lighter blue finials, red levers;** red DISTANT arms
p229	1933-36	**SIGNAL, No. 2E JUNCTION; green base and ladder, green finials, red levers;** red DISTANT arms
-	1936-38	**SIGNAL, No. 2E JUNCTION;** lighter blue base and ladder, lighter blue finials, red levers; **yellow** DISTANT arms
-	1936-38	**SIGNAL, No. 2E JUNCTION;** green base and ladder, green finials, red levers; **yellow** DISTANT arms
-	1938-39	**SIGNAL, No. 2E JUNCTION;** green base and ladder, **red finials,** red levers; yellow DISTANT arms
-	1939	**SIGNAL, No. 2E JUNCTION;** green base, **black ladder,** red finials, **black levers;** yellow DISTANT arms (PU)
-	1939-41	**SIGNAL, No. 2E JUNCTION;** green base, black ladder, **black finials,** black levers; yellow DISTANT arms

p23	1924-25	**SIGNAL FOR FOOTBRIDGE**; black lever, black finial, **tall** white post with black base; **DISTANT** (notched Home)
p199	1925-27	**SIGNAL FOR FOOTBRIDGE**; black lever, black finial, tall white post with black base; **HOME**
p155	1927-29	**SIGNAL FOR FOOTBRIDGE**; **grey-blue lever, grey-blue finial**, tall white post with **grey-blue** base; HOME
-	1929-33	**SIGNAL FOR FOOTBRIDGE**; **blue lever, blue finial**, tall white post with **blue** base; HOME
-	1933-34	**SIGNAL FOR FOOTBRIDGE**; **red lever, lighter blue finial**, tall **cream post** with **lighter blue** base; HOME
-	1933-34	**SIGNAL FOR FOOTBRIDGE**; **red lever, green finial**, tall **cream post** with **green** base; HOME
p49	1933-34	**SIGNAL FOR FOOTBRIDGE**; **red lever, red finial**, tall **cream post** with **red** base; HOME
		(For tinprinted and No. 1-type versions see Footbridge No. 1A)

p23	1924-27	**SIGNAL FOR FOOTBRIDGE**; black lever, black finial, **short** white post with black base; red **DISTANT** arm (notched Home)
-	1927-28	**SIGNAL FOR FOOTBRIDGE**; **grey-blue lever, grey-blue finial**, short white post with **grey-blue** base; red DISTANT arm (notched Home)
p155	1928-29	**SIGNAL FOR FOOTBRIDGE**; grey-blue lever, grey-blue finial, short white post with grey-blue base; red DISTANT arm **(printed chevron)**
-	1929-33	**SIGNAL FOR FOOTBRIDGE**; **blue lever, blue finial**, short white post with **blue** base; red DISTANT arm (printed chevron)
-	1933-34	**SIGNAL FOR FOOTBRIDGE**; **red lever, lighter blue finial**, short **cream post** with **lighter blue** base; red DISTANT arm
-	1933-34	**SIGNAL FOR FOOTBRIDGE**; **red lever, green finial**, short **cream post** with **green** base; red DISTANT arm
p49	1933-34	**SIGNAL FOR FOOTBRIDGE**; **red lever, red finial**, short **cream post** with **red** base; red DISTANT arm

p65	1933-38	**STANDS FOR TREES, DIECAST**; green
p69	1938-41	**STANDS FOR TREES, DIECAST; brown**

Station Staff.... see DINKY TOYS

p233	1927-28	**STATION No. 1**; red brick building; grey platform; 1st/2nd class booking office
p233	1928-29	**STATION No. 1**; red brick building; grey platform; **1st/3rd class booking office**
	1929-30	**STATION No. 1**; red brick building; **yellow-cream platform**; on reverse, car by entrance has 2 side windows
p233	1930-32	**STATION No. 1**; red brick building; yellow-cream platform; on reverse, car by entrance has **3 side windows**
-	1932-33	**STATION No. 1**; red brick building; yellow-cream platform; on reverse, car by entrance has **1 side window**
p49	1933-34	**STATION No. 1**; red brick building; **green platform**; pale blue/grey roof
p233	1934-37	**STATION No. 1**; red brick building; green platform; **blue roof**
p234	1937	**STATION No. 1**; red brick building; **tinprinted speckled platform**; blue roof

p19	1923-24	**STATION No. 2**; "**WINDSOR**"; red brick building; grey platform; 1st/2nd class booking office; non-opening doors
p23	1924-27	**STATION No. 2**; "**WINDSOR**"; red brick building; grey platform; 1st/2nd class booking office; **hinged doors**
-	1927-29	**STATION No. 2**; "**WINDSOR**"; red brick building; grey platform; **1st/3rd class booking office**
-	1929-30	**STATION No. 2**; "**WINDSOR**"; red brick building; **yellow-cream platform**; on reverse, car by entrance has 2 side windows
-	1930-32	**STATION No. 2**; "**WINDSOR**"; red brick building; yellow-cream platform; on reverse, car by entrance has **3 side windows**
-	1932-33	**STATION No. 2**; "**WINDSOR**"; red brick building; yellow-cream platform; on reverse, car by entrance has **1 side window** (PU)
p49	1933-34	**STATION No. 2**; "**WINDSOR**"; red brick building; **green platform**; pale blue/grey roof
p232	1934-36	**STATION No. 2**; "**WINDSOR**"; red brick building; green platform; **blue roof**
-	1936-37	**STATION No. 2**; "**WEMBLEY**"; red brick building; green platform; blue roof
-	1937	**STATION No. 2**; "**WEMBLEY**"; red brick building; green platform; **green roof** (PU)
-	1937	**STATION No. 2**; "**WEMBLEY**"; red brick building; **tinprinted speckled platform**; blue roof (PU)
-	1937	**STATION No. 2**; "**WEMBLEY**"; red brick building; tinprinted speckled platform; **green roof** (PU)
-	1936-37	**STATION No. 2**; "**RIPON**"; red brick building; **green platform**; **blue roof**

-	1937	**STATION No. 2**; "RIPON"; red brick building; green platform; **green roof** (PU)
-	1937	**STATION No. 2**; "RIPON"; red brick building; **tinprinted speckled platform**; **blue roof** (PU)
-	1937	**STATION No. 2**; "RIPON"; red brick building; tinprinted speckled platform; **green roof** (PU)
-	1936-37	**STATION No. 2**; **"BRISTOL"**; red brick building; **green platform**; **blue roof**
-	1937	**STATION No. 2**; **"READING"**; red brick building; green platform; **green roof** (PU)
-	1937	**STATION No. 2**; "READING"; red brick building; **tinprinted speckled platform**; **blue roof**
-	1937	**STATION No. 2**; "READING"; red brick building; tinprinted speckled platform; **green roof** (PU)
-	1936-37	**STATION No. 2**; **"MARGATE"**; red brick building; **green platform**; **blue roof**
-	1937	**STATION No. 2**; "MARGATE"; red brick building; green platform; **green roof** (PU)
-	1937	**STATION No. 2**; "MARGATE"; red brick building; **tinprinted speckled platform**; **blue roof** (PU)
-	1937	**STATION No. 2**; "MARGATE"; red brick building; tinprinted speckled platform; **green roof**
-	1932	**STATION No. 2E**; "WINDSOR"; red brick building; yellow-cream platform; on reverse, car by entrance has **3 side windows**
-	1932-33	**STATION No. 2E**; "WINDSOR"; red brick building; yellow-cream platform; on reverse, car by entrance has **1 side window** (PU)
-	1933-34	**STATION No. 2E**; "WINDSOR"; red brick building; **green platform**; pale blue/grey roof
-	1934-36	**STATION No. 2E**; "WINDSOR"; red brick building; green platform; **blue roof**
-	1936-37	**STATION No. 2E**; **"WEMBLEY"**; red brick building; green platform; blue roof
-	1937	**STATION No. 2E**; "WEMBLEY"; red brick building; green platform; **green roof** (PU)
-	1937	**STATION No. 2E**; "WEMBLEY"; red brick building; **tinprinted speckled platform**; **blue roof** (PU)
-	1937	**STATION No. 2E**; "WEMBLEY"; red brick building; tinprinted speckled platform; **green roof** (PU)
-	1936-37	**STATION No. 2E**; **"RIPON"**; red brick building; **green platform**; **blue roof**
p62	1937	**STATION No. 2E**; "RIPON"; red brick building; green platform; **green roof**
-	1937	**STATION No. 2E**; "RIPON"; red brick building; **tinprinted speckled platform**; **blue roof** (PU)
-	1937	**STATION No. 2E**; "RIPON"; red brick building; tinprinted speckled platform; **green roof** (PU)
p59	1936-37	**STATION No. 2E**; **"BRISTOL"**; red brick building; **green platform**; **blue roof**
-	1937	**STATION No. 2E**; **"READING"**; red brick building; green platform; **green roof** (PU)
-	1937	**STATION No. 2E**; "READING"; red brick building; **tinprinted speckled platform**; **blue roof** (PU)
-	1937	**STATION No. 2E**; "READING"; red brick building; tinprinted speckled platform; **green roof**
p60	1936-37	**STATION No. 2E**; **"MARGATE"**; red brick building; **green platform**; **blue roof**
-	1937	**STATION No. 2E**; "MARGATE"; red brick building; green platform; **green roof** (PU)
-	1937	**STATION No. 2E**; "MARGATE"; red brick building; **tinprinted speckled platform**; **blue roof** (PU)
-	1937	**STATION No. 2E**; "MARGATE"; red brick building; tinprinted speckled platform; **green roof** (PU)
p233	1937-39	**STATION No. 3**; buff building; tinprinted speckled platform; round-top arch over booking hall
p233	1939-41	**STATION No. 3**; buff building; tinprinted speckled platform; **square**-top arch over booking hall
-	1937-39	**STATION No. 4**; "WEMBLEY"; buff building; tinprinted speckled platform; round-top arch over booking hall
-	1939-41	**STATION No. 4**; "WEMBLEY"; buff building; tinprinted speckled platform; **square**-top arch over booking hall
p65	1937-39	**STATION No. 4**; **"RIPON"**; buff building; tinprinted speckled platform; round-top arch over booking hall
-	1939-41	**STATION No. 4**; "RIPON"; buff building; tinprinted speckled platform; **square**-top arch over booking hall
-	1937-39	**STATION No. 4**; **"READING"**; buff building; tinprinted speckled platform; round-top arch over booking hall
-	1939-41	**STATION No. 4**; "READING"; buff building; tinprinted speckled platform; **square**-top arch over booking hall
-	1937-39	**STATION No. 4**; **"MARGATE"**; buff building; tinprinted speckled platform; round-top arch over booking hall
-	1939-41	**STATION No. 4**; "MARGATE"; buff building; tinprinted speckled platform; **square**-top arch over booking hall

-	1937-39	**STATION No. 4E**; "**WEMBLEY**"; buff building; tinprinted speckled platform; round-top arch over booking hall
p66	1939-41	**STATION No. 4E**; "**WEMBLEY**"; buff building; tinprinted speckled platform; **square**-top arch over booking hall
-	1937-39	**STATION No. 4E**; "**RIPON**"; buff building; tinprinted speckled platform; round-top arch over booking hall
-	1939-41	**STATION No. 4E**; "**RIPON**"; buff building; tinprinted speckled platform; **square**-top arch over booking hall
p63	1937-39	**STATION No. 4E**; "**READING**"; buff building; tinprinted speckled platform; round-top arch over booking hall
p69	1939-41	**STATION No. 4E**; "**READING**"; buff building; tinprinted speckled platform; **square**-top arch over booking hall
p64	1937-39	**STATION No. 4E**; "**MARGATE**"; buff building; tinprinted speckled platform; round-top arch over booking hall
-	1939-41	**STATION No. 4E**; "**MARGATE**"; buff building; tinprinted speckled platform; **square**-top arch over booking hall
p45	1931-33	**STATION OR FIELD HOARDING**; blue
p53	1933-41	**STATION OR FIELD HOARDING**; **lighter blue**
-	1928-41	**TARPAULIN SHEETS**; LMS
-	1928-41	**TARPAULIN SHEETS**; NE
-	1928-41	**TARPAULIN SHEETS**; GW
-	1928-41	**TARPAULIN SHEETS**; SR
p234	1923	**TELEGRAPH POLE**; black cast base, grey post, 3 tin crossbars at 5/8" spacing
p234	1923	**TELEGRAPH POLE**; black **tinplate base**, grey post, 3 tin crossbars at 5/8" spacing
p234	1923-24	**TELEGRAPH POLE**; black tinplate base, grey post, 3 tin crossbars at **7/8" spacing**
p234	1924-27	**TELEGRAPH POLE**; black tinplate base, grey post, **2 tin crossbars** at 7/8" spacing
p234	1927-28	**TELEGRAPH POLE**; **grey-blue** tinplate base, **white post**, 2 tin crossbars at 7/8" spacing
p32	1928-29	**TELEGRAPH POLE**; grey-blue tinplate base, **grey-blue post**, **2 cast crossbars** at 7/8" spacing
p234	1929-33	**TELEGRAPH POLE**; **blue** tinplate base, **blue post**, 2 cast crossbars at 7/8" spacing
p234	1933-39	**TELEGRAPH POLE**; **lighter blue** base, **lighter blue** post, 2 cast crossbars at 7/8" spacing
p64	1938	**TELEGRAPH POLE**; **green** base, **green** post, 2 cast crossbars at 7/8" spacing

Train and Hotel Staff.... see DINKY TOYS

-	1932-35	**TRAIN NAME BOARDS**; No. 1, The Flying Scotsman; **tinprinted blue and gold**
-	1932-35	**TRAIN NAME BOARDS**; No. 2, The Scarborough Flier; tinprinted blue and gold
-	1932-35	**TRAIN NAME BOARDS**; No. 3, The Royal Scot; tinprinted blue and gold
p235	1932-35	**TRAIN NAME BOARDS**; No. 4, The Merseyside Express; tinprinted blue and gold
p235	1932-35	**TRAIN NAME BOARDS**; No. 5, The Golden Arrow; tinprinted blue and gold
p235	1932-35	**TRAIN NAME BOARDS**; No. 6, Bournemouth Belle; tinprinted blue and gold
p235	1932-35	**TRAIN NAME BOARDS**; No. 7, Cornish Riviera Express; tinprinted blue and gold
p235	1932-35	**TRAIN NAME BOARDS**; No. 8, Torbay Limited Express; tinprinted blue and gold
-	1932-35	**TRAIN NAME BOARDS**; No. 9, King's Cross, York and Edinburgh; tinprinted blue and gold
p235	1932-35	**TRAIN NAME BOARDS**; No. 10, King's Cross, Edinburgh & Aberdeen; tinprinted blue and gold
p235	1932-35	**TRAIN NAME BOARDS**; No. 11, London (Euston) & Liverpool (Lime Street); tinprinted blue and gold
p235	1932-35	**TRAIN NAME BOARDS**; No. 12, London (Euston) & Glasgow (Central); tinprinted blue and gold
p235	1932-35	**TRAIN NAME BOARDS**; No. 13, Victoria and Dover; tinprinted blue and gold
p235	1932-35	**TRAIN NAME BOARDS**; No. 14, Waterloo, Salisbury & Exeter; tinprinted blue and gold

| p235 | 1932-35 | **TRAIN NAME BOARDS**; No. 15, Paddington, Exeter & Plymouth; tinprinted blue and gold |
| p235 | 1932-35 | **TRAIN NAME BOARDS**; No. 16, Paddington & Bristol; tinprinted blue and gold |

p235	1935-38	**TRAIN NAME BOARDS**; No. 1, The Flying Scotsman; **blue fibreboard, gold letters**
-	1935-38	**TRAIN NAME BOARDS**; No. 2, The Scarborough Flier; blue fibreboard, gold letters
p235	1935-38	**TRAIN NAME BOARDS**; No. 3, The Royal Scot; blue fibreboard, gold letters
-	1935-38	**TRAIN NAME BOARDS**; No. 4, The Merseyside Express; blue fibreboard, gold letters
-	1935-38	**TRAIN NAME BOARDS**; No. 5, The Golden Arrow; blue fibreboard, gold letters (PU)
-	1935-38	**TRAIN NAME BOARDS**; No. 6, Bournemouth Belle; blue fibreboard, gold letters (PU)
-	1935-38	**TRAIN NAME BOARDS**; No. 7, Cornish Riviera Express; blue fibreboard, gold letters
-	1935-38	**TRAIN NAME BOARDS**; No. 8, Torbay Limited Express; blue fibreboard, gold letters (PU)
p235	1935-38	**TRAIN NAME BOARDS**; No. 9, King's Cross, York and Edinburgh; blue fibreboard, gold letters
-	1935-38	**TRAIN NAME BOARDS**; No. 10, King's Cross, Edinburgh & Aberdeen; blue fibreboard, gold letters (PU)
-	1935-38	**TRAIN NAME BOARDS**; No. 11, London (Euston) & Liverpool (Lime Street); blue fibreboard, gold letters (PU)
-	1935-38	**TRAIN NAME BOARDS**; No. 12, London (Euston) & Glasgow (Central); blue fibreboard, gold letters (PU)
-	1935-38	**TRAIN NAME BOARDS**; No. 13, Victoria and Dover; blue fibreboard, gold letters (PU)
-	1935-38	**TRAIN NAME BOARDS**; No. 14, Waterloo, Salisbury & Exeter; blue fibreboard, gold letters (PU)
-	1935-38	**TRAIN NAME BOARDS**; No. 15, Paddington, Exeter & Plymouth; blue fibreboard, gold letters
-	1935-38	**TRAIN NAME BOARDS**; No. 16, Paddington & Bristol; blue fibreboard, gold letters

p235	1938-41	**TRAIN NAME BOARDS**; No. 1, The Flying Scotsman; **tinprinted black on white**
p235	1938-41	**TRAIN NAME BOARDS**; No. 2, The Scarborough Flyer; tinprinted black on white
p235	1938-41	**TRAIN NAME BOARDS**; No. 3, The Royal Scot; tinprinted black on white
p235	1938-41	**TRAIN NAME BOARDS**; No. 4, The Merseyside Express - London (Euston) and Liverpool (Lime Street); tinprinted black on white
p235	1938-41	**TRAIN NAME BOARDS**; No. 5, The Golden Arrow; tinprinted black on white
p235	1938-41	**TRAIN NAME BOARDS**; No. 6, The Bournemouth Belle; tinprinted black on white
p235	1938-41	**TRAIN NAME BOARDS**; No. 7, Cornish Riviera Limited; tinprinted black on white
p235	1938-41	**TRAIN NAME BOARDS**; No. 8, Torbay Express; tinprinted black on white
p235	1938-41	**TRAIN NAME BOARDS**; No. 9, The Yorkshireman - London (St Pancras) and Bradford (Exchange); tinprinted black on white
-	1938-41	**TRAIN NAME BOARDS**; No. 10, King's Cross, Edinburgh & Aberdeen; tinprinted black on white (PU)
-	1938-41	**TRAIN NAME BOARDS**; No. 11, London (Euston) & Liverpool (Lime Street); tinprinted black on white (PU)
p235	1938-41	**TRAIN NAME BOARDS**; No. 12, The Mancunian - London (Euston) and Manchester (London Road); tinprinted black on white
-	1938-41	**TRAIN NAME BOARDS**; No. 13, The Queen of Scots; tinprinted black on white
-	1938-41	**TRAIN NAME BOARDS**; No. 14, Waterloo, Salisbury & Exeter; tinprinted black on white (PU)
p235	1938-41	**TRAIN NAME BOARDS**; No. 15, The Yorkshire Pullman; tinprinted black on white
p235	1938-41	**TRAIN NAME BOARDS**; No. 16, The Bristolian; tinprinted black on white
p235	1938-41	**TRAIN NAME BOARDS**; No. 17, Cheltenham Spa Express; tinprinted black on white
p235	1938-41	**TRAIN NAME BOARDS**; No. 18, London, Folkestone, Dover, Deal; tinprinted black on white
p235	1938-41	**TRAIN NAME BOARDS**; No. 19, Ocean Liner Express; tinprinted black on white

-	1933-36	**OAK TREES**
-	1936-41	**OAK TREES WITH STANDS**
-	1933-36	**POPLAR TREES**
-	1936-41	**POPLAR TREES WITH STANDS**
-	1933-41	**TREES (ASSORTED) WITH STANDS**
p23	1924-31	**TUNNEL**; tinprinted as moorland; tinprinted ends
p237	1931-32	**TUNNEL; enamelled centre section**; tinprinted ends
p237	1932-36	**TUNNEL; tinprinted, with hikers**; tinprinted ends
p237	1936-37	**TUNNEL**; tinprinted, with hikers; **enamelled ends**
p237	1930-41	**TUNNEL ENDS**
p211	1932-40	**TUNNEL No. O**
p211	1932-40	**TUNNEL No. 1**
p211	1932-41	**TUNNEL No. 2**
p211	1932-41	**TUNNEL No. 3**, curved
p211	1932-41	**TUNNEL No. 4**, curved
-	1932-36	**TUNNEL No. 5**, left hand, curved
p48	1932-36	**TUNNEL No. 6**, right hand, curved
p105	1927-30	**TURNTABLE No. 1; green**, red lining; rails aluminium finished
-	1930-33	**TURNTABLE No. 1; blue**, red lining; rails aluminium finished
-	1933-41	**TURNTABLE No. 1; lighter blue**, red lining; rails aluminium finished
p237	1933-41	**TURNTABLE No. 1; lighter green**, red lining; rails aluminium finished
p247	1933-41	**TURNTABLE No. 1; red, green** lining; rails aluminium finished
-	1923-25	**TURNTABLE No. 2; olive green**, red lining, large "Meccano Ltd" transfer; rails tinplate
p27	1925-27	**TURNTABLE No. 2**; olive green, red lining; **"Hornby Series" transfer; rails aluminium finished**
p32	1927-30	**TURNTABLE No. 2; green**, red lining; rails aluminium finished
-	1930-33	**TURNTABLE No. 2; blue**, red lining; rails aluminium finished
-	1933-41	**TURNTABLE No. 2; lighter blue**, red lining; rails aluminium finished
-	1933-41	**TURNTABLE No. 2; green**, red lining; rails aluminium finished
-	1933-41	**TURNTABLE No. 2; red, green** lining; rails aluminium finished
p143	1930-33	**TURNTABLE No. 2E; blue**, red lining; rails tinplate
p215	1933-41	**TURNTABLE No. 2E; lighter blue**, red lining; rails tinplate
-	1933-41	**TURNTABLE No. 2E; green**, red lining; rails tinplate
p61	1933-41	**TURNTABLE No. 2E; red, green** lining; rails tinplate
p23	1924-27	**VIADUCT**; dark green-grey sides
-	1927-33	**VIADUCT; green sides**
p238	1933-41	**VIADUCT; lighter green sides**
-	1925-27	**VIADUCT, CENTRE SECTION**; dark green-grey sides

| - | 1927-33 | **VIADUCT, CENTRE SECTION; green sides** |
| - | 1933-41 | **VIADUCT, CENTRE SECTION; lighter green sides** |

-	1925-27	**VIADUCT, ELECTRICAL**; dark green-grey sides
-	1927-33	**VIADUCT, ELECTRICAL; green sides**
p238	1933-41	**VIADUCT, ELECTRICAL; lighter green sides**
-	1925-27	**VIADUCT, CENTRE SECTION, ELECTRICAL**; dark green-grey sides
-	1927-33	**VIADUCT, CENTRE SECTION, ELECTRICAL; green sides**
-	1933-41	**VIADUCT, CENTRE SECTION, ELECTRICAL; lighter green sides**

p52	1934-39	**WATER TANK No. 1**; red tank, green base, yellow column, yellow ladder
-	1939	**WATER TANK No. 1**; red tank, green base, yellow column, **black ladder**
p69	1939-41	**WATER TANK No. 1**; red tank, green base, **buff column**, black ladder

-	1924	**WATER TANK No. 2**; red, yellow and black (PU)
p24	1924-27	**WATER TANK No. 2; olive green base** and column, red tank with grey-blue inside; hose drain grey-blue inside
p34	1927-30	**WATER TANK No. 2; green base** and column, red tank with grey-blue inside; hose drain grey-blue inside
p143	1930-31	**WATER TANK No. 2; blue base** and column, red tank with grey-blue inside; hose drain **green** inside
-	1931-33	**WATER TANK No. 2**; blue base and column, **yellow tank** with **red inside**; hose drain **all blue**
	1933-34	**WATER TANK No. 2; light green base** and column, yellow tank with red inside; hose drain **all light green**
p61	1934-39	**WATER TANK No. 2**; light green base and column, yellow tank with red inside; **no hose drain**

p47	1932-33	**WATER TANK No. 2E**; blue base, hose drain and column, yellow tank with red inside
-	1933-34	**WATER TANK No. 2E; light green base, hose drain and column**, yellow tank with red inside
p239	1934-39	**WATER TANK No. 2E**; light green base and column, yellow tank with red inside; **no hose drain**

p207	1926-29	**CONTROL SYSTEM OUTFIT No. 1**; 6-Lever Frame, 1' Radius Points LH and RH, Home and Distant Signals, 2 Rodding Compensators, No. 1 Control Rail, 20 Guide Brackets, 36 Nuts and Bolts, 3 Couplings, Wire Cutters
-	1926-29	**CONTROL SYSTEM OUTFIT No. 2**; 6-Lever Frame, 2' Radius Points LH and RH, Home and Distant Signals, 2 Rodding Compensators, No. 2 Control Rail, 20 Guide Brackets, 36 Nuts and Bolts, 3 Couplings, Wire Cutters
-	1931-39	**CONTROL ASSORTMENT No. 1**; 2-Lever Frame, 2 Points, 2 Rodding Compensators, 1 Coil of Wire, 12 Guide Brackets, Wire Cutters, 36 Nuts and Bolts, 3 Couplings
-	1931-39	**CONTROL ASSORTMENT No. 2**; 4-Lever Frame, 2 Points, 2 Rodding Compensators, 1 Coil of Wire, 24 Guide Brackets, Wire Cutters, 50 Nuts and Bolts, 4 Couplings, 2 Signals, Rodding Traverse
-	1931-39	**CONTROL ASSORTMENT No. 3**; 6-Lever Frame, 2 Points, 2 Rodding Compensators, 1 Coil of Wire, 24 Guide Brackets, Wire Cutters, 50 Nuts and Bolts, 4 Couplings, 2 Signals, Rodding Traverse, Junction Signal (Assortments with electric points were also available, to special order)
-	1926-27	**CONTROL BRAKE AND REVERSE RAIL** (PU)
p205	1926-29	**CONTROL RAIL No. 2**
p207	1927-29	**CONTROL RAIL No. 1**
p206	1926-39	**CONTROL COUPLING**
p206	1926-27	**CONTROL GUIDE BRACKETS**, 5 hole
p206	1927-39	**CONTROL GUIDE BRACKETS**, **10 hole**
-	1931-39	**CONTROL LEVER ASSEMBLY**
p207	1926-27	**CONTROL 6-LEVER FRAME**, black base
-	1927-29	**CONTROL 6-LEVER FRAME**, **grey-blue base**
-	1929-39	**CONTROL 6-LEVER FRAME**, **blue base**
-	1931-39	**CONTROL 4-LEVER FRAME**, blue base
p209	1931-39	**CONTROL 2-LEVER FRAME**, blue base
p207	1926-39	**CONTROL CLOCKWORK POINTS, 1' RADIUS**; LH and RH
-	1926-39	**CONTROL CLOCKWORK POINTS, 2' RADIUS**; LH and RH (Control Points with Reversed Switch may also have been made to special order)
-	SO	**CONTROL CLOCKWORK POINTS ON SOLID BASE, 2' RADIUS** (no lamps); LH and RH (PU) (Clockwork Points on Solid Base with Ground Disc and Lamp were fitted for both manual and Control operation; they are listed under Clockwork Rails)
-	SO	**CONTROL CLOCKWORK DOUBLE SYMMETRICAL POINTS, 1' RADIUS**; LH and RH (PU)
-	SO	**CONTROL CLOCKWORK DOUBLE SYMMETRICAL POINTS, 2' RADIUS**; LH and RH (PU)
-	SO	**CONTROL CLOCKWORK PARALLEL POINTS**; LH and RH (PU)
-	SO	**CONTROL CLOCKWORK CROSSOVERS**; LH and RH (PU)
p299	SO	**CONTROL ELECTRIC POINTS, 1' RADIUS**; LH and RH
p299	SO	**CONTROL ELECTRIC POINTS, 2' RADIUS**; LH and RH
p299	SO	**CONTROL ELECTRIC POINTS, 2' RADIUS REVERSED SWITCH**; LH and RH
p299	SO	**CONTROL ELECTRIC POINTS ON SOLID BASE, 2' RADIUS** (no lamps); LH and RH
-	SO	**CONTROL ELECTRIC POINTS ON SOLID BASE with GROUND DISC and LAMP, 2' RADIUS**; LH and RH
-	SO	**CONTROL ELECTRIC DOUBLE SYMMETRICAL POINTS, 1' RADIUS**; LH and RH (PU)
-	SO	**CONTROL ELECTRIC DOUBLE SYMMETRICAL POINTS, 2' RADIUS**; LH and RH (PU)
p299	SO	**CONTROL ELECTRIC PARALLEL POINTS**; LH and RH

p299	SO	CONTROL ELECTRIC CROSSOVERS; LH and RH
-	1926-27	CONTROL RODDING COMPENSATOR; black
p207	1927-29	**CONTROL RODDING COMPENSATOR; grey-blue**
-	1929-39	**CONTROL RODDING COMPENSATOR; blue**
-	1931-39	**CONTROL RODDING TRAVERSE**; blue
p206	1933?	**CONTROL RODDING TRAVERSE; lighter blue**
-	1926-27	CONTROL SIGNAL; black base, black lever, black finial; **HOME**
p207	1927-29	**CONTROL SIGNAL; grey-blue base, grey-blue lever, grey-blue finial**; HOME
-	1929-33	**CONTROL SIGNAL; blue base, blue lever, blue finial**; HOME
-	1933-34	CONTROL SIGNAL; blue base, **red lever,** blue finial; HOME (PU)
-	1934-39	CONTROL SIGNAL; blue base, red lever, blue **flat top**; HOME
-	1926-27	CONTROL SIGNAL; black base, black lever, black finial; red-arm **DISTANT** (notched Home)
p207	1927-28	**CONTROL SIGNAL; grey-blue base, grey-blue lever, grey-blue finial**; red-arm DISTANT (notched Home)
-	1928-29	CONTROL SIGNAL; grey-blue base, grey-blue lever, grey-blue finial; red-arm DISTANT **(printed chevron)**
-	1929-33	**CONTROL SIGNAL; blue base, blue lever, blue finial**; red-arm DISTANT (printed chevron)
-	1933-34	CONTROL SIGNAL; blue base, **red lever,** blue finial; red-arm DISTANT (PU)
-	1934-36	CONTROL SIGNAL; blue base, red lever, blue **flat top**; red-arm DISTANT (PU)
-	1936-39	CONTROL SIGNAL; blue base, red lever, blue flat top; **yellow-arm DISTANT** (PU)
-	SO	CONTROL ELECTRIC SIGNAL; blue base, blue lever, blue finial; **HOME** (PU)
-	SO	CONTROL ELECTRIC SIGNAL; blue base, **red lever,** blue finial; HOME
-	SO	CONTROL ELECTRIC SIGNAL; blue base, blue lever, blue finial; red-arm **DISTANT** (PU)
-	SO	CONTROL ELECTRIC SIGNAL; blue base, **red lever,** blue finial; red-arm DISTANT
p209	SO	CONTROL ELECTRIC SIGNAL; blue base, red lever, blue finial; **yellow-arm DISTANT**
p205	1926-27	CONTROL JUNCTION SIGNAL; black base, black lever, black finial; **HOME**
-	1927-29	CONTROL JUNCTION SIGNAL; **grey-blue base, grey-blue lever, grey-blue finial**; HOME
-	1929-33	**CONTROL JUNCTION SIGNAL; blue base, blue lever, blue finial**; HOME
-	1933-34	**CONTROL JUNCTION SIGNAL**; blue base, **red lever,** blue finial; HOME (PU)
-	1934-39	**CONTROL JUNCTION SIGNAL**; blue base, red lever, **blue flat top**; HOME
-	1926-27	CONTROL JUNCTION SIGNAL; black base, black lever, black finial; red-arm **DISTANT** (notched Home)
-	1927-28	CONTROL JUNCTION SIGNAL; **grey-blue base, grey-blue lever, grey-blue finial**; red-arm DISTANT (notched Home)
-	1928-29	CONTROL JUNCTION SIGNAL; grey-blue base, grey-blue lever, grey-blue finial; red-arm DISTANT **(printed chevron)** (PU)
-	1929-33	**CONTROL JUNCTION SIGNAL; blue base, blue lever, blue finial**; red-arm DISTANT (printed chevron) (PU)
-	1933-34	CONTROL JUNCTION SIGNAL; blue base, **red lever,** blue finial; red-arm DISTANT (PU)
-	1934-36	CONTROL JUNCTION SIGNAL; blue base, red lever, blue **flat top**; red-arm DISTANT
-	1936-39	CONTROL JUNCTION SIGNAL; blue base, red lever, blue flat top; **yellow-arm DISTANT** (PU)
-	SO	CONTROL ELECTRIC JUNCTION SIGNAL; blue base, blue lever, blue finial; **HOME** (PU)
-	SO	CONTROL ELECTRIC JUNCTION SIGNAL; blue base, **red lever,** blue finial; HOME
-	SO	CONTROL ELECTRIC JUNCTION SIGNAL; blue base, blue lever, blue finial; red-arm **DISTANT** (PU)
-	SO	CONTROL ELECTRIC JUNCTION SIGNAL; blue base, **red lever,** blue finial; red-arm DISTANT (PU)
-	SO	CONTROL ELECTRIC JUNCTION SIGNAL; blue base, red lever, blue finial; **yellow-arm DISTANT** (PU)
-	SO	CONTROL DOUBLE ARM SIGNAL; blue base, blue lever, blue finial; HOME/red-arm DISTANT (PU)
-	SO	CONTROL DOUBLE ARM SIGNAL; blue base, **red lever,** blue finial; HOME/red-arm DISTANT (PU)
-	SO	CONTROL DOUBLE ARM SIGNAL; blue base, red lever, **blue flat top**; HOME/red-arm DISTANT (PU)
p230	SO	CONTROL DOUBLE ARM SIGNAL; blue base, red lever, blue flat top; HOME/**yellow-arm DISTANT**

-	SO	**CONTROL ELECTRIC DOUBLE ARM SIGNAL**; blue base, blue lever, blue finial; HOME/red-arm DISTANT (PU)
-	SO	**CONTROL ELECTRIC DOUBLE ARM SIGNAL**; blue base, **red lever,** blue finial; HOME/red-arm DISTANT (PU)
-	SO	**CONTROL ELECTRIC DOUBLE ARM SIGNAL**; blue base, red lever, blue finial; HOME/**yellow-arm DISTANT** (PU)
-	SO	**CONTROL SLEEPER AND BELLCRANK**
p207	1926-39	**CONTROL WIRE**
p207	1926-39	**CONTROL WIRE CUTTERS**

PREWAR ELECTRICAL SUNDRIES

-	1926-29	**ACCUMULATOR,** 4 volt 8 ampere
-	1926-29	**ACCUMULATOR,** 4 volt 20 ampere
-	1930-35	**ACCUMULATOR,** 2 volt 20 ampere
-	1929-35	**ACCUMULATOR,** 6 volt 20 ampere
-	1933-41	**184a BULBS,** 2.5 volt
p245	1933-41	**184b BULBS,** 3.5 volt
-	1933-41	**184c BULBS,** 6 volt
-	1933-41	**184d BULBS,** 10 volt
p245	1933-41	**184e BULBS,** 20 volt
-	1936-38	**CIRCUIT BREAKER, 6 volt or 20 volt**
-	1938-41	**CIRCUIT BREAKER, 6 volt**
p244	1938-41	**CIRCUIT BREAKER, 20 volt**
p245	1935-41	**CONNECTING WIRE for electric accessories**
p245	1932-36	**DISTRIBUTION BOX**
p245	1935-41	**EARTHING or BONDING CLIP**
-	1932-37	**FLEXIBLE LEADS, 9"**
-	1932-37	**FLEXIBLE LEADS, 18"**
p245	1932-37	**FLEXIBLE LEADS, 36"**
p245	1934-41	**FUSE WIRE, 41 swg tinned copper**
p245	1934-41	**FUSE WIRE, 32 swg lead**
p245	1935-41	**FUSE WIRE, 24 swg lead**
p245	1938-41	**LIGHTING ACCESSORY for Buffer Stops**
p245	1935-40	**PLUGS**
p245		(a plug incorporating a fusewire holder was also included with certain Transformers)
p243	1925-26	**HV RHEOSTAT,** grey case, uncovered contacts
p243	1927-29	**HV RHEOSTAT, red case, covered contacts**
p244	1926-29	**RESISTANCE CONTROLLER, 4 VOLT;** maroon body, white lettering
p244	1929-33	**RESISTANCE CONTROLLER, 6 VOLT;** maroon body, gold lettering
p244	1933-41	**RESISTANCE CONTROLLER, 6 VOLT; red body,** gold lettering
		(Some 6V Resistance Controllers with blue bodies also appeared)
-	1933-34	**RESISTANCE CONTROLLER, 20 VOLT;** blue body, "OFF-MAX" lettering
-	1934-36	**RESISTANCE CONTROLLER, 20 VOLT;** blue body, **"OFF-FAST-SLOW"** lettering; lever on lh side
p244	1936-41	**RESISTANCE CONTROLLER, 20 VOLT;** blue body, "OFF-FAST-SLOW" lettering; **lever on rh side**

p245	1935-40	**SOCKETS**
-	1929-33	**SPEED AND REVERSE CONTROL SWITCH, 6 volt**; maroon body
-	1933	**SPEED AND REVERSE CONTROL SWITCH, 6 volt; blue body**
p125	1933-39	**SPEED AND REVERSE CONTROL SWITCH, 6 volt; red body**
-	1925-29	**TERMINAL CONNECTING PLATE, HIGH VOLTAGE**; black fibre base, no provision for fusewire
-	1926-27	**TERMINAL CONNECTING PLATE, LOW VOLTAGE**; red fibre base, with provision for fusewire
-	1927-29	**TERMINAL CONNECTING PLATE, LOW VOLTAGE; black fibre** base, with provision for fusewire
p244	1929-41	**TERMINAL CONNECTING PLATE, 6 VOLT**; black fibre base
-	1932-41	**TERMINAL CONNECTING PLATE, 20 VOLT**; black fibre base; plug connections; fusewire holder
p241	1937-41	**TERMINALS TSR for Solid Steel Rails**
-	1927-29	**FERRANTI TRANSFORMER, 4 volt**
-	1929-30	**FERRANTI TRANSFORMER, for 6 volt** trains, 3-piece case
p243	1930-33	**FERRANTI TRANSFORMER, for 6 volt** trains, **2-piece case**
p243	1931-41	**TRANSFORMER T6**, green case; label green on brass
p243	1933-41	**TRANSFORMER T6A**, green case; label green on brass
p243	1933-41	**TRANSFORMER T6M**, red case; label red on brass
-	1935-41	**TRANSFORMER T26M**, green case; label green on brass
-	1932-33	**TRANSFORMER T20, blue case**, blue scroll label
-	1933-34	**TRANSFORMER T20, lighter blue case, rectangular label** blue on brass (PU)
-	1934-36	**TRANSFORMER T20**, lighter blue case, **label green on brass**
p243	1936-41	**TRANSFORMER T20**, lighter blue case, **label green on aluminium**
-	?	**TRANSFORMER T20**, lighter blue case, **label red on aluminium** (PU)
p243	1932-33	**TRANSFORMER T20A**, blue case, blue scroll label
-	1933-34	**TRANSFORMER T20A, lighter blue case, rectangular label** blue on brass
-	1934-36	**TRANSFORMER T20A**, lighter blue case, **label green on brass**
-	1936-41	**TRANSFORMER T20A**, lighter blue case, **label green on aluminium**
-	?	**TRANSFORMER T20A**, lighter blue case, **label red on aluminium**
p243	1933-41	**TRANSFORMER T20M**, red case; label red on brass
p243	1935-41	**TRANSFORMER T22M**, blue case; label green on aluminium
-	ca1937?	**TRANSFORMER T22M**, blue case; label **dark red on aluminium**
p125	1934-41	**TRANSFORMER-RECTIFIER TR6**, red case; label red on aluminium

p298		**RAIL GAUGE**; (supplied in early electric sets)
p298	1930-41	**COMBINED RAIL GAUGE, SCREWDRIVER and SPANNER**
-	1932-36	**DIECAST SPOKED WHEELS**; (No. 2 Special Tender wheel size)
-	1936-41	**DIECAST SPOKED WHEELS**; **(smaller size)**
p240	1933-41	**GRAPHITE GREASE**
p241	1936-39	**"A" KEY**, for MO, Silver Jubilee and Streamline Locos (shown 2nd row, 4th from left)
p241	1920-21	**KEY**; no rail gauge; for No. 1 and Tinprinted Trains (shown top row, 1st from left)
p241	1921-28	**KEY, with rail gauge**; round shaft; for No. 1 etc (shown top row, 2nd from left)
p241	1928-30	**KEY**, with rail gauge; **square shaft**; for No. 1 etc (shown top row, 3rd from left)
p241	1930-36	**KEY, with concave rail gauge to clear centre rail**; square shaft press fitted to head; for No. 1 etc (shown top row, 4th from left)
p241	1936-39	**"L" KEY**, for M1, M3 Tank, No. O and No. 1 Locos; formed from folded sheet (shown top right)
p241	1921-29	**KEY**, larger size for **No. 2** and No. 3 Locos (shown 2nd row, 2nd from left)
-	1929-36	**KEY**, for **No. 1 Special** Locos
-	1936-39	**"H" KEY**, for No. 1 Special Locos
-	1929-36	**KEY**, for **No. 2 Special**, No. 3 and Metro Locos
p241		Meccano Motor Keys were supplied with certain of these Locos (shown 2nd row, 1st on left)
p241	1936-39	**"J" KEY**, for No. 2 Special, No. 3 and Metro Locos (shown 2nd row, 3rd from left)
-	1929-41	**DETACHABLE HEAD LAMP**, black with white bull
-	1938-41	**DETACHABLE HEAD LAMP**, red with white bull, for Princess Elizabeth Locomotive; not sold separately
-	1935-41	**DETACHABLE REAR LAMP**, black with light red bull (GW rear lamp)
-	1935-37	**DETACHABLE REAR LAMP**, aluminium with dark red bull (LMS rear lamp)
-	1937-41	**DETACHABLE REAR LAMP**, aluminium with **light red** bull (LMS rear lamp)
-	1935-41	**DETACHABLE REAR LAMP**, red with dark red bull (LNER, GW, SR rear lamp)
-	1935-41	**DETACHABLE ROUTE INDICATOR DISC** for "Eton" Locomotive; not sold separately
-	1920-24	**HORNBY No. 1 TRAIN PARTS**: HT1, Clockwork
-	1920-24	**HORNBY No. 1 TRAIN PARTS**: HT2, Milled Nuts for Brake Rod
-	1920-24	**HORNBY No. 1 TRAIN PARTS**: HT3, Loco Frame With Wheel Guards (with couplings, from 1921)
-	1920-24	**HORNBY No. 1 TRAIN PARTS**: HT4, Cylinder Frame
-	1920-24	**HORNBY No. 1 TRAIN PARTS**: HT5, Boiler with Dome
-	1920-24	**HORNBY No. 1 TRAIN PARTS**: HT6, Chimney
-	1920-24	**HORNBY No. 1 TRAIN PARTS**: HT7, Boiler End
-	1920-24	**HORNBY No. 1 TRAIN PARTS**: HT8, Boiler Stay, Complete
-	1920-24	**HORNBY No. 1 TRAIN PARTS**: HT9, Screwed Rod for Boiler Stay
-	1920-24	**HORNBY No. 1 TRAIN PARTS**: HT10, Handle for Boiler Stay
-	1920-21	**HORNBY No. 1 TRAIN PARTS**: HT11, Handrail, Complete (not listed in 1921 instructions or later lists)
-	1920-24	**HORNBY No. 1 TRAIN PARTS**: HT12, Handrail
-	1920-24	**HORNBY No. 1 TRAIN PARTS**: HT13, Handrail Support with Set Screw
-	1920-24	**HORNBY No. 1 TRAIN PARTS**: HT14, Curved Washer for Handrail, set of 4
-	1920-24	**HORNBY No. 1 TRAIN PARTS**: HT15, Cab Side
-	1920-24	**HORNBY No. 1 TRAIN PARTS**: HT16, Cab Top
-	1920-24	**HORNBY No. 1 TRAIN PARTS**: HT17, Tender Frame (with couplings, from 1921)

-	1920-24	**HORNBY No. 1 TRAIN PARTS:** HT18, Tender Side
-	1920-24	**HORNBY No. 1 TRAIN PARTS:** HT19, Wagon Frame (with couplings, from 1921)
-	1920-24	**HORNBY No. 1 TRAIN PARTS:** HT20, Wagon Side, two sections
-	1920-24	**HORNBY No. 1 TRAIN PARTS:** HT21, Wheel
-	1920-24	**HORNBY No. 1 TRAIN PARTS:** HT22, Axle
-	1920-22	**HORNBY No. 1 TRAIN PARTS:** HT23, Split Pin (not listed in 1922 and 1923 lists)
-	1920-24	**HORNBY No. 1 TRAIN PARTS:** HT24, Winding Key
-	1921-24	**HORNBY No. 1 TRAIN PARTS:** HT25, Coach Frame
-	1921-24	**HORNBY No. 1 TRAIN PARTS:** HT26, Trunnion
-	1921-24	**HORNBY No. 1 TRAIN PARTS:** HT27, Coach Side, 2 sections
-	1921-24	**HORNBY No. 1 TRAIN PARTS:** HT28, Coach Top
-	1921-24	**HORNBY No. 2 TRAIN PARTS:** HT101, Clockwork
-	1921-24	**HORNBY No. 2 TRAIN PARTS:** HT102, Loco Frame with Wheel Guards
-	1921-24	**HORNBY No. 2 TRAIN PARTS:** HT103, Bogie, complete
-	1921-24	**HORNBY No. 2 TRAIN PARTS:** HT104, Boiler with Dome
-	1921-24	**HORNBY No. 2 TRAIN PARTS:** HT105, Boiler Stay, Complete
-	1921-24	**HORNBY No. 2 TRAIN PARTS:** HT106, Handrail
-	1921-24	**HORNBY No. 2 TRAIN PARTS:** HT107, Curved Washer for Handrail, set of 6
-	1921-24	**HORNBY No. 2 TRAIN PARTS:** HT108, Cab Weight
-	1921-24	**HORNBY No. 2 TRAIN PARTS:** Cab Top (given as HT15 in first list)
-	1921-24	**HORNBY No. 2 TRAIN PARTS:** Cab Side (given as HT16 in first list)
-	1921-24	**HORNBY No. 2 TRAIN PARTS:** HT109, Tender Frame
-	1921-24	**HORNBY No. 2 TRAIN PARTS:** HT110, Tender Side
		(no HT111; the Hornby Trains used Meccano Part 111A, ½" Bolt)
-	1921-24	**HORNBY No. 2 TRAIN PARTS:** HT112, Coach Frame with Cylinders
-	1921-24	**HORNBY No. 2 TRAIN PARTS:** HT113, Coach Side
-	1921-24	**HORNBY No. 2 TRAIN PARTS:** HT114, Coach End
-	1921-24	**HORNBY No. 2 TRAIN PARTS:** HT115, Coach Top
-	1921-24	**HORNBY No. 2 TRAIN PARTS:** HT116, Coach Top Support
-	1921-24	**HORNBY No. 2 TRAIN PARTS:** HT117, Screw for Coach Top
-	1921-24	**HORNBY No. 2 TRAIN PARTS:** HT118, Bogie Frame
-	1921-24	**HORNBY No. 2 TRAIN PARTS:** HT119, Bolt for Bogie
		(no HT120; the Hornby Trains used Meccano Part 120, Buffer)
-	1921-22	**HORNBY No. 2 TRAIN PARTS:** HT121, Step (not included in 1922 or 1923 lists)
-	1921-24	**HORNBY No. 2 TRAIN PARTS:** HT122, Winding Key
-	1928-35	**LUBRICATING OIL**, round bottle, blue label
p240	1935-41	**LUBRICATING OIL, flat bottle, yellow label**
-	1928-41	**MANSELL WHEELS**
-	1928	**OIL CAN, "K"-TYPE**; early small pattern
-	1928	**OIL CAN, "K" TYPE; larger pattern**; copper body, **brass spout**
p240	1928-41	**OIL CAN, "K"-TYPE**; larger pattern; copper body, **copper spout**
-	?	**OIL CAN, "K" TYPE**; larger pattern; **steel** body, copper spout
-		Some "K" oil cans carry no Meccano Ltd trademark, and may have been sold elsewhere.
p240	1928-32	**OIL CAN No. 1**; square-bodied

- 1932-41 **OIL CAN No. 1; round** body with flat base

PREWAR RAILS FOR CLOCKWORK TRAINS

Throughout this section, "unslotted" and "slotted" sleepers refer to provision for centre rail conversion.
Notes on sleepers refer to turnout end throughout the Points section. "Reversed Switch" points were also available to special order.

p297	1920	**STRAIGHT RAIL B1**; 3 early flat/sloped/flat sleepers; no locking wires
p297	1920-21	**STRAIGHT RAIL B1**; 3 early **sloping** sleepers; no locking wires
p297	1921-25	**STRAIGHT RAIL B1**; 3 early sloping sleepers **with locking wires**
-	1925-26	**STRAIGHT RAIL B1**; 3 unpainted sloping sleepers **for rail connecting plates**
-	1926-30	**STRAIGHT RAIL B1**; 3 **black** unslotted sloping sleepers for rail connecting plates
-	1930-36	**STRAIGHT RAIL B1**; 3 black **slotted** sloping sleepers for rail connecting plates
-	1936-41	**STRAIGHT RAIL B1**; 3 black **unslotted** sloping sleepers for rail connecting plates
-	1921	**STRAIGHT HALF RAIL B½**; 3 early **sloping** sleepers; no locking wires
-	1922-25	**STRAIGHT HALF RAIL B½**; 3 early sloping sleepers **with locking wires**
-	1925-26	**STRAIGHT HALF RAIL B½**; **2** unpainted sloping sleepers **for rail connecting plates**
-	1926-30	**STRAIGHT HALF RAIL B½**; 2 **black** unslotted sloping sleepers for rail connecting plates
-	1930-36	**STRAIGHT HALF RAIL B½**; 2 black **slotted** sloping sleepers for rail connecting plates
-	1936-41	**STRAIGHT HALF RAIL B½**; 2 black **unslotted** sloping sleepers for rail connecting plates
-	1921	**STRAIGHT QUARTER RAIL B¼**; 2 early **sloping** sleepers; no locking wires (PU)
-	1922-25	**STRAIGHT QUARTER RAIL B¼**; 2 early sloping sleepers **with locking wires**
-	1925-26	**STRAIGHT QUARTER RAIL B¼**; 2 unpainted sloping sleepers **for rail connecting plates**
-	1926-30	**STRAIGHT QUARTER RAIL B¼**; 2 **black** unslotted sloping sleepers for rail connecting plates
-	1930-36	**STRAIGHT QUARTER RAIL B¼**; 2 black **slotted** sloping sleepers for rail connecting plates
-	1936-41	**STRAIGHT QUARTER RAIL B¼**; 2 black **unslotted** sloping sleepers for rail connecting plates
p9	1920	**CURVED 9" RADIUS RAIL**; 3 early flat/sloped/flat sleepers; no locking wires; 4 per circle
p11	1920-21	**CURVED 9" RADIUS RAIL**; 3 early **sloping** sleepers; no locking wires; 4 per circle
-	1922-27	**CURVED 9" RADIUS RAIL A9**; 3 early sloping sleepers; no locking wires; **6 per circle**
-	1921	**CURVED 9" RADIUS HALF RAIL**; 2 early **sloping** sleepers; no locking wires (PU)
-	1921	**CURVED 9" RADIUS QUARTER RAIL**; 2 early **sloping** sleepers; no locking wires (PU)
-	1921-25	**CURVED 1' RADIUS RAIL A1**; 5 early sloping sleepers **with locking wires**; 6 per circle
-	1925-26	**CURVED 1' RADIUS RAIL A1**; 3 unpainted sloping sleepers **for rail connecting plates**; 6 per circle
-	1926-30	**CURVED 1' RADIUS RAIL A1**; 3 **black** unslotted sloping sleepers for rail connecting plates; 6 per circle
-	1930-36	**CURVED 1' RADIUS RAIL A1**; 3 black **slotted** sloping sleepers for rail connecting plates; 6 per circle
-	1936-41	**CURVED 1' RADIUS RAIL A1**; 3 black **unslotted** sloping sleepers for rail connecting plates; 6 per circle

-	1922-25	**CURVED 1' RADIUS HALF RAIL A1½**; 3 early sloping sleepers **with locking wires**
-	1925-26	**CURVED 1' RADIUS HALF RAIL A1½**; **2** unpainted sloping sleepers **for rail connecting plates**
-	1926-30	**CURVED 1' RADIUS HALF RAIL A1½**; 2 **black** unslotted sloping sleepers for rail connecting plates
-	1930-36	**CURVED 1' RADIUS HALF RAIL A1½**; 2 black **slotted** sloping sleepers for rail connecting plates
-	1936-41	**CURVED 1' RADIUS HALF RAIL A1½**; 2 black **unslotted** sloping sleepers for rail connecting plates
-	1922-25	**CURVED 1' RADIUS QUARTER RAIL A1¼**; 2 early sloping sleepers **with locking wires**
-	1925-26	**CURVED 1' RADIUS QUARTER RAIL A1¼**; 2 unpainted sloping sleepers **for rail connecting plates**
-	1926-30	**CURVED 1' RADIUS QUARTER RAIL A1¼**; 2 **black** unslotted sloping sleepers for rail connecting plates
-	1930-36	**CURVED 1' RADIUS QUARTER RAIL A1¼**; 2 black **slotted** sloping sleepers for rail connecting plates
-	1936-41	**CURVED 1' RADIUS QUARTER RAIL A1¼**; 2 black **unslotted** sloping sleepers for rail connecting plates
-	1921-25	**CURVED 2' RADIUS RAIL A2**; 5 early sloping sleepers **with locking wires**; 12 per circle
-	1925-26	**CURVED 2' RADIUS RAIL A2**; 3 unpainted sloping sleepers **for rail connecting plates**; 12 per circle
-	1926-30	**CURVED 2' RADIUS RAIL A2**; 3 **black** unslotted sloping sleepers for rail connecting plates; 12 per circle
-	1930-36	**CURVED 2' RADIUS RAIL A2**; 3 black **slotted** sloping sleepers for rail connecting plates; 12 per circle
-	1936-41	**CURVED 2' RADIUS RAIL A2**; 3 black **unslotted** sloping sleepers for rail connecting plates; 12 per circle
-	1922-25	**CURVED 2' RADIUS HALF RAIL A2½**; 3 early sloping sleepers **with locking wires**
-	1925-26	**CURVED 2' RADIUS HALF RAIL A2½**; 2 unpainted sloping sleepers **for rail connecting plates**
-	1926-30	**CURVED 2' RADIUS HALF RAIL A2½**; 2 **black** unslotted sloping sleepers for rail connecting plates
-	1930-36	**CURVED 2' RADIUS HALF RAIL A2½**; 2 black **slotted** sloping sleepers for rail connecting plates
-	1936-41	**CURVED 2' RADIUS HALF RAIL A2½**; 2 black **unslotted** sloping sleepers for rail connecting plates
-	1922-25	**CURVED 2' RADIUS QUARTER RAIL A2¼**; 2 early sloping sleepers **with locking wires**
-	1925-26	**CURVED 2' RADIUS QUARTER RAIL A2¼**; 2 unpainted sloping sleepers **for rail connecting plates**
-	1926-30	**CURVED 2' RADIUS QUARTER RAIL A2¼**; 2 **black** unslotted sloping sleepers for rail connecting plates
-	1930-36	**CURVED 2' RADIUS QUARTER RAIL A2¼**; 2 black **slotted** sloping sleepers for rail connecting plates
-	1936-41	**CURVED 2' RADIUS QUARTER RAIL A2¼**; 2 black **unslotted** sloping sleepers for rail connecting plates
p34	1928-30	**DOUBLE TRACK STRAIGHT RAIL DS1**; unpainted sleepers
p45	1930-41	**DOUBLE TRACK STRAIGHT RAIL DS1**; **black sleepers**
p32	1928-30	**DOUBLE TRACK CURVED RAIL DC2**; unpainted sleepers
-	1930-41	**DOUBLE TRACK CURVED RAIL DC2**; **black sleepers**
p247	1930-41	**MO STRAIGHT RAIL BM**; sloping MO rail sleepers
p247	1931-41	**MO STRAIGHT HALF RAIL BM½**; sloping MO rail sleepers (sold only with M Level Crossing)
p246	1930-41	**MO 9" RADIUS CURVED RAIL M9**; sloping MO rail sleepers
p297	1921	**POINTS, roughly 9" RADIUS**; LH and RH
p297	1922-27	**POINTS, 9" RADIUS PL9/PR9**; early sloping sleepers with locking wires or holes for wires; LH and RH
p246	1930-41	**MO 9" RADIUS POINTS ML9/MR9**; sloping MO rail sleepers; LH and RH

A100

p297	1921-24	POINTS, 1' RADIUS PL1/PR1; early sloping sleepers with locking wires or holes for wires; LH and RH
p22	1924-25	POINTS, 1' RADIUS PL1/PR1; early **flat sleepers** with locking wires or holes for wires; LH and RH
-	1925-26	POINTS, 1' RADIUS PL1/PR1; unpainted sloping sleepers **for rail connecting plates**; LH and RH
-	1926-30	POINTS, 1' RADIUS PL1/PR1; **black** unslotted sloping sleepers for rail connecting plates; LH and RH
-	1930-36	POINTS, 1' RADIUS PL1/PR1; black **slotted** sloping sleepers for rail connecting plates; LH and RH
-	1936-41	POINTS, 1' RADIUS PL1/PR1; black **unslotted** sloping sleepers for rail connecting plates; LH and RH
p297	1921-24	POINTS, 2' RADIUS PL2/PR2; early sloping sleepers with locking wires or holes for wires; LH and RH
-	1924-25	POINTS, 2' RADIUS PL2/PR2; early **flat sleepers** with locking wires or holes for wires; LH and RH
-	1925-26	POINTS, 2' RADIUS PL2/PR2; unpainted sloping sleepers **for rail connecting plates**; LH and RH
-	1926-30	POINTS, 2' RADIUS PL2/PR2; **black** unslotted sloping sleepers for rail connecting plates; LH and RH
p39	1930-36	POINTS, 2' RADIUS PL2/PR2; black **slotted** sloping sleepers for rail connecting plates; LH and RH
-	1936-41	POINTS, 2' RADIUS PL2/PR2; black **unslotted** sloping sleepers for rail connecting plates; LH and RH
p17	1922-24	POINTS, 1' RADIUS PARALLEL PPL1/PPR1; early sloping sleepers with locking wires or holes for wires; LH and RH
-	1924-25	POINTS, 1' RADIUS PARALLEL PPL1/PPR1; early **flat sleepers** with locking wires or holes for wires; LH and RH
-	1925-28	POINTS, 1' RADIUS PARALLEL PPL1/PPR1; unpainted sloping sleepers **for rail connecting plates**; LH and RH
-	1924-25	POINTS, 2' RADIUS PARALLEL PPL2/PPR2; early **flat sleepers** with locking wires or holes for wires; LH and RH
-	1925-26	POINTS, 2' RADIUS PARALLEL PPL2/PPR2; unpainted sloping sleepers **for rail connecting plates**; LH and RH
-	1926-30	POINTS, 2' RADIUS PARALLEL PPL2/PPR2; **black** unslotted sloping sleepers for rail connecting plates; LH and RH
p43	1930-36	POINTS, 2' RADIUS PARALLEL PPL2/PPR2; black **slotted** sloping sleepers for rail connecting plates; LH and RH
-	1936-41	POINTS, 2' RADIUS PARALLEL PPL2/PPR2; black **unslotted** sloping sleepers for rail connecting plates; LH and RH
-	1922-24	POINTS, 1' RADIUS DOUBLE SYMMETRICAL DSL1/DSR1; early sloping sleepers with locking wires or holes for wires; LH and RH
-	1924-25	POINTS, 1' RADIUS DOUBLE SYMMETRICAL DSL1/DSR1; early **flat sleepers** with locking wires or holes for wires; LH and RH
p255	1925-26	POINTS, 1' RADIUS DOUBLE SYMMETRICAL DSL1/DSR1; unpainted sloping sleepers **for rail connecting plates**; LH and RH
-	1926-30	POINTS, 1' RADIUS DOUBLE SYMMETRICAL DSL1/DSR1; **black** unslotted sloping sleepers for rail connecting plates; LH and RH
-	1930-36	POINTS, 1' RADIUS DOUBLE SYMMETRICAL DSL1/DSR1; black **slotted** sloping sleepers for rail connecting plates; LH and RH
-	1936-41	POINTS, 1' RADIUS DOUBLE SYMMETRICAL DSL1/DSR1; black **unslotted** sloping sleepers for rail connecting plates; LH and RH
-	1922-24	POINTS, 2' RADIUS DOUBLE SYMMETRICAL DSL2/DSR2; early sloping sleepers with locking wires or holes for wires; LH and RH
-	1924-25	POINTS, 2' RADIUS DOUBLE SYMMETRICAL DSL2/DSR2; early **flat sleepers** with locking wires or holes for wires; LH and RH
-	1925-26	POINTS, 2' RADIUS DOUBLE SYMMETRICAL DSL2/DSR2; unpainted sloping sleepers **for rail connecting plates**; LH and RH
-	1926-30	POINTS, 2' RADIUS DOUBLE SYMMETRICAL DSL2/DSR2; **black** unslotted sloping sleepers for rail connecting plates; LH and RH
-	1930-36	POINTS, 2' RADIUS DOUBLE SYMMETRICAL DSL2/DSR2; black **slotted** sloping sleepers for rail connecting plates; LH and RH
-	1936-41	POINTS, 2' RADIUS DOUBLE SYMMETRICAL DSL2/DSR2; black **unslotted** sloping sleepers for rail connecting plates; LH and RH
p31	1928-30	**POINTS ON SOLID BASE WITH GROUND DISC AND LAMP PSL2/PSR2**; Control and manual levers; black base; LH and RH
p209	1930-39	**POINTS ON SOLID BASE WITH GROUND DISC AND LAMP PSL2/PSR2**; Control and manual levers; **blue base**; LH and RH
p300	1935-39	**POINTS ON SOLID BASE SPSL2/SPSR2**, no ground disc or lamp; unpainted base; LH and RH
p115	1925-28	**POINTS, 1' RADIUS CROSSOVER CO1**; early wide spaced pattern; **LH only**

| p25 | 1925-28 | **POINTS, 2' RADIUS CROSSOVER CO2**; early wide-spaced pattern; **LH only** |
| p31 | 1928-41 | **POINTS, 2' RADIUS CROSSOVER COL2/COR2**; double-track spacing; **LH and RH** |

p18	1921-24	**CROSSING, 2' RADIUS ACUTE ANGLE CA2**; open pattern; early sloping sleepers with locking wires
-	1924-26	**CROSSING, 2' RADIUS ACUTE ANGLE CA2**; open pattern; early **flat sleepers** with locking wires
-	1926-28	**CROSSING, 2' RADIUS ACUTE ANGLE CA2**; unpainted **solid base**
-	1928-30	**CROSSING, 2' RADIUS ACUTE ANGLE CA2**; **black** solid base
-	1930-33	**CROSSING, 2' RADIUS ACUTE ANGLE CA2**; **blue** solid base
p50	1933-38	**CROSSING, 2' RADIUS ACUTE ANGLE CA2**; **lighter blue** solid base
-	1938-39	**CROSSING, 2' RADIUS ACUTE ANGLE CA2**; **green** solid base
-	1939-41	**CROSSING, 2' RADIUS ACUTE ANGLE CA2**; **black** solid base

-	1921-24	**CROSSING, 2' RADIUS RIGHT ANGLE CR2**; open pattern; early sloping sleepers with locking wires
-	1924-26	**CROSSING, 2' RADIUS RIGHT ANGLE CR2**; open pattern; early **flat sleepers** with locking wires
-	1926-28	**CROSSING, 2' RADIUS RIGHT ANGLE CR2**; unpainted **solid base**
-	1928-30	**CROSSING, 2' RADIUS RIGHT ANGLE CR2**; **black** solid base
-	1930-33	**CROSSING, 2' RADIUS RIGHT ANGLE CR2**; **blue** solid base
-	1933-38	**CROSSING, 2' RADIUS RIGHT ANGLE CR2**; **lighter blue** solid base
-	1938-39	**CROSSING, 2' RADIUS RIGHT ANGLE CR2**; **green** solid base
-	1939-41	**CROSSING, 2' RADIUS RIGHT ANGLE CR2**; **black** solid base

-	1926-28	**CROSSING, 1' RADIUS ACUTE ANGLE CA1**; unpainted solid base; unpainted flat sleepers for rail connecting plates
-	1928-30	**CROSSING, 1' RADIUS ACUTE ANGLE CA1**; **black** solid base; **black** flat sleepers
-	1930-33	**CROSSING, 1' RADIUS ACUTE ANGLE CA1**; **blue** solid base; black flat sleepers
-	1933-38	**CROSSING, 1' RADIUS ACUTE ANGLE CA1**; **lighter blue** solid base; black flat sleepers
-	1938-39	**CROSSING, 1' RADIUS ACUTE ANGLE CA1**; **green** solid base; black flat sleepers
-	1939-41	**CROSSING, 1' RADIUS ACUTE ANGLE CA1**; **black** solid base; black flat sleepers

-	1926-28	**CROSSING, 1' RADIUS RIGHT ANGLE CR1**; unpainted solid base; unpainted flat sleepers for rail connecting plates
-	1928-30	**CROSSING, 1' RADIUS RIGHT ANGLE CR1**; **black** solid base; **black** flat sleepers
-	1930-33	**CROSSING, 1' RADIUS RIGHT ANGLE CR1**; **blue** solid base; black flat sleepers
-	1933-38	**CROSSING, 1' RADIUS RIGHT ANGLE CR1**; **lighter blue** solid base; black flat sleepers
-	1938-39	**CROSSING, 1' RADIUS RIGHT ANGLE CR1**; **green** solid base; black flat sleepers
-	1939-41	**CROSSING, 1' RADIUS RIGHT ANGLE CR1**; **black** solid base; black flat sleepers

-	1920	**CURVED 9" RADIUS BRAKE RAIL**; 3 early flat/sloped/flat sleepers; no locking wires; 4 per circle
-	1920-21	**CURVED 9" RADIUS BRAKE RAIL**; 3 early **sloping** sleepers; no locking wires; 4 per circle
p246	1930-41	**MO 9" RADIUS CURVED BRAKE RAIL MB9**; sloping MO rail sleepers; 6 per circle

-	1921-25	**CURVED 1' RADIUS BRAKE RAIL AB1**; 5 early sloping sleepers **with locking wires**; 6 per circle
-	1925-26	**CURVED 1' RADIUS BRAKE RAIL AB1**; 3 unpainted sloping sleepers **for rail connecting plates**; 6 per circle
-	1926-30	**CURVED 1' RADIUS BRAKE RAIL AB1**; 3 **black** unslotted sloping sleepers for rail connecting plates; 6 per circle
-	1930-36	**CURVED 1' RADIUS BRAKE RAIL AB1**; 3 black **slotted** sloping sleepers for rail connecting plates; 6 per circle
-	1936-41	**CURVED 1' RADIUS BRAKE RAIL AB1**; 3 black **unslotted** sloping sleepers for rail connecting plates; 6 per circle

-	1921-25	**CURVED 2' RADIUS BRAKE RAIL AB2**; 5 early sloping sleepers **with locking wires**; 12 per circle
-	1925-26	**CURVED 2' RADIUS BRAKE RAIL AB2**; 3 unpainted sloping sleepers **for rail connecting plates**; 12 per circle
-	1926-30	**CURVED 2' RADIUS BRAKE RAIL AB2**; 3 **black** unslotted sloping sleepers for rail connecting plates; 12 per circle
-	1930-36	**CURVED 2' RADIUS BRAKE RAIL AB2**; 3 black **slotted** sloping sleepers for rail connecting plates; 12 per circle
-	1936-41	**CURVED 2' RADIUS BRAKE RAIL AB2**; 3 black **unslotted** sloping sleepers for rail connecting plates; 12 per circle

-	1924-25	**STRAIGHT BRAKE RAIL BB1**; 4 early sloping sleepers **with locking wires**
p298	1925-26	**STRAIGHT BRAKE RAIL BB1**; **3** unpainted sloping sleepers **for rail connecting plates**
-	1926-30	**STRAIGHT BRAKE RAIL BB1**; 3 **black** unslotted sloping sleepers for rail connecting plates
-	1930-36	**STRAIGHT BRAKE RAIL BB1**; 3 black **slotted** sloping sleepers for rail connecting plates
-	1936-41	**STRAIGHT BRAKE RAIL BB1**; 3 black **unslotted** sloping sleepers for rail connecting plates

-	1927-30	**STRAIGHT BRAKE AND REVERSE RAIL BBR1**; black unslotted sloping sleepers; tall point-type lever
p298	1930	**STRAIGHT BRAKE AND REVERSE RAIL BBR1**; black **slotted** sloping sleepers; tall point-type lever
-	1930-36	**STRAIGHT BRAKE AND REVERSE RAIL BBR1**; **revised horizontal-type lever**; black slotted sloping sleepers for rail connecting plates
p298	1936-41	**STRAIGHT BRAKE AND REVERSE RAIL BBR1**; revised horizontal-type lever; black **unslotted** sloping sleepers for rail connecting plates

p299	1925-26	**RAIL CONNECTING PLATES RCP**; unpainted, unembossed, large size
p299	1926?	**RAIL CONNECTING PLATES RCP**; **black, embossed**, large size
p299	1926-27	**RAIL CONNECTING PLATES RCP**; **unpainted, standard pattern**
p299	1927-41	**RAIL CONNECTING PLATES RCP**; **black**, standard pattern

| - | 1938-41 | **MO RAIL CONNECTING CLIPS MCC** |
| - | 1938-41 | **POINT CONNECTING CLIPS PCC** |

p299	1930-35	**CENTRE RAIL CONVERSION ACCESSORIES; BC1 Straight Centre Rail**
p299	1930-35	**CENTRE RAIL CONVERSION ACCESSORIES; BC½ Straight Half Centre Rail**
-	1930-35	**CENTRE RAIL CONVERSION ACCESSORIES; BC¼ Straight Quarter Centre Rail**
-	1930-35	**CENTRE RAIL CONVERSION ACCESSORIES; AC1 Curved Centre Rail, 1' Radius**
-	1930-35	**CENTRE RAIL CONVERSION ACCESSORIES; AC1½ Curved Half Centre Rail, 1' Radius**
-	1930-35	**CENTRE RAIL CONVERSION ACCESSORIES; AC1¼ Curved Quarter Centre Rail, 1'Radius**
p299	1930-35	**CENTRE RAIL CONVERSION ACCESSORIES; AC2 Curved Centre Rail, 2' Radius**
p299	1930-35	**CENTRE RAIL CONVERSION ACCESSORIES; AC2½ Curved Half Centre Rail, 2' Radius**
-	1930-35	**CENTRE RAIL CONVERSION ACCESSORIES; AC2¼ Curved Quarter Centre Rail, 2'Radius**
p299	1930-35	**CENTRE RAIL CONVERSION ACCESSORIES; CCR Clips for Centre Rails**
p299	1930-35	**CENTRE RAIL CONVERSION ACCESSORIES; ICR Insulators for Centre Rails**

(The November 1921 MM also offered conversion accessories; Straight, 1' and 2' radius centre rails, chairs, insulating bushes and washers, and 6BA nut and bolt)

-	1922-25	**ELECTRIC STRAIGHT RAIL EB1**; 4 early sloping sleepers **with locking wires**
-	1925-26	**ELECTRIC STRAIGHT RAIL EB1**; 3 unpainted **flat sleepers for rail connecting plates**
-	1926-27	**ELECTRIC STRAIGHT RAIL EB1**; 3 unpainted **sloping** sleepers for rail connecting plates
p47	1927-41	**ELECTRIC STRAIGHT RAIL EB1**; 3 **black** sloping sleepers for rail connecting plates
-	1922-25	**ELECTRIC STRAIGHT HALF RAIL EB½**; 3 early sloping sleepers **with locking wires**
-	1925-26	**ELECTRIC STRAIGHT HALF RAIL EB½**; **2** unpainted **flat sleepers for rail connecting plates**
-	1926-27	**ELECTRIC STRAIGHT HALF RAIL EB½**; 2 unpainted **sloping** sleepers for rail connecting plates
-	1927-41	**ELECTRIC STRAIGHT HALF RAIL EB½**; 2 **black** sloping sleepers for rail connecting plates
-	1922-25	**ELECTRIC STRAIGHT QUARTER RAIL EB¼**; 2 early sloping sleepers **with locking wires**
-	1925-26	**ELECTRIC STRAIGHT QUARTER RAIL EB¼**; 2 unpainted **flat sleepers for rail connecting plates**
-	1926-27	**ELECTRIC STRAIGHT QUARTER RAIL EB¼**; 2 unpainted **sloping** sleepers for rail connecting plates
-	1927-41	**ELECTRIC STRAIGHT QUARTER RAIL EB¼**; 2 **black** sloping sleepers for rail connecting plates
p298	1922-25	**ELECTRIC 2' RADIUS CURVED RAIL EA2**; 5 early sloping sleepers **with locking wires**
p298	1925	**ELECTRIC 2' RADIUS CURVED RAIL EA2**; 4 unpainted **flat sleepers for rail connecting plates**
p298	1925-26	**ELECTRIC 2' RADIUS CURVED RAIL EA2**; 3 unpainted flat sleepers for rail connecting plates
p298	1926-27	**ELECTRIC 2' RADIUS CURVED RAIL EA2**; 3 unpainted **sloping** sleepers for rail connecting plates
p298	1927-41	**ELECTRIC 2' RADIUS CURVED RAIL EA2**; 3 **black** sloping sleepers for rail connecting plates
-	1922-25	**ELECTRIC 2' RADIUS CURVED HALF RAIL EA2½**; 3 early sloping sleepers **with locking wires**
-	1925-26	**ELECTRIC 2' RADIUS CURVED HALF RAIL EA2½**; **2** unpainted **flat sleepers for rail connecting plates**
-	1926-27	**ELECTRIC 2' RADIUS CURVED HALF RAIL EA2½**; 2 unpainted **sloping** sleepers for rail connecting plates
-	1927-41	**ELECTRIC 2' RADIUS CURVED HALF RAIL EA2½**; 2 **black** sloping sleepers for rail connecting plates
-	1922-25	**ELECTRIC 2' RADIUS CURVED QUARTER RAIL EA2¼**; 2 early sloping sleepers **with locking wires**
-	1925-26	**ELECTRIC 2' RADIUS CURVED QUARTER RAIL EA2¼**; 2 unpainted **flat sleepers for rail connecting plates**
-	1926-27	**ELECTRIC 2' RADIUS CURVED QUARTER RAIL EA2¼**; 2 unpainted **sloping** sleepers for rail connecting plates
-	1927-41	**ELECTRIC 2' RADIUS CURVED QUARTER RAIL EA2¼**; 2 **black** sloping sleepers for rail connecting plates
-	1922-25	**ELECTRIC 1' RADIUS CURVED RAIL EA1**; 5 early sloping sleepers **with locking wires**
-	1925-26	**ELECTRIC 1' RADIUS CURVED RAIL EA1**; 3 unpainted **flat sleepers for rail connecting plates**
-	1926-27	**ELECTRIC 1' RADIUS CURVED RAIL EA1**; 3 unpainted **sloping** sleepers for rail connecting plates
-	1927-41	**ELECTRIC 1' RADIUS CURVED RAIL EA1**; 3 **black** sloping sleepers for rail connecting plates
-	1922-25	**ELECTRIC 1' RADIUS CURVED HALF RAIL EA1½**; 3 early sloping sleepers **with locking wires**
-	1925-26	**ELECTRIC 1' RADIUS CURVED HALF RAIL EA1½**; **2** unpainted **flat sleepers for rail connecting plates**
-	1926-27	**ELECTRIC 1' RADIUS CURVED HALF RAIL EA1½**; 2 unpainted **sloping** sleepers for rail connecting plates
-	1927-41	**ELECTRIC 1' RADIUS CURVED HALF RAIL EA1½**; 2 **black** sloping sleepers for rail connecting plates

-	1922-25	**ELECTRIC 1' RADIUS CURVED QUARTER RAIL EA1¼**; 2 early sloping sleepers **with locking wires**
-	1925-26	**ELECTRIC 1' RADIUS CURVED QUARTER RAIL EA1¼**; 2 unpainted **flat sleepers for rail connecting plates**
-	1926-27	**ELECTRIC 1' RADIUS CURVED QUARTER RAIL EA1¼**; 2 unpainted **sloping** sleepers for rail connecting plates
-	1927-41	**ELECTRIC 1' RADIUS CURVED QUARTER RAIL EA1¼**; 2 **black** sloping sleepers for rail connecting plates
-	1929-30	**ELECTRIC DOUBLE TRACK STRAIGHT RAILS EDS1**; unpainted sleepers
-	1930-41	**ELECTRIC DOUBLE TRACK STRAIGHT RAILS EDS1**; **black** sleepers
-	1929-30	**ELECTRIC DOUBLE TRACK CURVED RAILS EDC2**; unpainted sleepers
-	1930-41	**ELECTRIC DOUBLE TRACK CURVED RAILS EDC2**; black sleepers
-	1922-24	**ELECTRIC POINTS, 1' RADIUS EPL1/EPR1**; early sloping sleepers with locking wires or holes for wires; LH and RH
-	1924-25	**ELECTRIC POINTS, 1' RADIUS EPL1/EPR1**; early **flat sleepers** with locking wires or holes for wires; LH and RH
-	1934-41	**ELECTRIC POINTS, 1' RADIUS EPL1/EPR1**; **black** sloping sleepers for rail connecting plates; LH and RH
-	1922-24	**ELECTRIC POINTS, 2' RADIUS EPL2/EPR2**; early sloping sleepers with locking wires or holes for wires; LH and RH
-	1924-25	**ELECTRIC POINTS, 2' RADIUS EPL2/EPR2**; early **flat sleepers** with locking wires or holes for wires; LH and RH
-	1925-26	**ELECTRIC POINTS, 2' RADIUS EPL2/EPR2**; unpainted flat sleepers **for rail connecting plates**; LH and RH
-	1926-27	**ELECTRIC POINTS, 2' RADIUS EPL2/EPR2**; unpainted **sloping sleepers** for rail connecting plates; LH and RH
p53	1927-36	**ELECTRIC POINTS, 2' RADIUS EPL2/EPR2**; **black** sloping sleepers for rail connecting plates; LH and RH
p60	1936-39	**ELECTRIC POINTS ON SOLID BASE ESPSL2/ESPSR2** or EPL2/EPR2, no ground disc or lamp; unpainted base; LH and RH
-	1923-24	**ELECTRIC POINTS, 1' RADIUS PARALLEL EPPL/EPPR**; early sloping sleepers with locking wires or holes for wires; LH and RH
-	1925-26	**ELECTRIC POINTS, 2' RADIUS PARALLEL EPPL2/EPPR2**; unpainted flat sleepers for rail connecting plates; LH and RH
-	1926-27	**ELECTRIC POINTS, 2' RADIUS PARALLEL EPPL2/EPPR2**; unpainted **sloping** sleepers for rail connecting plates; LH and RH
p37	1927-41	**ELECTRIC POINTS, 2' RADIUS PARALLEL EPPL2/EPPR2**; **black** sloping sleepers for rail connecting plates; LH and RH
-	1922-24	**ELECTRIC POINTS, 1' RADIUS DOUBLE SYMMETRICAL EDSL1/EDSR1**; early sloping sleepers with locking wires or holes for wires; LH/RH
-	1924-25	**ELECTRIC POINTS, 1' RADIUS DOUBLE SYMMETRICAL EDSL1/EDSR1**; early **flat sleepers** with locking wires or holes for wires; LH and RH
p259	1934-41	**ELECTRIC POINTS, 1' RADIUS DOUBLE SYMMETRICAL EDSL1/EDSR1**; **black** sloping sleepers for rail connecting plates; LH and RH
-	1922-24	**ELECTRIC POINTS, 2' RADIUS DOUBLE SYMMETRICAL EDSL2/EDSR2**; early sloping sleepers with locking wires or holes for wires; LH/RH
-	1924-25	**ELECTRIC POINTS, 2' RADIUS DOUBLE SYMMETRICAL EDSL2/EDSR2**; early **flat sleepers** with locking wires or holes for wires; LH and RH
-	1925-26	**ELECTRIC POINTS, 2' RADIUS DOUBLE SYMMETRICAL EDSL2/EDSR2**; unpainted flat sleepers **for rail connecting plates**; LH and RH
-	1926-27	**ELECTRIC POINTS, 2' RADIUS DOUBLE SYMMETRICAL EDSL2/EDSR2**; unpainted **sloping sleepers** for rail connecting plates; LH and RH
p51	1927-41	**ELECTRIC POINTS, 2' RADIUS DOUBLE SYMMETRICAL EDSL2/EDSR2**; **black** sloping sleepers for rail connecting plates; LH and RH
p215	1931-41	**ELECTRIC POINTS, 2' RADIUS CROSSOVER ECOL2/ECOR2**; double-track spacing; LH and RH
-	1922-24	**ELECTRIC CROSSING, 2' RADIUS ACUTE ANGLE ECA**; open pattern; early sloping sleepers with locking wires
-	1924-26	**ELECTRIC CROSSING, 2' RADIUS ACUTE ANGLE ECA**; open pattern; early **flat sleepers** with locking wires
-	1926-28	**ELECTRIC CROSSING, 2' RADIUS ACUTE ANGLE ECA**; unpainted solid base
-	1928-30	**ELECTRIC CROSSING, 2' RADIUS ACUTE ANGLE ECA**; **black** solid base

-	1930-33	**ELECTRIC CROSSING, 2' RADIUS ACUTE ANGLE ECA; blue** solid base
-	1933-38	**ELECTRIC CROSSING, 2' RADIUS ACUTE ANGLE ECA; lighter blue** solid base
-	1938-39	**ELECTRIC CROSSING, 2' RADIUS ACUTE ANGLE ECA; green** solid base
-	1939-41	**ELECTRIC CROSSING, 2' RADIUS ACUTE ANGLE ECA; black** solid base
p131	1922-24	**ELECTRIC CROSSING, 2' RADIUS RIGHT ANGLE ECR;** open pattern; early sloping sleepers with locking wires
-	1924-26	**ELECTRIC CROSSING, 2' RADIUS RIGHT ANGLE ECR;** open pattern; early **flat sleepers** with locking wires
-	1926-28	**ELECTRIC CROSSING, 2' RADIUS RIGHT ANGLE ECR;** unpainted solid base
-	1928-30	**ELECTRIC CROSSING, 2' RADIUS RIGHT ANGLE ECR; black** solid base
-	1930-33	**ELECTRIC CROSSING, 2' RADIUS RIGHT ANGLE ECR; blue** solid base
p210	1933-38	**ELECTRIC CROSSING, 2' RADIUS RIGHT ANGLE ECR; lighter blue** solid base
-	1938-39	**ELECTRIC CROSSING, 2' RADIUS RIGHT ANGLE ECR; green** solid base
-	1939-41	**ELECTRIC CROSSING, 2' RADIUS RIGHT ANGLE ECR; black** solid base
-	1922-26	**CURVED RAIL WITH TERMINAL, 1' RADIUS, EAT1**
-	1922-26	**CURVED RAIL WITH TERMINAL, 2' RADIUS, EAT2**
-	1934-39	**SWITCH RAIL, 6 VOLT, EMC6**
-	1934-39	**SWITCH RAIL, 20 VOLT, EMC20**
-	1937-41	**SOLID STEEL STRAIGHT RAILS EB3**
-	1937-41	**SOLID STEEL STRAIGHT HALF RAILS EB3½**
-	1937-41	**SOLID STEEL STRAIGHT QUARTER RAILS EB3¼**
-	1937-41	**SOLID STEEL CURVED RAILS EA3**
-	1937-41	**SOLID STEEL CURVED HALF RAILS EA3½**
-	1937-41	**SOLID STEEL POINTS EPL3/EPR3;** LH and RH
p241	1937-41	**SOLID STEEL RAIL ADAPTING PIECES**
p241	1937-41	**SOLID STEEL RAIL FISHPLATES**

-	1947-54	**MO GOODS TRAIN SET**; red MO Loco, Tender and two green MO Wagons
-	1947-54	**MO GOODS TRAIN SET**; green MO Loco, Tender and two red MO Wagons
-	1954-66	**No. 20 GOODS TRAIN SET**; BR No. 20 Loco, Tender and two No. 20 Wagons
-	1947-54	**MO PASSENGER SET**; red MO Loco, Tender and two MO Pullman Coaches
-	1947-54	**MO PASSENGER SET**; green MO Loco, Tender and two MO Pullman Coaches
-	1954-66	**No. 21 PASSENGER SET**; BR No. 20 Loco, Tender and two No. 21 Coaches
-	1947-57	**M1 PASSENGER SET**; red M1 Loco, Tender and two M1 Pullman Coaches
p75	1947-57	**M1 PASSENGER SET**; green M1 Loco, Tender and two M1 Pullman Coaches
-	1956-65	**No. 31 PASSENGER SET**; BR No. 30 Loco, Tender, and two No. 31 Coaches (1st/2nd and Brake/2nd)
-	1947-57	**M1 GOODS SET**; red M1 Loco, Tender and two LMS M1 Wagons
-	1947-57	**M1 GOODS SET**; green M1 Loco, Tender and two LNE M1 Wagons
-	1956-65	**No. 30 GOODS SET**; BR No. 30 Loco, Tender, No. 30 Wagon and No. 30 Goods Van
-	1947-54	**201 TANK GOODS SET**; LMS red 101 Tank Loco, LMS No. 1 Wagon, Tank wagon, No. 1 Timber Wagon
-	1947-54	**201 TANK GOODS SET**; LNER green 101 Tank Loco, NE No. 1 Wagon, Tank Wagon, No. 1 Timber Wagon
p72	1947-49	**201 TANK GOODS SET**; GW green 101 Tank Loco, GW No. 1 Wagon, Tank Wagon, No. 1 Timber Wagon
-	1947-49	**201 TANK GOODS SET**; SR green 101 Tank Loco, SR No. 1 Wagon, Tank Wagon, No. 1 Timber Wagon
-	1954-58	**No. 40 TANK GOODS SET**; BR black No. 40 Tank Loco, BR No. 1 Wagon, No. 1 Tank Wagon, No. 1 Timber Wagon
-	1957-65	**No. 45 TANK GOODS SET**; BR black No. 40 Tank Loco, BR No. 50 Wagon, No. 50 Tank Wagon, No. 50 Lumber Wagon
-	1947-54	**101 TANK PASSENGER SET**; LMS red 101 Tank Loco, two LMS No. 1 Coaches and Passenger Brake Van
-	1947-54	**101 TANK PASSENGER SET**; LNER green 101 Tank Loco, two NE No. 1 Coaches and Passenger Brake Van
p72	1947-49	**101 TANK PASSENGER SET**; GW green 101 Tank Loco, two GW No. 1 Coaches and Passenger Brake Van
-	1947-49	**101 TANK PASSENGER SET**; SR green 101 Tank Loco, two SR No. 1 Coaches and Passenger Brake Van
-	1954-65	**No. 41 TANK PASSENGER SET**; BR black No. 40 Loco, two No. 41 Passenger Coaches and No. 41 Passenger Brake Van
-	1948-54	**No. 601 GOODS SET**; LMS red 501 Loco and Tender, LMS No. 1 Wagon, LMS Flat Truck, LMS Brake Van
-	1948-54	**No. 601 GOODS SET**; LNER green 501 Loco and Tender, NE No. 1 Wagon, NE Flat Truck, NE Brake Van
-	1948-49	**No. 601 GOODS SET**; GW green 501 Loco and Tender, GW No. 1 Wagon, GW Flat Truck, GW Brake Van
-	1948-49	**No. 601 GOODS SET**; SR green 501 Loco and Tender, SR No. 1 Wagon, SR Flat Truck, SR Brake Van (Set PU)
-	1954-58	**No. 50 GOODS SET**; BR black No. 50 Loco and Tender, No. 1 Wagon, Low Sided Wagon, Brake Van
-	1957-61	**No. 55 GOODS SET**; BR black No. 50 Loco and Tender, No. 50 Wagon, No. 50 Low Sided Wagon, No. 50 Brake Van
-	1948-54	**No. 501 PASSENGER SET**; LMS red 501 loco, two LMS No. 1 Coaches, and LMS Passenger Brake Van
-	1948-54	**No. 501 PASSENGER SET**; LNER red 501 loco, two LNER No. 1 Coaches, and LNER Passenger Brake Van
-	1948-49	**No. 501 PASSENGER SET**; GW green 501 loco, two GW No. 1 Coaches, and GW Passenger Brake Van
-	1948?	**No. 501 PASSENGER SET**; SR 501 loco, two SR No. 1 Coaches, and SR Passenger Brake Van (Set PU)
-	1954-61	**No. 51 PASSENGER SET**; BR green 51 Loco, two BR No. 51 Coaches, and No. 51 Passenger Brake Van

| | | POSTWAR LOCOMOTIVES |

-	1946-54	**MO LOCOMOTIVE**; **green**, tender number 2595
p80	1946-54	**MO LOCOMOTIVE**; **red**, tender number 6161
p83	1954-68	**TYPE 20 LOCOMOTIVE**; **BR** livery
p71	1946-58	**M1 LOCOMOTIVE**; **green**, tender number 3435
p79	1946-58	**M1 LOCOMOTIVE**; **red**, tender number 3435
p85	1956-65	**TYPE 30 LOCOMOTIVE**; **BR** livery
p73	1947-54	**101 LOCOMOTIVE**; **LMS** livery, number 2270
p82	1947-54	**101 LOCOMOTIVE**; **LNER** livery, number 460
p72	1947-49	**101 LOCOMOTIVE**; **GW** livery, number 6600
p77	1947-49	**101 LOCOMOTIVE**; **SR** livery, number E126
p82	1954-60	**TYPE 40 TANK LOCOMOTIVE**; "lion over wheel" BR emblem
p86	1960-65	**TYPE 40 TANK LOCOMOTIVE**; **"lion holding wheel"** BR emblem
p73	1948-49	**501 LOCOMOTIVE**; **LMS** livery, serif cabside number 5600
p76	1949-54	**501 LOCOMOTIVE**; **LMS** livery, **sans-serif cabside number 5600**
p75	1948-54	**501 LOCOMOTIVE**; **LNER** livery, cabside number 1842
p75	1948-49	**501 LOCOMOTIVE**; **GW** livery, cabside number 9319
p76	1948-49	**501 LOCOMOTIVE**; **SR** livery, cabside number 793 (PU)
p83	1954-61	**TYPE 50 LOCOMOTIVE**; BR goods livery, number 60199
p83	1954-61	**TYPE 51 LOCOMOTIVE**; BR passenger livery, number 50153

| | | POSTWAR COACHES |

p71	1946-47	**MO PULLMAN COACH, JOAN**; cream roof
p71	1946-47	**MO PULLMAN COACH, ZENA**; cream roof
p80	1947-54	**MO PULLMAN COACH, JOAN**; **grey** roof
p80	1947-54	**MO PULLMAN COACH, ZENA**; **grey** roof
p83	1954-69	**No. 21 COACH**
p71	1946-47	**M1 PULLMAN COACH, VIKING**; white roof, prewar base
-	1946-47	**M1 PULLMAN COACH, MARJORIE**; white roof, prewar base
p71	1946-47	**M1 PULLMAN COACH, AURELIA**; white roof, prewar base
p75	1947-49	**M1 PULLMAN COACH, MARJORIE**; **grey roof**, prewar base
p75	1947-49	**M1 PULLMAN COACH, AURELIA**; **grey roof**, prewar base
p79	1949-57	**M1 PULLMAN COACH, MARJORIE**; grey roof, **postwar type base**
p79	1949-57	**M1 PULLMAN COACH, AURELIA**; grey roof, **postwar type base**
p85	1956-68	**No. 31 COACH, 1st/3rd**; (later called 1st/2nd)
p85	1956-65	**No. 31 COACH, Brake/3rd**; (later called brake/2nd)

p75	1947-59	**No. 1 COACH; LMS** livery
-	1947-59	**No. 1 COACH; LNER** livery
p77	1947-49	**No. 1 COACH; GW** livery
p77	1947-49	**No. 1 COACH; SR** livery
p75	1947-57	**No. 1 PASSENGER BRAKE; LMS** livery
p81	1947-57	**No. 1 PASSENGER BRAKE; LNER** livery
p77	1947-49	**No. 1 PASSENGER BRAKE; GW** livery
p77	1947-49	**No. 1 PASSENGER BRAKE; SR** livery
p82	1954-58	**No. 41 COACH; 1st/3rd** (later called 1st/2nd)
p82	1954-58	**No. 41 PASSENGER BRAKE**
p84	1954-58	**No. 51 COACH, 1st class**
p84	1954-58	**No. 51 COACH, 3rd** (later called 2nd) class
p84	1954-58	**No. 51 PASSENGER BRAKE**
p76	1948-50	**No. 2 COACH, LMS**
p76	1948-50	**No. 2 COACH, LNER**
p77	1948-50	**No. 2 COACH, GW**
p77	1948-50	**No. 2 COACH, SR**
p76	1948-50	**No. 2 COACH, Brake/3rd LMS**
p76	1948-50	**No. 2 COACH, Brake/3rd LNER**
p77	1948-50	**No. 2 COACH, Brake/3rd GW**
p77	1948-50	**No. 2 COACH, Brake/3rd SR**

POSTWAR SUNDRIES

p241	1966-68	**AUTOMATIC COUPLINGS**
p245	1950-53	**FUSE WIRE, 32SWG LEAD**
-	1949-53	**TRANSFORMER T20**; black case, with controller
-		**GRAPHITE GREASE**
p241	1946-51	**"A" KEY**; for MO Trains; nickel plated (shown bottom left)
p241	1951-52	**"A" KEY**; for MO Trains; **blackened** (shown bottom row, 2nd from left)
p241	1952-53	**"S" KEY**; for MO Trains; blackened (shown bottom row, 3rd from left)
p241	1953-54	**"S" KEY**; for MO Trains; **nickel plated** (shown bottom row, 4th from left)
p241	1954-69	**"S" KEY**; for MO Trains; **diecast**, Hornby trademark (shown bottom row, 2nd from right)
p241		Later versions had Meccano trademark (shown bottom right)
p241	1946-51	**"H" KEY**; for M1 up Trains; nickel plated (shown 3rd row, 1st from left)
p241	1951-53	**"H" KEY**; for M1 up Trains; **blackened** (shown 3rd row, 2nd from left)
-	1953-54	**"H" KEY**; for M1/30 up Trains; **nickel plated**
p241	1954-60	**"H" KEY**; for M1/30 up Trains; **diecast**, unpainted (shown 3rd row, 2nd from right)
p241	1960-69	**"H" KEY**; mainly for Meccano Motors; diecast, **black painted** (shown 3rd row, 1st from right)

(late unpainted and black versions, such as those sold with "PERCY", had no Hornby trademark or rail gauge marking)

p75	1952-66	**HEAD LAMP for LOCOMOTIVE**; no wire handle; black with aluminium bull
-	1952-66	**TAIL LAMP for LOCOMOTIVE**; no wire handle; **aluminium with red bull**
p81	1952-66	**TAIL LAMP for LOCOMOTIVE**; no wire handle; **red with dark red bull**
p73	1952-66	**SIDE LAMP for BRAKE VAN**; black with red and aluminium bulls
p241	1952-68	**WHEELS and AXLES FOR ROLLING STOCK**
p241	c1948?	**MANSELL WHEELS** (uncatalogued)
-	c1948?	**SPOKED WHEELS** (uncatalogued)

POSTWAR RAILS

-	1947-68	**STRAIGHT RAILS, B1**
-	1948-68	**STRAIGHT HALF RAILS, B½**
-	1948-68	**STRAIGHT QUARTER RAILS, B¼**
-	1949-54	**STRAIGHT RAILS FOR MO TRAINS, BM**
-	1947-69	**CURVED RAILS 2ft RADIUS, A2**
-	1948-69	**CURVED RAILS 2ft RADIUS, A2½**
-	1947-69	**CURVED RAILS 1ft RADIUS, A1**
-	1948-69	**CURVED RAILS 1ft RADIUS, A1½**
-	1947-54	**CURVED RAILS 9 inch RADIUS, M9**
-	1948-69	**POINTS 2ft RADIUS, PL2/PR2**
-	1948-69	**POINTS 1ft RADIUS, PL1/PR1**
-	1948-69	**ACUTE ANGLE CROSSING 2ft RADIUS, CA2**
-	1948-69	**ACUTE ANGLE CROSSING 1ft RADIUS, CA1**
-	1949-69	**RIGHT ANGLE CROSSING 2ft RADIUS, CR2**
-	1949-69	**RIGHT ANGLE CROSSING 1ft RADIUS, CR1**
p300	1947-51	**BRAKE RAIL, STRAIGHT BB1**
p300	1948-51	**BRAKE AND REVERSE RAIL, STRAIGHT BBR2**; separate brake and reverse trips
p300	1951-69	**BRAKE AND REVERSE RAIL, STRAIGHT BBR**; single trip
-	1950-54	**BRAKE RAIL, STRAIGHT BBM, FOR MO TRAINS**
-	1947-50	**BRAKE RAIL, CURVED 9in RADIUS FOR MO TRAINS**
-	1947-69	**RAIL CONNECTING PLATES**
-	1947-54	**RAIL CONNECTING CLIPS FOR MO RAILS, MCC**
-	1949-69	**POINT CONNECTING CLIPS, PCC**

Throughout, "unslotted" refers to bases of the prewar style but lacking axlebox slots; slotted bases have axlebox slots.

p73	1948	**GOODS BRAKE VAN; LMS**, brown body and solebar, grey roof; unslotted prewar-type base
p78	1948-54	**GOODS BRAKE VAN; LMS**, brown body and solebar, grey roof; **postwar-type base**
p76	1948	**GOODS BRAKE VAN; NE**, bauxite body and solebar, white roof; unslotted prewar-type base
p78	1948-54	**GOODS BRAKE VAN; NE**, bauxite body and solebar, white roof; **postwar-type base**
-	1948	**GOODS BRAKE VAN; GW**, grey body, black solebar, white roof; unslotted prewar-type base (PU)
p77	1948-51	**GOODS BRAKE VAN; GW**, grey body, black solebar, white roof; **postwar-type base**
-	1948	**GOODS BRAKE VAN; SR**, dark brown body and solebar, white roof; unslotted prewar-type base (PU)
p77	1948-51	**GOODS BRAKE VAN; SR**, dark brown body and solebar, white roof; **postwar-type base**
p84	1954-57	**GOODS BRAKE VAN; BR**, brown body and solebar, grey roof; postwar-type base
p86	1957-69	**GOODS BRAKE VAN No. 50; BR**, brown tinprinted body
-	1949-50	**BREAKDOWN VAN AND CRANE; LMS**, brown body, black base, red crane, grey roof
-	1949-50	**BREAKDOWN VAN AND CRANE; unlettered** brown body, black base, unlettered red crane, grey roof
-	1948	**CATTLE TRUCK No. 1; LMS**, brown body and solebar, grey roof; unslotted prewar-type base
p78	1948-54	**CATTLE TRUCK No. 1; LMS**, brown body and solebar, grey roof; **postwar-type base**
-	1948	**CATTLE TRUCK No. 1; NE**, bauxite body and solebar, white roof; unslotted prewar-type base
p78	1948-54	**CATTLE TRUCK No. 1; NE**, bauxite body and solebar, white roof; **postwar-type base**
-	1948	**CATTLE TRUCK No. 1; GW**, grey body and solebar, white roof; unslotted prewar-type base (PU)
p77	1948-51	**CATTLE TRUCK No. 1; GW**, grey body and solebar, white roof; **postwar-type base**
-	1948	**CATTLE TRUCK No. 1; SR**, dark brown body and solebar, white roof; unslotted prewar-type base (PU)
p77	1948-51	**CATTLE TRUCK No. 1; SR**, dark brown body and solebar, white roof; **postwar-type base**
p84	1954-57	**CATTLE TRUCK No. 1; BR**, brown body and solebar, grey roof; postwar-type base
p86	1957-65	**CATTLE TRUCK No. 50; BR**, tinprinted brown body
p75	1949-50	**CATTLE TRUCK NO. 2;** unlettered bauxite body, white roof
-	1948	**CEMENT WAGON;** Portland Cement, yellow body; unslotted prewar-type base (PU)
p79	1948-57	**CEMENT WAGON;** Portland Cement, yellow body; **postwar-type base**
-	1948	**CRANE TRUCK;** black base, red jib; slotted prewar-type base
-	1948	**CRANE TRUCK;** black base, red jib; **unslotted prewar-type base**
p79	1948-57	**CRANE TRUCK;** black base, red jib; **postwar-type base**
p86	1957-69	**CRANE TRUCK No. 50;** black base, red jib
-	1948	**FLAT TRUCK; LMS**, brown; slotted prewar-type base
p73	1948	**FLAT TRUCK; LMS**, brown; **unslotted prewar-type base**
p78	1948-54	**FLAT TRUCK; LMS**, brown; **postwar-type base**
-	1948	**FLAT TRUCK; NE**, bauxite; slotted prewar-type base
-	1948	**FLAT TRUCK; NE**, bauxite; **unslotted prewar-type base**

p78	1948-54	**FLAT TRUCK**; NE, bauxite; **postwar-type base**
-	1948	**FLAT TRUCK; GW**, grey; slotted prewar-type base
-	1948	**FLAT TRUCK; GW**, grey; **unslotted prewar-type base**
-	1948-51	**FLAT TRUCK; GW**, grey; **postwar-type base**
-	1948	**FLAT TRUCK; SR**, dark brown; slotted prewar-type base
-	1948	**FLAT TRUCK; SR**, dark brown; **unslotted prewar-type base**
-	1948-51	**FLAT TRUCK; SR**, dark brown; **postwar-type base**
p84	1954-59	**FLAT TRUCK; BR**, brown; postwar-type base
-	1957-66	**FLAT TRUCK No. 50**; BR brown
-	1948	**FLAT TRUCK WITH CABLE DRUM; LMS**, brown; slotted prewar-type base
-	1948	**FLAT TRUCK WITH CABLE DRUM**; LMS, brown; **unslotted prewar-type base**
p78	1948-54	**FLAT TRUCK WITH CABLE DRUM**; LMS, brown; **postwar-type base**
p76		(above with LEC drum; also circa 1948 with "Electric Cables" drum)
-	1948	**FLAT TRUCK WITH CABLE DRUM; NE, bauxite; slotted prewar-type base**
p76	1948	**FLAT TRUCK WITH CABLE DRUM; NE**, bauxite; **unslotted prewar-type base**
p78	1948-54	**FLAT TRUCK WITH CABLE DRUM; NE**, bauxite; **postwar-type base**
-	1948	**FLAT TRUCK WITH CABLE DRUM; GW**, grey; slotted prewar-type base
-	1948	**FLAT TRUCK WITH CABLE DRUM; GW**, grey; **unslotted prewar-type base**
-	1948-51	**FLAT TRUCK WITH CABLE DRUM; GW**, grey; **postwar-type base**
-	1948	**FLAT TRUCK WITH CABLE DRUM; SR**, dark brown; slotted prewar-type base
-	1948	**FLAT TRUCK WITH CABLE DRUM; SR**, dark brown; **unslotted prewar-type base**
-	1948-51	**FLAT TRUCK WITH CABLE DRUM; SR**, dark brown; **postwar-type base**
p84	1954-59	**FLAT TRUCK WITH CABLE DRUM; BR**, brown; postwar-type base
p86	1957-69	**FLAT TRUCK No. 50 WITH CABLE DRUM**; BR, brown
-	1948	**FLAT TRUCK WITH CONTAINER; LMS**, brown; slotted prewar-type base
-	1948	**FLAT TRUCK WITH CONTAINER; LMS**, brown; **unslotted prewar-type base**
p78	1948-54	**FLAT TRUCK WITH CONTAINER; LMS**, brown; **postwar-type base**
-	1948	**FLAT TRUCK WITH CONTAINER; NE**, bauxite; slotted prewar-type base
-	1948	**FLAT TRUCK WITH CONTAINER; NE**, bauxite; **unslotted prewar-type base**
p78	1948-54	**FLAT TRUCK WITH CONTAINER; NE**, bauxite; **postwar-type base**
-	1948	**FLAT TRUCK WITH CONTAINER; GW**, grey; slotted prewar-type base
-	1948	**FLAT TRUCK WITH CONTAINER; GW**, grey; **unslotted prewar-type base**
p77	1948-51	**FLAT TRUCK WITH CONTAINER; GW**, grcy; **postwar-type base**
-	1948	**FLAT TRUCK WITH CONTAINER; SR**, dark brown; slotted prewar-type base
-	1948	**FLAT TRUCK WITH CONTAINER; SR**, dark brown; **unslotted prewar-type base**
p77	1948-51	**FLAT TRUCK WITH CONTAINER; SR**, dark brown; **postwar-type base**
p84	1954-59	**FLAT TRUCK WITH FURNITURE CONTAINER; BR**, brown; postwar-type base
p84	1955-59	**FLAT TRUCK WITH INSULATED MEAT CONTAINER; BR**, brown; postwar-type base
-	1957-69	**FLAT TRUCK No. 50 WITH FURNITURE CONTAINER**; BR, brown
p86	1957-69	**FLAT TRUCK No. 50 WITH INSULATED MEAT CONTAINER; BR, brown**
-	1948	**GAS CYLINDER WAGON**; red cylinders, black unslotted prewar-type base

p79	1948-57	GAS CYLINDER WAGON; red cylinders, black postwar-type base
p86	1957-69	**GAS CYLINDER WAGON No. 50**
p85	1956-69	**GOODS VAN No. 30**
-	1948	**GOODS VAN No. 1**; **LMS**, brown body with flat lettering panel, brown solebar, grey roof; unslotted prewar-type base
p78	1948-54	GOODS VAN No. 1; **LMS**, brown body with flat lettering panel, brown solebar, grey roof; postwar-type base
p76	1948	**GOODS VAN No. 1**; **NE**, bauxite body and solebar, white roof; unslotted prewar-type base
p78	1948-54	**GOODS VAN No. 1**; **NE**, bauxite body and solebar, white roof; **postwar-type base**
p77	1948	**GOODS VAN No. 1**; **GW**, grey body, black solebar, white roof; unslotted prewar-type base
-	1948-51	**GOODS VAN No. 1**; **GW**, grey body, white roof; **postwar-type base** (PU)
p77	1948	**GOODS VAN No. 1**; **SR**, dark brown body, black solebar, white roof; unslotted prewar-type base
-	1948-51	**GOODS VAN No. 1**; **SR**, dark brown body, white roof; **postwar-type base** (PU)
p84	1954-57	**GOODS VAN No. 1**; **BR**, brown body and solebar, grey roof; postwar-type base
p86	1957-69	**GOODS VAN No. 50**; BR, brown tinprinted body
p76	1948-50	**GOODS VAN No. 2**; **LMS**, brown body, grey roof
p76	1948-50	**GOODS VAN No. 2**; **NE**, bauxite body, white roof
-	1949-50	**HIGH CAPACITY WAGON**; **LMS** (PU)
-	1949-50	**HIGH CAPACITY WAGON**; **NE** (PU)
p77	1949-50	**HIGH CAPACITY WAGON**; **GW**
p73	1948	**HOPPER WAGON**; **LMS**, green body, black unslotted prewar-type base
p78	1948-54	**HOPPER WAGON**; **LMS**, green body, black **postwar-type base**
p84	1954-57	**HOPPER WAGON**; **BR**, grey body, black postwar-type base
p86	1957-69	**HOPPER WAGON No. 50**; BR, grey body
-	1948	**LUMBER WAGON No. 1**; red bolsters, black unslotted prewar-type base
p79	1948-57	**LUMBER WAGON No. 1**; red bolsters, black **postwar-type base**
p86	1957-69	**LUMBER WAGON No. 50**
-	1949-50	**LUMBER WAGON No. 2** (PU)
-	1948	**MILK TRAFFIC VAN**; unlettered green body (embossed planking, no lettering panel), black solebar, black unslotted prewar-type base
p77	1948	**MILK TRAFFIC VAN**; **SOUTHERN** green body (**no planking**), black solebar; black unslotted prewar-type base
-	1948	**MILK TRAFFIC VAN**; SOUTHERN green body, **green solebar**, black unslotted prewar-type base
p78	1948-54	**MILK TRAFFIC VAN**; SOUTHERN green body, green solebar, black **postwar-type base**
p84	1954-57	**MILK TRAFFIC VAN**; **BR** maroon body and solebar, black postwar-type base

-	1952	**MO CRANE TRUCK**; green base, light blue top (same blue as Dinky Goods Yard Crane base p82)
p80	1952-54	**MO CRANE TRUCK**; green base, **blue top**
p83	1954-69	**No. 20 CRANE TRUCK; lighter green base**, blue top
p80	1952-60	**MO PETROL TANK WAGON**; red base, silver tank, "BP" one side, "Shell" other
p80	1952-65	**MO ROTARY TIPPER**; red base, green top
p80	1952-66	**MO SIDE TIPPER**; green base, yellow top
p80	1946-54	**MO WAGON; green** body
p80	1946-54	**MO WAGON; red** body
p83	1954-66	**No. 20 WAGON**; BR grey body
-	1946-47	**M1 WAGON; LMS, buff** body, open axleguard long thin base (PU)
-	1947	**M1 WAGON**; LMS, **light grey** body (inside walls grey), open axleguard long thin base
-	1947-48	**M1 WAGON**; LMS, **grey** body (inside walls black), open axleguard long thin base
-	1948-49	**M1 WAGON**; LMS, **brown** body, open axleguard long thin base
p79	1949-57	**M1 WAGON**; LMS, brown body, **postwar long thin base**
-	1946-47	**M1 WAGON; LNE, buff** body, open axleguard long thin base
-	1947	**M1 WAGON**; LNE, **light grey** body (inside walls grey), open axleguard long thin base (PU)
-	1947-48	**M1 WAGON**; LNE, **brown** body, open axleguard long thin base
-	1948-49	**M1 WAGON**; LNE, **grey** body (inside walls black), open axleguard long thin base
p79	1949-57	**M1 WAGON**; LNE, grey body, **postwar long thin base**
p85	1956-68	**WAGON No. 30**; BR grey body
p73	1948	**REFRIGERATOR VAN No. 1; LMS**, buff body without flat lettering panel, grey roof; black solebar, unslotted prewar-type base
p78	1948-53	**REFRIGERATOR VAN No. 1**; LMS, buff body with **one flat lettering panel** each side, **buff solebar**, grey roof; **postwar-type base**
p82	1953-54	**REFRIGERATOR VAN No. 1**; LMS, buff body with **two flat lettering panels** each side, buff solebar, grey roof; postwar-type base
-	1948	**REFRIGERATOR VAN No. 1; NE**, white body, with flat lettering panel, white roof; black buffer beam, black solebar, unslotted prewar-type base
-	1948	**REFRIGERATOR VAN No. 1**; NE, white body, **no flat lettering panel**, white roof; black buffer beam, black solebar, unslotted prewar-type base
-	1948-54	**REFRIGERATOR VAN No. 1**; NE, white body, no flat lettering panel, white roof; black buffer beam, **postwar-type base**
p78	1948-54	**REFRIGERATOR VAN No. 1**; NE, white body, **one flat lettering panel** each side, white roof; black buffer beam, postwar-type base
p84	1954-57	**REFRIGERATOR VAN No. 1; BR**, white body with two flat lettering panels each side, grey roof, black buffer beam; black solebar, postwar-type base
p86	1957-69	**REFRIGERATOR VAN No. 50**; BR, white body, grey roof
-	1948	**ROTARY TIPPING WAGON**; Trinidad Lake Asphalt, buff body, black slotted prewar-type base
-	1948	**ROTARY TIPPING WAGON**; Trinidad Lake Asphalt, buff body, black **unslotted prewar-type base**
p79	1948-59	**ROTARY TIPPING WAGON**; Trinidad Lake Asphalt, buff body, black **postwar-type base**
p86	1957-69	**ROTARY TIPPING WAGON No. 50**; Trinidad Lake Asphalt, buff body
p86	1957-69	**SAXA SALT WAGON No. 50**

-	1948	**SIDE TIPPING WAGON**; McAlpine, buff body, black unslotted prewar-type base
p79	1948-56	**SIDE TIPPING WAGON**; McAlpine Public Works Contractors, buff body, black **postwar-type base**
p84	1956-57	**SIDE TIPPING WAGON**; McAlpine Public Works Contractors, **green** body, black postwar-type base
p86	1957-69	**SIDE TIPPING WAGON No. 50**; McAlpine **Civil Engineering Contractors**, green body

p73	1947-48	**TANK WAGON No. 1, ROYAL DAYLIGHT**; grey, slotted prewar-type base
p73	1947-48	**TANK WAGON No. 1, POOL**; grey, slotted prewar-type base
p73	1947-48	**TANK WAGON No. 1, POOL**; **darker grey**, slotted prewar-type base
-	1947-48	**TANK WAGON No. 1, POOL**; grey, **unslotted prewar-type base**
p73	1948	**TANK WAGON No. 1, SHELL**; red tank, black unslotted prewar-type base
p79	1948-50	**TANK WAGON No. 1, SHELL**; red tank, black **postwar-type base**
p79	1950-53	**TANK WAGON No. 1, ESSO**; silver tank, black postwar-type base
p79	1953-55	**TANK WAGON No. 1, NATIONAL BENZOLE**; silver tank, black postwar-type base
p84	1955-57	**TANK WAGON No. 1, SHELL LUBRICATING OIL**; yellow tank, black postwar-type base
p84	1955-57	**TANK WAGON No. 1, MANCHESTER OIL REFINERIES**; green tank, black postwar-type base
p86	1957-69	**TANK WAGON No. 50, SHELL LUBRICATING OIL**; yellow tank
p86	1957-61	**TANK WAGON No. 50, MANCHESTER OIL REFINERIES**; green tank

p72	1947-48	**TIMBER WAGON No. 1**; red stanchions, black slotted prewar-type base
-	1948	**TIMBER WAGON No. 1**; red stanchions, black **unslotted prewar-type base**
p79	1948-59	**TIMBER WAGON No. 1**; red stanchions, black **postwar-type base**

| - | 1949-50 | **TROLLEY WAGON**; grey with red stanchions |

p73	1947-48	**WAGON No. 1**; **LMS**, tinprinted large-letter buff body; with tinprinted solebars; slotted prewar-type base
-	1948	**WAGON No. 1**; LMS, tinprinted large-letter **brown** body; with tinprinted solebars; **unslotted prewar-type base**
p73	1948	**WAGON No. 1**; LMS, tinprinted large-letter brown body; **no tinprinted solebars**; unslotted prewar-type base
p79	1948-49	**WAGON No. 1**; LMS, tinprinted large-letter brown body; no tinprinted solebars; **postwar-type base**
p79	1949-54	**WAGON No. 1**; LMS, tinprinted **small-letter** brown body; postwar-type base
-	1947-48	**WAGON No. 1**; **NE**, tinprinted large-letter buff body; with tinprinted solebars; slotted prewar-type base
p76	1948	**WAGON No. 1**; NE, tinprinted large-letter **grey** body; with tinprinted solebars; **unslotted prewar-type base**
-	1948	**WAGON No. 1**; NE, tinprinted large-letter grey body; **no tinprinted solebars**; unslotted prewar-type base
p79	1948-49	**WAGON No. 1**; NE, tinprinted large-letter grey body; no tinprinted solebars; **postwar-type base**
p79	1949-54	**WAGON No. 1**; NE, tinprinted **small-letter** grey body; postwar-type base
p77	1947-48	**WAGON No. 1**; **GW**, tinprinted large-letter buff body; with tinprinted solebars; slotted prewar-type base
p77	1947-48	**WAGON No. 1**; **SR**, tinprinted large-letter dark brown body; with tinprinted solebars; slotted prewar-type base
p84	1954-58	**WAGON No. 1**; **BR**, tinprinted grey body; postwar-type base
p86	1957-68	**WAGON No. 50**; BR, tinprinted grey body

-	1948	**WAGON WITH SHEET RAIL**; **LMS**, tinprinted large-letter brown body; unslotted prewar-type base
p79	1949-54	**WAGON WITH SHEET RAIL**; LMS, tinprinted **small-letter** brown body; **postwar-type base**
p76	1948	**WAGON WITH SHEET RAIL**; **NE**, tinprinted large-letter grey body; unslotted prewar-type base
p79	1949-54	**WAGON WITH SHEET RAIL**; NE, tinprinted **small-letter** grey body; **postwar-type base**
p84	1954-58	**WAGON WITH SHEET RAIL**; **BR**, tinprinted grey body; postwar-type base

p77   1948-50   **BUFFER STOP No. 1**; grey body, grey rails; bracket for lighting accessory; pierced base
p85   1950-66   **BUFFER STOP No. 1**; grey body, grey rails; **no bracket** for lighting accessory; **solid base**

p241   1956-69   **CABLE DRUM No. 1**; LEC
-      1956-62   **INSULATED MEAT CONTAINER No. 1**
-      1956-69   **FURNITURE CONTAINER No. 1**

p81   1952-56   **DINKY TOYS No. 1, STATION STAFF; Porter**, dark blue
p81   1952-56   **DINKY TOYS No. 1, STATION STAFF; Porter with Luggage**, dark blue
p81   1952-56   **DINKY TOYS No. 1, STATION STAFF; Guard**, dark blue
p81   1952-56   **DINKY TOYS No. 1, STATION STAFF; Ticket Collector**, dark blue
p81   1952-56   **DINKY TOYS No. 1, STATION STAFF; Engine Driver**, blue
p80   1952-56   **DINKY TOYS No. 2, FARMYARD ANIMALS; Cow**, light brown
p80   1952-56   **DINKY TOYS No. 2, FARMYARD ANIMALS; Cow**, brown
p80   1952-56   **DINKY TOYS No. 2, FARMYARD ANIMALS; Sheep**, cream
p80   1952-56   **DINKY TOYS No. 2, FARMYARD ANIMALS; Pig**
p80   1952-56   **DINKY TOYS No. 2, FARMYARD ANIMALS; Horse**, brown
p80   1952-56   **DINKY TOYS No. 2, FARMYARD ANIMALS; Horse**, light yellow-cream
p81   1952-56   **DINKY TOYS No. 3, PASSENGERS; Hiker (Woman)**, light blue
p81   1952-56   **DINKY TOYS No. 3, PASSENGERS; Business Man**, brown
p81   1952-56   **DINKY TOYS No. 3, PASSENGERS; Mother and Child**, green
p81   1952-56   **DINKY TOYS No. 3, PASSENGERS; Hiker (Man)**, brown
p81   1952-56   **DINKY TOYS No. 3, PASSENGERS; Newsboy**
p81   1952-56   **DINKY TOYS No. 3, PASSENGERS; Woman**
p81   1952-56   **DINKY TOYS No. 4, ENGINEERING STAFF; Fitter**, brown
p81   1952-56   **DINKY TOYS No. 4, ENGINEERING STAFF; Fitter**, blue
p81   1952-56   **DINKY TOYS No. 4, ENGINEERING STAFF; Greaser**, brown
p81   1952-56   **DINKY TOYS No. 4, ENGINEERING STAFF; Engine Room Attendant**, blue
p81   1952-56   **DINKY TOYS No. 4, ENGINEERING STAFF; Storekeeper**, brown
p81   1952-56   **DINKY TOYS No. 5, TRAIN & HOTEL STAFF; Dining Car Conductor**
p81   1952-56   **DINKY TOYS No. 5, TRAIN & HOTEL STAFF; Dining Car Attendant**
p81   1952-56   **DINKY TOYS No. 5, TRAIN & HOTEL STAFF; Hotel Porter**; dark blue, brown and dark green cases
p81   1952-56   **DINKY TOYS No. 5, TRAIN & HOTEL STAFF; Hotel Porter**; dark blue, brown and green cases
p80   1952-56   **DINKY TOYS No. 6, SHEPHERD SET; Sheep**, cream
p80   1952-56   **DINKY TOYS No. 6, SHEPHERD SET; Shepherd**, light brown
p80   1952-56   **DINKY TOYS No. 6, SHEPHERD SET; Sheepdog**, black

p76	1949-52	**FOOTBRIDGE No. 1**; grey enamel, green lining; latticed sides
p81	1952-54	**FOOTBRIDGE No. 1**; **cream enamel**, green lining; **solid sides**
p82	1954-57	**FOOTBRIDGE No. 1**; **buff tinprinted** solid sides
-	1948	**GOODS PLATFORM No. 1**; tinprinted "speckled" platform, identical to prewar printings (PU)
p82	1949-55	**GOODS PLATFORM No. 1**; tinprinted buff platform, **postwar printing** with **green roof**
p85	1955-57	**GOODS PLATFORM No. 1**; tinprinted buff platform, **later printing** with **red roof**, lettered "GOODS DEPOT" over doors
p82	1953-60	**GOODS YARD CRANE, DINKY TOY No. 752**
-	1949-52	**ISLAND PLATFORM; WEMBLEY**, lattice posts
-	1949-52	**ISLAND PLATFORM; RIPON**, lattice posts (PU)
p77	1949-52	**ISLAND PLATFORM; READING**, lattice posts
-	1949-52	**ISLAND PLATFORM; MARGATE**, lattice posts (PU)
p81	1952-54	**ISLAND PLATFORM; WEMBLEY**, **shorter non-lattice** posts
p81	1952-54	**ISLAND PLATFORM; RIPON**, **shorter non-lattice** posts
-	1952-54	**ISLAND PLATFORM; READING**, **shorter non-lattice** posts
p77	1952-54	**ISLAND PLATFORM; MARGATE**, **shorter non-lattice** posts
-	1952-54	**ISLAND PLATFORM; BRISTOL**, **shorter non-lattice** posts
p82	1954-55	**ISLAND PLATFORM; TRENT**, white posts, green roof
p84	1955-57	**ISLAND PLATFORM; TRENT**, **orange** posts, **orange** roof
p71	1949-69	**LEVEL CROSSING**
p71	1948?	**M LEVEL CROSSING**; green posts
p71	1946	**M STATION SET**; including M Signals (2) and M Telegraph Poles (2) with **plain white posts**; M Station, M Wayside Station and M Signal Box
p241	1954-69	**MILK CAN**
p85	1949-69	**PLATFORM CRANE**; buff base, red centre, grey crane
p224	1949-69	**POSTERS, SET 1**; small, BIRD'S Custard, "Something to sing about"
p224	1949-69	**POSTERS, SET 1**; small, CADBURY'S Bourn-vita
p224	1949-69	**POSTERS, SET 1**; small, CAPSTAN, "Have a Capstan"
p224	1949-69	**POSTERS, SET 1**; small, LIFEBUOY Soap "For health"
p224	1949-69	**POSTERS, SET 1**; small, RALEIGH, "Reg rides a Raleigh"
p224	1949-69	**POSTERS, SET 1**; small, SPRATTS "Builds up a dog"
p224	1949-69	**POSTERS, SET 1**; large, BEV
p224	1949-69	**POSTERS, SET 1**; large, BRYLCREAM "..your hair and be set for the day"
p224	1949-69	**POSTERS, SET 1**; large, CASTROL, "Give me Castrol every time"
p224	1949-69	**POSTERS, SET 1**; large, HARTLEY'S, "The greatest name in jam making"
p224	1949-69	**POSTERS, SET 1**; large, HP SAUCE, "Improves all meals"
p224	1949-69	**POSTERS, SET 1**; large, SMITHS KLG
p224	1949-69	**POSTERS, SET 2**; small, BRYLCREAM "..your hair for perfect control"
p224	1949-69	**POSTERS, SET 2**; small, CASTROL, "The masterpiece in oils"
p224	1949-69	**POSTERS, SET 2**; small, HARTLEY'S, "The greatest name in jam making"
p224	1949-69	**POSTERS, SET 2**; small, HP SAUCE, "Improves all meals"

p224	1949-69	**POSTERS**, SET 2; small, LYONS' Tea, "Always the best - on sale here"
p224	1949-69	**POSTERS**, SET 2; small, SMITHS KLG
p224	1949-69	**POSTERS**, SET 2; large, BIRD'S CUSTARD, "Something to sing about"
p224	1949-69	**POSTERS**, SET 2; large, CADBURY'S Bournville Cocoa
p224	1949-69	**POSTERS**, SET 2; large, LIFEBUOY Soap "For health"
p224	1949-69	**POSTERS**, SET 2; large, RALEIGH, "The all steel bicycle"
p224	1949-69	**POSTERS**, SET 2; large, SPRATTS Bonio "..is what we're waiting for"
p224	1949-69	**POSTERS**, SET 2; large, WILLS CAPSTAN Cigarettes (with yachts and liner)
		(a different version with steam fishing boats appeared on early postwar hoardings)
-	1948-49	**SIGNAL CABIN No. 2**; hinged roof, prewar-style tinprinting
p81	1949-55	**SIGNAL CABIN No. 2**; **fixed** green roof, **revised tinprinting**
p84	1955-57	**SIGNAL CABIN No. 2**; **orange roof**
-	1948	**SIGNAL No. 2; HOME**, white lattice post with black lower section and lever; green base
-	1948-50	**SIGNAL No. 2; HOME**, **all-white** lattice post, black lever; green base
p81	1950-54	**SIGNAL No. 2; HOME**, **shorter non-lattice** all-white post, black lever, white lamp; green base
-	1954-69	**SIGNAL No. 2; HOME**, shorter non-lattice all-white post, black lever, **black** lamp; green base
-	1948	**SIGNAL No. 2; DISTANT**, white lattice post with black lower section and lever; green base
-	1948-50	**SIGNAL No. 2; DISTANT**, **all-white** lattice post, black lever; green base
p81-	1950-54	**SIGNAL No. 2; DISTANT**, **shorter non-lattice** all-white post, black lever, white lamp; green base
-	1954-69	**SIGNAL No. 2; DISTANT**, shorter non-lattice all-white post, black lever, **black** lamp; green base
p76	1948	**SIGNAL, DOUBLE ARM No. 2**, white lattice post with black lower section and lever; green base
p76	1948-50	**SIGNAL, DOUBLE ARM No. 2**, **all-white** lattice post, black lever; green base
-	1950-54	**SIGNAL, DOUBLE ARM No. 2**, **shorter non-lattice** all-white post, black lever, white lamp; green base
p85	1954-69	**SIGNAL, DOUBLE ARM No. 2**, shorter non-lattice all-white post, black lever, **black** lamp; green base
-	1953-54	**JUNCTION SIGNAL No. 2; HOME**, white lamps
-	1954-69	**JUNCTION SIGNAL No. 2; HOME**, **black** lamps
-	1953-54	**JUNCTION SIGNAL No. 2; DISTANT**, white lamps
p85	1954-69	**JUNCTION SIGNAL No. 2; DISTANT**, **black** lamps
-	1948-49	**STATION No. 3**; prewar-style tinprinting
p82	1949-55	**STATION No. 3**; **green** roof; **revised tinprinting**
p84	1955-57	**STATION No. 3**; **orange** roof; **new revised tinprinting**
p84	1949-69	**STATION HOARDINGS**; buff
p83	1949-69	**TURNTABLE No. 2**
p83	1949-68	**WATER TANK No. 1**

Many new items of literature have been found since we compiled the list in HCS Volume 5, and it has become rather inconvenient to use because of the large number of additions. We are, therefore, including this new list which replaces that on pages 311-317. Codes not given in the previous list are in bold type.

We are very grateful to the many people who have contributed information for this section, including Roger Beardsley, Ian Button, Jim Gamble, Richard Lines, Peter Matthews, Henry Pearce, John Rausch, Doug Taylor, David Uttley, Ken Vernon, Patrick Whitehouse and Roy Young.

HORNBY BOOKS of TRAINS
All with full colour cover and full colour catalogue section.

No code	1925 HBT, 44pp inc. cover, LNER 1471 on cover (2 editions; among other differences, the first has p34 headed "No. OO Clockwork Trains", later "Hornby Trains"
926/50	1926 HBT, 48pp inc. cover, GWR 4079
1226/25	1926 HBT, 48pp inc. cover, GWR 4079
927/75	1927/28 HBT, 48pp inc. cover, GWR 4082
1127/15	1927/28 HBT, 48pp inc. cover, GWR 4082
828/100	1928/29 HBT, 44pp & cover, LMS 6100
3/929/100	1929/30 HBT, 44pp & cover, LMS 5986
3/1029/130	1929/30 HBT, 44pp & cover, LMS 5986
16/830/75	1930/31 HBT, 44pp & cover, LMS 6100
16/1130/15(2)	1930/31 HBT, 44pp & cover, LMS 6100
16/831/120	1931/32 HBT, 44pp & cover, LMS 5957
16/832/105	1932/33 HBT, 48pp & cover, LMS 6110
16/833/100	1933/34 HBT, 48pp & cover, LMS 6100
16/934/100	1934/35 HBT, 64pp & cover, LMS 6200
7/835/65	1935/36 BHT&MP, 56pp & cover
7/837/100	1937/38 HBT, 56pp & cover, LMS 6201
7/837/117	1938/39 HBT, 56pp & cover, GWR 6005
7/739/100	1939/40 HBT, 56pp & cover, LMS 6231

"HORNBY TRAIN" CATALOGUES and FOLDERS:

No code	(no date) black/white folder; shows 1922 range
1023/200	(no date) black/white folder
1024/150	(no date) black/white folder
1224/30	(no date) black/white folder

826/100	(no date) black/white folder
1126/25	(no date) black/white folder
927/250	(no date) black/white folder
1128/150	(no date) blue/white 16pp booklet
3/729/300	(no date) blue/white 16pp booklet
3/1029/100(3)	(no date) brown/white 16pp booklet
3/1129/50(4)	(no date) brown/white 16pp booklet
3/1229/20(5)	(no date) brown/white 16pp booklet
5/830/500	1930/31, dark brown/white 20pp booklet
5/1130/50(IR)	1930/31, dark brown/white 20pp booklet
2/831/450	1931/32, brown/white 20pp booklet
2/1131/100	1931/32, brown/white 20pp booklet
13/832/500(1P)	(no date) green/white folder
13/1132/50(2P)	(no date) green/white folder
13/833/550	(no date) blue/white folder
13/1133/50(2P)	(no date) blue/white folder
15/834/500(1P)	(no date) blue/white electric train folder
15/834/500(1P)	(no date) brown/white clockwork train folder
13/634/610(1P)	1935/36, red/white 24pp booklet
13/837/80	(no date) black/green/white folder
8/938/200	(no date) black/blue/white folder
2/739/160(1P)	(no date) black/blue/white folder

13/1053/100	1953 sepia/white folder
16/754/100	1954/5 black/blue/white folder
	also with label "Revised Prices 1st February 1955. Please refer to enclosed list."
20/855/200	1955/6 full colour folder
11/756/250	1956/7 full colour folder
11/757/250	(no date) full colour folder
11/858/250	1958 full colour folder
8/10/59/175	(no date) black/green/white folder
16/860/175	(no date) black/yellow/white folder
	also overprinted "Revised prices 1st February 1961. Please refer to new list"
9/661/175	(no date) black/orange/white folder
12/4/62/150	(no date) black/yellow/white folder

MECCANO PRODUCTS FOLDERS, CATALOGUES and ILLUSTRATED PRICE LISTS

which include Hornby Trains:

Code	Description
No code	1920/21 catalogue, 20pp, 7" by 9"
No code	1921/22 catalogue, 20pp, 7" by 9"
No code	1922/23 catalogue, 20pp, 7" by 9"
No code	1923/24 catalogue, 20pp, 7" by 9"
No code	1924/25 catalogue, 20pp, 5" by 7"
No code	1924/25 catalogue, 20pp, 7" by 9"
825/50	1925/26 catalogue, 20pp, 7" by 9"
No code	1925/26 catalogue, 20pp, 5" by 7"
No code	1926/27 catalogue, 24pp, 5" by 7"
527/300	1927/28 catalogue, 24pp, 5" by 7"
928/400	1928/29 catalogue, 24pp, 5" by 7"
4/829/400	1929/30 catalogue, 28pp, 5" by 7"
2/830/500	1930/31 catalogue, 32pp, 5" by 7"
7/731/500	Meccano/Hornby folder
13/831/500	1931/32 catalogue, 32pp, 5" by 7"
2/1231/25	Meccano/Hornby folder
13/832/500	1932/33 catalogue, 36pp, 5" by 7"
13/633/750(1P)	1933/34 catalogue, 40pp, 5" by 7"
13/834/900	1934/35 catalogue, 64pp, 5" by 7"
13/635/938.5	1935/36 catalogue, 64pp, 5" by 7"
13/736/1302	1936/37 catalogue, 72pp, 5" by 7"
13/737/1,150	1937/38 catalogue, 72pp, 8½" by 5½"
13/638/1150	1938/39 catalogue, 72pp, 8½" by 5½"
13/639/1,1500	1939/40 catalogue, 72pp, 8½" by 5½"
16/347/50	MARCH 1947, black/white 2pp
No code	12th NOVEMBER 1947, 4pp
16/248/10	1948, blue/white
16/448/30	1st MAY 1948, pale green/white 4pp
16/948/200	OCTOBER 1948, violet/white 4pp
16/449/100	APRIL-MAY 1949, light brown/white 6pp folder
16/1049/100	OCTOBER 1949, violet/white 6pp folder
13/1049/150	black/buff/white 8pp booklet
16/250/100	1st FEBRUARY 1950, brown/white 6pp folder
16/450/150	JUNE 1950, black/blue/white 8pp folder
16/1050/160	OCTOBER 1950, blue/white 8pp folder
16/251/33	MARCH 1951, brown/white 8pp folder
16/651/75	MARCH 1951, blue/white 8pp folder
16/1051/25	OCTOBER 1951, purple/white 8pp folder
16/1151/10	OCTOBER 1951, purple/white 8pp folder

Code	Description
16/152/50	FEBRUARY 1952, brown/white 16pp booklet
16/452/50	APRIL 1952, blue/white 16pp booklet
16/852/500	SEPTEMBER 1952, brown/white 16pp booklet
16/153/50	1st FEBRUARY 1953, blue/white booklet
16/453/50	15th APRIL 1953, violet/white 16pp booklet
13/953/678	1st OCTOBER 1953, 20pp booklets:
	"Meccano, Toys of Quality" shop window cover
	"Magic Carpet to the World of Thrills" cover
	"Meccano, Toys of Quality" pirate's cave cover
	"Meccano, Dinky, Hornby Trains, Hornby Dublo" cover
13/1053/350 2P	do. (same choice of covers)
13/654/995	1954-5, 24pp booklet; colour desert island cover
13/655/797	1955/6, 28pp booklet; schoolboys at shop window cover
13/756/525	(No date), 32pp full colour booklet
7/457/150	1957, full colour folder
13/757/500	1957, 32pp full colour booklet
13/758/450	1958, 20pp full colour booklet
7/263/400	(No date), 20pp full colour booklet (includes price list 7/463/400)
9/464/150 1stP	(No date), 8pp full colour booklet (includes price list 9/464/150 1st P)
9/464/150 2ndP	(No date), 8pp full colour booklet (includes price list 9/664/150 2nd P)

MECCANO PRODUCTS CATALOGUE COVERS, PREWAR

"Boys' Hobbies" (Crane loading goods train); black and brown on white, 5" by 7"

"The Boys' Treasure book"; (showing Meccano red/green models, Hornby No. 2 Locos), 5" by 7"

"The Boys' Treasure book"; (showing Meccano blue/gold models, Hornby No. 2 Specials), 5" by 7"

"Choice Gifts for Boys", full colour 5" by 7", with boy & Meccano red/green steam shovel

"For Interesting Toys." Halfords; black, blue and yellow, 8.5" by 5.5"

"For Meccano and Hornby Trains"; black and blue on white, 5" by 7"

"The Golden Gate to Funland"; full colour, 5" by 7"

"Halfords. For Sensible Toys"; showing shop front, black/red on white, 5" by 7"

"Halfords. For Toys of Interest"; full colour, 5" by 7"

"Hamleys, the Finest Toy Shop in the World"; full colour, 5" by 7"

"Hornby Trains. Meccano. Known all round the world"; full colour, 5" by 7"

"The Magic Carpet". Full colour, 7" by 9".

"Meccano and Hornby Trains". Full colour, 5" by 7". Meccano monorail

"Meccano. Hornby Trains". Full colour, 5" by 7". LMS 6110 and train

"Meccano. Motor Car Constructor. Aeroplane Constructor". Full colour, 5" by 7"

Description	Code	Notes
"Meccano Products". Green and gold on grey, 7" by 9"	No code	Revised Prices, Hornby Train Sets (pasted in Standard Mechanisms Manual, eg 127/10)
"Meccano Products". Full colour, 7" by 9"; Meccano bridge and funfair, at night		
"Meccano Products". Full colour, 5" by 7". Boy in circle, products in diagonal stripes	No code	Revised Prices, Hornby Trains Sets, Wagons and Accessories; (pasted in Meccano Instruction Manuals)
"Meccano Products". Full colour, 5" by 7". Boy with crane in circle, products in circular bands	1928	Revised prices, revisions and deletions; Meccano and Hornby Train Sets, Rolling Stock and Accessories
"Meccano Products. For boys of all ages". Full colour, 5" by 7"	1 929.55.	1929-30, revised prices, Meccano and Hornby Train Sets
"Meccano. Quality Gifts for Boys". Full colour, 8.5" by 5.5"	2/1229/1	Price list, Meccano and Hornby Train Sets
"Meccano. Quality Toys". Full colour, 8.5" by 5.5"	1/330/10(2)	1st March 1930, revised prices and deletions, Meccano and Hornby
"A Message From Meccano Town". Full colour, 7" by 9". Meccano bridge and funfair, at night	6/930/6	Revised prices for Hornby rails (pasted on "How to Get More Fun..", 1127/25)
No Title. Boys looking into shop window, with 2711 etc. 5" by 7".		
No title. Black and brown on white. Boy inside toyshop, at counter. 5" by 7"	1/1035/31.5	1935-36 revised prices (inserted in 1934-35 Meccano Products Catalogues)
"Obtainable from Halfords"; full colour, 8.5" by 5.5"		
"Products of Meccano Ltd Liverpool". Full colour, 5" by 7"	1/836/13	SEASON 1936-37, revised prices (inserted in Meccano Products Catalogues)
"The Stars Send Their Message". Full colour, 8.5" by 5.5"		
"To the Best Toy-Shop in Town". Block colour, 5" by 7"		
"Toy Trains and Model Building for Pleasure". Shows Royal Scot front end. Full colour, 5" by 7"	1/138/50 (2P)	1st JANUARY 1938, full Meccano Products price list
	1/138 50 (3P)	1st JANUARY 1938, full Meccano Products price list
"Toys of Quality". Meccano boys with crystal set etc. Full colour, 7" by 9"	1/238/50 (3P)	1st JANUARY 1938, full Meccano Products price list
"Toys of Quality". Red loco on viaduct. Green and red on white, 5" by 7"	1/238/10 (4P)	1st JANUARY 1938, full Meccano Products price list
"Toys of Quality". Full colour, 5" by 7". Meccano boys with silver/green Meccano Models, Hornby 2710s, 2711, Metro etc	1/338/25 (5P)	1st JANUARY 1938, full Meccano Products price list
	1/538/10 (6P)	1st JANUARY 1938, full Meccano Products price list
"Toys of Quality". Full colour, 8.5" by 5.5". Princess Elizabeth, Gantry, Signal box	1/638/10 (7P)	1st JANUARY 1938, full Meccano Products price list
"Toys of Quality from Meccano Land". Full colour, 8.5" by 5.5"	1/140/50	1st JANUARY 1940
"The Treasure Chest". Full colour, 5" by 7". Boys with pirates	1/440/100	APRIL 1940
"A Wonder Book of Toys". Full colour, 8.5" by 5.5"	16/840/50	AUGUST 1940
"The World's Best Toys". Full colour, 5" by 7"	16/1040/100	21st OCTOBER 1940
	16/141/25	JANUARY 1941
	16/641/25	MAY 1941
	16/1141/20	1st NOVEMBER 1941

PRICE LISTS, MECCANO PRODUCTS and HORNBY:

(Illustrated price lists are included with catalogues and folders.)

Code	Description
821/50	(No date) Revised prices, Hornby and Tinprinted Trains (pasted in 1920-21 Meccano Products catalogue)
222/10	1st MARCH 1922, revised prices
No code	17th JULY 1922, revised prices for Hornby rails (pasted on Rail Formations leaflet)
No code	19th FEBRUARY 1923, revised prices (inserted in 1922-23 Meccano Products catalogue)
No code	1st AUGUST 1924, revised prices and additions, Hornby Trains (pasted on Rail Formations booklet)
No code	1st SEPTEMBER 1925, revised prices and additions
726/5	Revised Price list, Meccano and Hornby Train Sets (for Meccano Manuals)

Code	Date
16/753/100	1st JULY 1953
16/1053/150	1st OCTOBER 1953
16/354/50	1st APRIL 1954
16/454/50	1st MAY 1954
16/754/20	(no date). Hamleys.
16/954/50	(no date)
16/155/100	FEBRUARY 1955
16/255/100	FEBRUARY 1955
16/355/100	MARCH 1955
16/555/100	MAY 1955
16/1055/500	27th OCTOBER 1955
16/156/100M 1stP	1st FEBRUARY 1956

16/456/100M 2ndP	APRIL 1956
13/656/525	JULY 1956
16/956/200	SEPTEMBER 1956
16/157/100M	1st FEBRUARY 1957
16/457/100M 2ndP	APRIL 1957
16/757/100 3rdP	AUGUST 1957
16/857/500	SEPTEMBER 1957
16/1057/100 4thP	OCTOBER 1957
16/158/100 1stP	1st FEBRUARY 1958
16/558/50 2ndP	1st MAY 1958
16/658/30 3rdP	1st JULY 1958
16/658/70 3rdP	1st JULY 1958
10/758/450	1958
16/858/58 4thP	1st AUGUST 1958
16/958/50 5thP	1st NOVEMBER 1958
16/1258/70 6thP	DECEMBER 1958
16/459/100 1stP	1st MAY 1959
16/859/75	1959. Hamleys
16/959/100 2ndP	1st SEPTEMBER 1959
16/1059/145 3rdP	1st OCTOBER 1959
16/1259/145 4thP	DECEMBER 1959
8/760/70	1960. Hamleys
8/760/125 1stP	AUGUST 1960
16/1060/100 2ndP	AUGUST 1960
16/261/100 1stP	1st FEBRUARY 1961
16/561/50 2ndP	1st MAY 1961
16/761/60	1961. Hamleys
16/861/60	1961
16/861/100 3rdP	1st SEPTEMBER 1961
16/1161/100 4thP	1st NOVEMBER 1961
16/1261/100 1stP	FEBRUARY 1962
16/462/170m 3rdP	APRIL 1962
16/662/100M 4thP	JUNE 1962
16/962/150m 5thP	SEPTEMBER 1962
16/163/50m 1stP	JANUARY 1963
7/463/400	(stapled inside 7/263/400 Catalogue)
16/963/125 2ndP	SEPTEMBER 1963
16/164/100	1964
9/464/150 1st P	1964 (stapled inside 9/464/150 1st P catalogue)
9/664/150 2ndP	1964 (stapled inside 9/464/150 2nd P catalogue)
16/1264/150 1stP	1965
16/665/50	SEPTEMBER 1965, Hamleys
16/766/50m	JULY 1966 (misprinted as 1/766/150 in previous list)
No code	JANUARY 1967 (in two editions)
No code	1969

MISC. HORNBY and MECCANO PRODUCT LEAFLETS

etc. which include Hornby advertisements

620/45	Black/white 2pp
820/250	Black/white 2pp
1220/100	Black/white 2pp
921/350	Black/white 2pp
No code	Full colour, similar to 921/350
122/10	Lattice Girder Bridge and Timber Wagon, 2pp
No code	'Hornby Presentation Sets'
No code	'Birthday Gifts..', entry form
No code	'The Hornby Electric Train', 4pp colour
725/400	'Run your own Railway' throwaway
426/10	'Jackie Coogan Visits a Meccano Factory', booklet
526/15	'Hornby Clockwork Trains' throwaway
826/205	'The New Meccano', folder, colour cover
1026/50	'Jackie Coogan Visits a Meccano Factory', booklet
1026/100	'The New Meccano', folder, colour cover
527/175	'Hornby Trains', blue/cream single sheet
727/80	'Adventures in Meccanoland', booklet
No code	'Three New Hornby Trains' (No. 3 Trains, MM insert)
No code	'To Hornby Train Users' postcard (re HRC)
528/275	'Which is the Greatest Railway Company in the World?' (throwaway advertising HRC)
928/25	'Adventures in Meccanoland', booklet
1/430/280	'Right Away for Happy Days' throwaway
2/1030/50	'Boys! Here is a plan..', part exchange leaflet
1/331/350	'Longer Runs, Heavier Loads' throwaway
1/531/40	Hornby Accessories & Rolling Stock, illustrated list, 2pp
1/731/375	'Longer Runs, Heavier Loads' (also has 1/332/150 code on reverse, showing Meccano Aeroplanes)
1/432/250	'Boys, Run Your Own Railway!'
?	'Longer Runs with Heavier Loads' (similar to 1/832/200)
1/832/200(1P)	'Boys, Start a Railway of your Own'
1/932/5	'Boys! Here is a plan..'; exchange scheme leaflet
1/1232/25	Hornby Countryside Sections
1/233/100	Meccano Products and Hornby, 2pp leaflet
1/633/250	Meccano Products and Hornby, 2pp leaflet
1/534/240	Meccano Products and Hornby, 2pp leaflet
1/634/240	Meccano Products and Hornby, 2pp leaflet
2/834/10	British Express, descriptive colour leaflet and instructions
1/1134/150	Meccano Products and Hornby, 2pp leaflet

1/1234/50	Meccano Products and Hornby, 2pp
1/737/5	Princess Elizabeth, 1 page leaflet
1/539/5	JUNE 1939, Exchange scheme leaflet
16/865/35	'Percy the Small Engine', full colour
No code	'Meet Percy in Person!', black/orange/white
No code	'Meet Percy in Person!', full colour
No code	1st MAY 1969, 'The Play Train by Meccano', full colour
No code	1st JAN 1970, 'The Play Train by Meccano', full colour

MECCANO INSTRUCTION MANUALS with HORNBY ADVERTISEMENTS:
(English Edition only)

921/15	Book No. 3, full colour or black/white 2pp insert
622/8	No. 22, pages 203-206
622/50	No. 22A, pages 59-62
922/10	No. 22.0, page 17
1022/85	No. 22A, pages 59-62
1222/5	No. 22, pages 203-206
1223/2.5	No. 23, pages 203-206
724/25	No. 24A, pages 59-62
No code	Standard Mechanisms (1925 edition)
725/100	No. 25A, pages 59-62
1125/10	No. 25A, pages 59-62
626/50	No. 26.0, page 17
626/75	No. 26A, pages 59-62
626/10.5	No. 26, pages 205-208
726/5	'Standard Mechanisms' Manual
926/5	'Standard Mechanisms' Manual
	(was listed in error as 'no code')
127/10	'Standard Mechanisms' Manual
127(F)30	No. 27.0, page 17
127(F)5	No. 27, pages 205-208
127(F)30	No. 27A, pages 59-62
427/75	No. 27A, pages 59-62
427/10	No. 27, pages 205-208
1027/5	No. 27, pages 205-208
528/15	No. 28, pages 136-138
628/75	No. 28.0, pages 27-28
628/100	No. 28A, pages 108-110
728/5	'Standard Mechanisms' Manual
1028/50	No. 28A, pages 108-110
1028/5	No. 28, pages 136-138
1128/15	No. 28.0, pages 27-28

1128/3	'Standard Mechanisms' Manual
329/50	No. 29.0, pages 42-44
329/50	No. 29A, pages 132-134
329/10	No. 29, pages 137-138
629/3(2)	No. 29, pages 137-138
729/39(2)	No. 29.0, pages 42-44
2/130/15(1)	No. 30A, pages 132-134
2/330/75(2)	No. 30A, pages 131-134
2/730/100(2)	No. 30A, pages 131-134

(Various 1937-1941 Manuals advertised Hornby Trains on the back cover.)

'HORNBY CONTROL SYSTEM' LEAFLET: 4pp

926/12	
1126/20	
627/35	
728/20	
2/831/45	
13/532/15	
1/433/40	
1/935/7.5	
1/1235/2.5	
1/436/15	
1/1236/1	
1/237/2	
1/937/1	
1/1237/1	(overprinted "Revised prices 1st January 1938")

'HOW TO PLAN YOUR HORNBY RAILWAY' and similar leaflets:

926/35	'The Hornby Train System', 8pp
1127/10	'How to Get More Fun out of Hornby Trains', 12pp
1127/25	'How to Get More Fun out of Hornby Trains', 12pp
628/80	'How to Get More Fun out of Hornby Trains', 12pp
2/929/10	'How to Plan Your Hornby Railway', 12pp
16/430/50	'How to Plan Your Hornby Railway', 12pp
2/531/40	'How to Plan Your Hornby Railway', 12pp
2/632/2.5	'How to Plan Your Hornby Electric Railway', 4pp
13/732/15	'How to Plan Your Hornby Railway', 12pp
2/433/35	'How to Plan Your Hornby Railway', 12pp
1/533/4	'How to Plan Your Hornby Electric Railway', 4pp
2/1134/10	'How to Plan Your Hornby Railway'
7/1134/20	'How to Plan Your Hornby Electric Railway', 4pp

15/1134/10	'How to Choose and Use a Hornby Electric Railway'
2/1035/15(2P)	'How to Plan Your Hornby Railway', 12pp
2/336/16(1P)	'How to Plan Your Hornby Railway', 12pp
2/636/5(2P)	'How to Plan Your Hornby Railway, 12pp
1/636/50	'How to Develop Your Hornby Model Railway', 2pp
1/1036/6	'How to Plan Your Hornby Electric Railway', 4pp
7/737/14(IP)	'How to Plan Your Hornby Railway', 12pp
	(also overprinted "Prices Revised 1st January 1938")
1/937/3.5	'How to Plan Your Hornby Electric Railway', 4pp
7/338/12.5(IP)	'How to Plan Your Hornby Railway', 4pp
1/438/10	'How to Plan Your Hornby Electric Railway', 4pp
1/938/3	'How to Plan Your Hornby Electric Railway', 4pp
1/1238/20	'How to Develop Your Hornby Clockwork Railway'
7/1039/10	'How to Plan Your Hornby Railway', 12pp

RAIL FORMATION LEAFLETS:

No code	'Rail Formations', 8pp
522/10	'Rail Formations', 8pp
922/20	'Rail Formations', 8pp
1122/10	'Rail Formations', 8pp
123/10	'Rail Formations', 8pp
523/35	'Rail Formations', 8pp
525/40	'Rail Formations', 8pp
1025/15	'Rail Formations', 8pp
1/1034/30	'Hornby Layouts. 100 Suggestions', 12pp
1/735/40	'Hornby Layouts. 100 Suggestions', 12pp
1/1235/5	'Hornby Layouts. 100 Suggestions', 12pp
1/136/50	'Hornby Layouts. 100 Suggestions', 12pp
1/737/55	'Hornby Layouts. 100 Suggestions', 12pp
	(also overprinted "Prices Revised 1st January 1938")
1/737/10	'Hornby Layouts. 100 Suggestions', 12pp (1938 edition)
1/1238/25	'Hornby Layouts. 100 Suggestions', 12pp
1/140/30	'Hornby Layouts. 60 Suggestions', 8pp
15/849/25	'Layouts for Clockwork Track', 8pp
15/949/50	'Layouts for Clockwork Track', 8pp
15/1149/150	'Layouts for Clockwork Track', 8pp
15/151/150	'Layouts for Clockwork Track', 8pp
16/152/100	'Layouts for Clockwork Track', **4pp**
16/1052/50	'Layouts for Clockwork Track', 4pp
16/953/50	'Layouts for Clockwork Track', 4pp
16/1253/200	'Layout Suggestions for Clockwork Track', 4pp
16/1154/100	'Layout Suggestions for Clockwork Track', 4pp

16/1055/100	'Layout Suggestions for Clockwork Track', 4pp
15/157/100	'Layout Suggestions for Clockwork Track', 4pp
15/258/75	'Layout Suggestions for Clockwork Track', 4pp
10/259/75	'Layout Suggestions for Clockwork Track', 4pp
10/260/100	'Layout Suggestions for Clockwork Track', 4pp
10/261/120	'Layout Suggestions for Clockwork Track', 4pp
10/1261/100	'Layout Suggestions for Clockwork Track', 4pp

HORNBY RAILWAY COMPANY SENIOR SECTION BOOKLET:
24 page booklets titled 'The Hornby Railway Company'

1028/9-10.	Horizontal format
129/10.	Horizontal format
13/331/5	Vertical format
13/1132/5	do.
13/434/5(2P)	do.
13/137/5(3R)	do.
13/140/2	do.
13/241/2	do.
13/1148/20	do.
13/1149/20	do.
13/350/20	do.
13/1250/12	do.
13/1151/12	do.
13/1252/30	do.
13/1254/10	do.
13/1055/12	do.
13/256/10	do.
13/1058/20	do.

HORNBY RAILWAY COMPANY JUNIOR SECTION BOOKLET:
24 page booklets titled 'How to Get More Fun from Your Hornby Train'

2/331/5
2/332/5
2/335/5
2/137/5
2/239/5
2/1140/5
2/946/1

HRC FORMS:

Pads of fifty forms: no code, 1/1130/200pds, or 1/232/250pds

GW1 General Working Timetable, black/yellow
SD4 Stationmaster's Arrivals and Departures, black/cream
EJ5 Engineman's Job Card, black/buff
SB6 Signal Box instructions, black/pink
SR7 Stationmaster's Report Form

HRC MEMBERSHIP APPLICATION FORMS:

1128/50	4pp
1228/50	do.
429/175	do.
1/430/100	2pp
1.530.190	do.
1/1130/95	do.
1/431/160	do.
1/232/160	do.
1/433/125	do.
1/234/250	do.
No code	do.
1/236/200	do.
1/636/100	do.
1/537/150.	do.
1/138 200	do.
1/238/200	do.
1/638/15	do.
1/738/200	do.
1/139/210	do.
2/440/75	do.
16/946/50	2pp
5/447/50	do.
5/448/150	do.
5/1048/150	do.
5/649/200	do.
5/350/200	do.
5/1250/250	do.
5/1051/100	do.
5/352/100	do.
5/752/100	do.
17/953/100	do.
17/354/200	do.

17/1154/250	do.
17/1255/250	do.
17/157/250	do.
17/1258/250	do.
10/860/250	do.
10/961/250	do.

HRC CORRESPONDENCE CLUB APPLICATION FORM:

17/348/2	Postcard
17/749/2	Postcard

GUARANTEES and INSTRUCTIONS, CLOCKWORK LOCOS AND SETS:

No code	Instructions, Meccano Clockwork Trains. Multilingual, no pictures. (With Tinprinted Train Set)
No code	Instructions, Hornby Train Set (1920, Loco and Truck only)
No code	Instructions, Hornby No. 1 Train Set (1921, with coaches)
No code	Instructions, Hornby No. 2 Train Set
921-10	Instructions, Hornby No. 1 Loco
921/5	Instructions, Hornby No. 2 Loco
1121/25	Instructions, Hornby No. 1 Loco
1121/20.	Instructions, Hornby No. 2 Loco
No code	60 day Guarantees, Instructions on back:
	with border of squares
	with border of diamonds in squares
	with border of blocks inside squares
	with border of double hollow squares
625/25	60 day Guarantee, Instructions on back
925/30	60 day Guarantee, Instructions on back
No code	'Important', note on radii for No. 0, 1, 2 Trains.
426/75	60 day Guarantee, Instructions on back
926/50	Unlimited Guarantee, Instructions on back (for M Series)
227/75	60 day Guarantee, Instructions on back
1227/50	60 day Guarantee, Instructions on back
No code	'Important', note on radii for No. 0, 1, 2, Metropolitan and Riviera Blue
428/25	60 day Guarantee, Instructions on back
428/75	Unlimited Guarantee, Instructions on back (for M Series)
329/150	Unlimited Guarantee & Instructions (for M Series)
429/50	60 day Guarantee & Instructions
No code	'Important'; note on radii for M, 0, 1, 2, 3 and Met
6/1129/50	60 day Guarantee & Instructions

1/430/50	60 day Guarantee & Instructions	1/936/7.5	No. 1 up Train Sets and Loco 60 day Guarantee
1/530/10 (2)	60 day Guarantee & Instructions	**1/1036/20**	MO & Silver Jubilee sets and locos, Instructions
1/830/60	Unlimited Guarantee & Instructions (for M Series)	1/1136/2.5	MO and No. 0 Siver Jubilee Train Sets and Locos, Instructions
1/1230/20	60 day Guarantee & Instructions		
1/431/75	'Important'; note on radii	1/437/60	M1/2 Set and Loco Instructions
1/431/120 M	Unlimited Guarantee & Instructions	1/437/55	M3 up Instructions
1/531/120 M	Unlimited Guarantee & Instructions	1/537/100	MO set and loco Instructions
1/531/60 C	60 day Guarantee & Instructions	1/537/40	No. 1 up 60 day Guarantee
1/132/15	M1/2 Loco, Unlimited Guarantee & Instructions	**1/637/30**	No. 1 up Loco 60 day Guarantee
1/132/55	'Important'; note on radii	1/1037/10	M3 up Instructions
1/232/5	(for MO). On pink.	1/338/75	M1/2 Set and Loco Instructions
1/232/15	M3 loco Guarantee & Instructions (was listed as 1/232/16)	1/338/50	M3 & No. 0 Sets and Locos, 30 day Guarantee
1/232/2	M3 30 day Guarantee & Instructions	1/438/75	M1/2 Set and Loco Instructions
1/232/20	No. 1 up sets, Guarantee & Instructions	**1/538/15**	MO set and loco Instructions
1/232/80	No. 1 up loco, Guarantee & Instructions (was listed as 1/232/30)	**1/139/30**	M1/2 Instructions
1/1232/15	M1/2 Loco Instructions	1/439/35	M1/2 up Instructions
1/233/75	M1/2 up 'Read This First', re oiling/radii	1/1139/100	MO Set and Loco Instructions
1/233/10	M3 and No. O sets, 30 day Guarantee & Instructions	1/1239/30	M3 & No. 0 Guarantee (also found in early postwar sets)
1/333/15	M3 Loco 30 day Guarantee and Instructions	No code	No. 1 up 60 day Guarantee (probably 1939; found in early postwar 501 sets)
1/333/20	No. 1 up 60 day Guarantee & Instructions		
1/533/25	M1/2 up 'Read This First', re oiling/radii	16/646/100	M1 up 'Hints on Running Your Hornby Railway'
1/1233/20	M1/2 up 'Read This First', re oiling/radii	17/647/100	M1 up 'Hints on Running Your Hornby Railway'
1/134/75	MO 'Read This First', re oiling	16/248/75	M1 up 'Hints on Running Your Hornby Railway'
1/134/200	M1/2 up 'Read This First', re oiling/radii	17/348/40	MO 'Hints on Running Your Hornby Railway'
1/134/15	MO Instructions	**16/1248/40**	MO 'Hints on Running Your Hornby Railway'
1/234/30	M1/2 Instructions	16/449/100	M1 up 'Hints on Running Your Hornby Railway'
1/234/15	No. 1-3 Loco, 60 day Guarantee & Instructions	16/1049/30	M1 up 'Hints on Running Your Hornby Railway'
1/135/15	MO Instructions	16/150/125	M1 up 'Hints on Running Your Hornby Railway'
1/235/25	No. 1 up 60 day Guarantee & Instructions	17/1050/125	M1 up 'Hints on Running Your Hornby Railway'
1/335/60	M1/2 up 'Read This First', re oiling/radii	**17/1250/100**	MO 'Hints on Running Your Hornby Railway'
1/335/15	M3 & No. 0 Guarantee & Instructions	**16/151/255**	"Before running this train.."; Oiling instructions, multilingual
1/335/15	No. 1-3 Loco, 60 day Guarantee & Instructions		
1/1035/7.5	M3 & No. 0 Guarantee & Instructions	17/751/110	M1 up 'Hints on Running Your Hornby Railway'
1/1035/10	No. 1 up Guarantee & Instructions	17/1151/150	M1 up 'Hints on Running Your Hornby Railway'
1/136/35	M3 & No. O Train Sets and Locos, Instructions	7/1151/2501	"Before running this train.."; Oiling instructions, multilingual
1/136/35	M3 and No. 0 30 day Guarantee		
1/336/82.5	MO Train Set and Locomotive Instructions	17/253/80	M1 up 'Hints on Running Your Hornby Railway'
1/336/62.5	M1/2 Set and Loco Instructions	**17/1053/100**	"Before running this train.."; Oiling instructions, multilingual
1/336/27.5	M3 and No. 0 Train Sets and Locos, Instructions		
1/336/9.7	M3 and No. 0 Train Sets and Locos, 30 day Guarantee	17/254/150	30 up 'Hints on Running Your Hornby Railway'
1/336/40	No. 1 up Train Sets and Locos, 60 day Guarantee	17/1154/75	30 up 'Hints on Running Your Hornby Railway'
1/436/40	No. 1 up Instructions	17/155/110	30 up 'Hints on Running Your Hornby Railway'
		17/255/100	No. 20/21 'Hints on Running Your Hornby Railway'

10/1255/75	No. 20/21 'Hints on Running Your Hornby Railway'
10/1255/110	30 up 'Hints on Running Your Hornby Railway'
10/1256/75	No. 20/21 'Hints on Running Your Hornby Railway'
10/1256/75	30 up 'Hints on Running Your Hornby Railway'
10/658/25	30 up 'Hints on Running Your Hornby Railway'
10/758/50	No. 20/21 'Hints on Running Your Hornby Railway'
10/359/50	No. 20/21 'Hints on Running Your Hornby Railway'
10/359/25	30 up 'Hints on Running Your Hornby Railway'
10/559/25	30 up 'Hints on Running Your Hornby Railway'
10/161/10	30 up 'Hints on Running Your Hornby Railway'
10/1161/15	30 up 'Hints on Running Your Hornby Railway'

INSTRUCTIONS, ELECTRIC LOCOMOTIVES and SETS:

No Code	Hornby Electric Train
1126/5	Metropolitan No. 2 and other 4V trains 4pp
527/1.5	Metropolitan No. 1 HV 4pp
228/1	Metropolitan High Voltage 4pp
628/5	No. 3E Train Sets, 4 volt 4pp; (was listed as "No code")
629/5	No. 1 Electric Tank Loco (6V DC) 2pp
629/3.5	No. 3E (6 volt) Train Sets
6/331/.5	Metropolitan LV (6 Volt)
6/331/5	No. 3E (6 volt) Train Sets
1/632/2	LSTM3/20 Tank, LE1/20, LST1/20 Tank, LE2/20 2pp
1/933/1	LSTM3/20 Tank, LE1/20, LST1/20 Tank, LE2/20, LST2/20 Tank, E3/20
2/1134/1	EPM16 Special Tank 2pp
2/1134/2.5	E26 Special Tank and E36 4pp
2/1134/.5	Metropolitan E36 4pp
2/1134/5	EM36 Tank, E06, E16, E16 Tank 4pp
2/1134/10	EM320 Tank, E020, E120, E120 Tank 4pp
2/1134/7.5	20 volt Auto Reverse locos 4pp
2/235/10	20 volt Auto Reverse locos 4pp
1/335/1	EM16 Loco 2pp
1/336/12.5	20 volt Auto Reverse locos 4pp
1/536/2.5	EM320 Tank, E020, E120, E120 Tank 4pp
1/936/.25	Metropolitan E36, 4pp
1/1236/1	E26 Special Tank, 4pp
1/1236/1.5	EM320 Tank, E020, E120, E120 Tank 4pp
No code	EM320 Tank, E020, E120, E120 Tank 4pp
1/137/1.5	EM120 Loco 2pp
1/537/2.5	'Princess Elizabeth' Loco 4pp
1/637/2.5	EM320 Tank, E020, E120, E120 Tank 4pp
1/637/15	20 Volt Auto Reverse 4pp

No code	ADDENDA for Eton E420 Locomotive
1/737/.35	Metropolitan E36
1/338/15	20 Volt Auto Reverse 4pp
1/939/5	20 Volt Auto Reverse 4pp
1/1139/1	E26 Special Tank 4pp
1/440/5	EM320 Tank, E020, E120, E120 Tank 4pp
No code	EM320 Tank, E020, E120, E120 Tank 4pp
No code	20 volt Auto Reverse 4pp
	(All auto reverse instructions covered the E120 Special, E120 Special Tank, E220 Special, E220 Special Tank, and the E320. This last version also included the E420.)
16/948/5	E502 and E602 Train Sets 4pp
16/850/2.5	E502 and E602 Train Sets 4pp

GUARANTEES, ELECTRIC LOCOMOTIVES and SETS:

428/5	60 day
429/3	60 day
6/331/5 E	60 day
1/531/6 E	60 day
1/132/4	60 day
1/1232/5	60 day
1/1233/5	60 day (also version overstamped '30 days')
1/1134/6	30 day, for locos up to E120/E16
1/135/4.5	60 day, for E120 Special up
1/1235/1	60 day, for E120 Special up, also E26 Special Tank and E36 Locos
1/136/10	60 day, for E120 Special up
1/537/15	60 day, for E120 Special up
No code	for Princess Elizabeth Loco
1/1237/2.5	60 day, for E120 Special up
1/338/22.5	60 day, for E120 Special up
1/338/3.	30 day, for EM320 Tank/EM36 Tank/EO20 Sets and Locos

INSTRUCTIONS FOR TRANSFORMERS:

6/432/2	Ferranti Transformer
6/632/1	T20A
1/732/1	T20
1/833?/1.5	T20A
1/834/1.7	T6A
1/834/2.2	T20
1/135/12.5	T20
1/135/2.5	T20M
1/135/8	T20A
1/335/.3	TR6
1/735/12.5	T20A
1/636/5.	T20A
1/337/3	T20A
1/537/.5	T6A
1/537/.25	T22M
1/537/.6	T22M
1/637/1.	T20M
1/737/4	T20A
1/338/2.7	T22M
1/438/.3	T6M
1/438/7.5	T20
1/538/6	T20A
No code	T20A (1939 issue?)
1/639/.5	T20
1/1039/.25	T6
1/1039/.25	T26M
1/1039/7.5	T20
16/848/5	T20
16/949/20	T20
16/351/25	T20M

INSTRUCTIONS FOR DISTRIBUTION BOX:

1/832/1
1/932/5
1/1232/5
1/1233/5

INSTRUCTIONS FOR ELECTRICALLY LIGHTED ACCESSORIES:

1/735/10
1/835/4(2P)
1/1135/5.
1/136/17.5
1/936/3.5
1/1036/2
1/1136/20
1/537/40
1/539/20
1/739/5.2

INSTRUCTIONS FOR CIRCUIT BREAKERS:

1/835/5	
1/336/5	
1/836/5.	
1/1136/10.5	
1/437/20	
1/239/5.25	20V
1/439/1.25	20V
1/739/.25	6V
1/640/6.	20V